Cacti for the Connoisseur

A GUIDE FOR GROWERS AND COLLECTORS

CACTI
FOR THE
CONNOISSEUR

A Guide for Growers & Collectors

John Pilbeam

Photography by Bill Weightman

(signature: John Pilbeam)

B. T. BATSFORD LTD · LONDON

ISBN 0 7134 4861 X

Typeset and printed by
Butler & Tanner Ltd, Frome and London

for the publishers
B. T. Batsford Ltd
4 Fitzhardinge Street London W1H 0AH

CONTENTS

ACKNOWLEDGEMENTS

The chief acknowledgement I make with great pleasure is to my good friend Bill Weightman for his superb photography, which graces these pages and makes the book so much more useful than it would be with the results I could have achieved.

The list of further help goes far and wide, and is far too long to include here. It includes all my friends in the hobby, whose opinions and arguments I have enjoyed over the past thirty-odd years.

My thanks are due to Ken Burke, Tom Jenkins, Derek Bowdery, Terry Hewitt and Dave Clark for the loan of their photographs for use in the book.

LIST OF COLOUR ILLUSTRATIONS

List of colour illustrations

INTRODUCTION

A few years ago I found that I had talked myself into giving a talk to judges and potential judges of cacti on the woes of judging what I jokingly referred to as 'Aristocacti', that is to say, those cacti coming from generally harsh surroundings in the wild, which often present problems in cultivation.

In the following few years this talk was adapted to be more suitable for branches of the British Cactus & Succulent Society, by broadening it to embrace in addition the more popular, more easily grown genera of cacti, with a view to selecting from the latter the more choice species – a sort of recommended short-list based on as objective an assessment as an individual choice can be. Those chosen are often the plants which, all things being equal, will walk off with the prizes at cactus shows. As well as being more difficult to cultivate successfully, which tends to sway the judging in their favour, they are often more eye-catching; perhaps from a more dense covering of spines associated with fending off the sun in their more exposed position in the wild. Sometimes they represent the last bastion clinging on in the wild in difficult terrain, and in doing so have reduced their size to that of a miniature, in contrast to their fellow species in less hostile conditions.

Whatever their particular appeal I found that when I came to make the choice, they almost chose themselves; I suspect that a poll taken among those who know their cacti well would come up with many of the same species in their selection of 'connoisseur's cacti'.

This talk became the inspiration for this book, and I have set out in the following pages to produce for enthusiasts a guide to these wonderful, spiny plants that grip the imagination and aesthetic appreciation of so many who grow them – a guide to the various genera and some indication of those species that are regarded as the more 'choice'. Of course such a choice is for the individual, but as I have suggested above it is not so subjective as might be thought. Bill Weightman's photographs will I hope give an indication of why these species are so chosen.

So what we have here is a book for the enthusiast who wants to know what are the choicer cacti to grow, both in terms of the more choice genera, and the select species from the more widely grown genera. But often in this hobby the beginner rapidly becomes the enthusiast, and this book will at least help the beginner become an enthusiast more easily. For the more seasoned enthusiasts it collects together the names published in recent years as well as those appearing in older books which have provided complete listings, with an indication of their validity where known. It also provides a guide to the more up-to-date thinking on amalgamation of genera, too splintered by far in the Backebergian philosophy. For want of any comparable publication since Backeberg's massive works *Die Cactaceae* and the *Kakteenlexicon*, the latter (available in English as the *Cactus Lexicon*) still tends to be used by most amateurs as their source of information, out of date as it is.

Finally I must acknowledge and endorse the need to conserve these beautiful plants in the wild, and encourage readers to seek their plants from skilful nurserymen who propagate their sales plants from seed or cuttings, rather than from those who still import direct from the wild.

John Pilbeam   JANUARY 1987

CULTIVATION

Rather like motorway or freeway driving, cultivation of some of these more choice cacti takes more care than the 'side-road' cacti usually acquired in the early days of your collecting. Where you can get away with a degree of carelessness by way of overwatering or heavy-handed repotting with the old faithfuls, the 'aristocacti' require a more delicate touch: a gentle throttle by way of the watering can and, to risk straining the metaphor, a constant lookout for hazard signs.

Watering

Perhaps the most vital aspect of cultivation and the most frequent query to experienced growers is the watering requirements of some of those cacti which come from the more arid areas. The more experienced the grower the more the answer tends to be evasive, or at least to sound so, but it comes down to regulation according to each individual's conditions of growing, with all factors playing a part. Points to consider are: where are you? England, with its short summer growing period, frequently cloudy days, and high humidity, or America (and which state)? Do your plants get good exposure to sunshine? What are the weather conditions at the time of watering? Do you use clay or plastic pots, soil based or soil-less compost? And what balance of grit to compost? All these things will affect the frequency of your watering programme, but in general you should water the 'aristocacti' perhaps a little less frequently than the rest, unless you increase the grit content – in which case you can treat them the same as the rest of your collection, bearing in mind the remarks about compost below. Some of the more arid growing cacti come from the Chihuahuan desert which is exceptional for its lack of winter rains. These plants tend to come into growth much later than most cacti, and this should be reflected in their watering – not starting in earnest until about June in England, and a month or two later than normal elsewhere.

Potting on

I use the term potting on rather than repotting, since with many of the more difficult plants moving them into a fresh pot is a hazardous time, and the process should preferably be achieved with as little root disturbance as possible, commensurate with normal pest control checks.

If clay pots are being used, it is often safer (if uneconomic) to break the old pot if the plant is proving difficult to remove, rather than risk excessive root damage. With plastic pots a little judicious squeezing of the sides of the pot will usually free the roots and allow the soil-ball to be removed in one piece. With either method a moderate watering a week or so before the operation will facilitate removal from the pot and reduce the risk of root damage, but ensure that the soil-ball is not still excessively damp from this watering before potting on, replacing in the pot loosely for a few days if so. Have the new pot (only slightly larger and thoroughly clean) ready and ensure that the fresh soil to be used both matches the former compost, if it has proved successful, and is fairly dry, though not completely so. Firm the fresh soil around the root-ball gently but enough to ensure good contact between the two, and add a top-dressing of grit, which stops too-rapid drying-out, helps prevent moss or green algae getting a hold on the surface and looks more sightly. Leave the freshly potted plant at least two weeks before lightly watering, and another two weeks before giving the first thorough dousing to get the roots going again.

The potting medium

If you have already found a satisfactory compost for growing your plants successfully, then stick to it. If you decide to change to a different mix, do so gradually, trying a few plants first (preferably duplicates) to see how they fare. All too often I have heard of someone changing from soil-based to soil-less compost or vice versa, and going the whole hog with all their plants, only to find sooner or later that they are changing back to what they had before, because the results are not up to their expectations, or even downright disastrous.

Considerations of pH (the degree of acidity or alkalinity) of the composts you are using must not be overlooked, as some plants have a distinct preference one way or the other, especially those which grow just on limestone in the wild, or those which grow in a very acid soil, such as is found in afforested areas, where some plants grow in the leaf detritus. In general soil-less, peat-based composts are acid, whether mixed for ericaceous plants or not, while soil-based composts are often slightly alkaline. Gypsum may be added to composts to reduce acidity if required, and watering with hard tap-water will have a similar effect, but it is more difficult to reduce the alkalinity of composts, and better to start with an acid mixture, using soft, distilled or rainwater to maintain the acidity, if this is what is required. Where possible in the *Commentary on Genera* I have indicated where plants are known to have a marked preference for either end of the pH scale. A soil-testing kit can be purchased from most garden centres. Whatever compost is used, the more difficult a plant is rated is generally an indication that a higher grit content in the mixture is needed. Do not use sand at all. Most grades which are available tend to compact rather than open up the compost for better drainage, which should be the purpose of their incorporation. A fine grit with no dust is needed. Most cacti seem to give less trouble and grow well in a proportion of 1 part grit (by bulk) to about 4 parts compost, but for the more touchy genera or species a mix of 1 to 1 is advised.

Shading

In England shading is rarely needed, except perhaps in the spring in years when a lengthy overcast period has coincided with the plants' starting into growth. A few clear days, with the sun having gained some strength in the meanwhile, will scorch the new growth. Glasshouses which are very exposed to the sun may need some shading in the sunniest months to keep growth moving, as there seems to be a tendency for the plants to stand still and just bask in the sunshine. Particular genera seem to do better in less full exposure to sunshine than others; in particular *Gymnocalycium* springs to mind. But these are few, with most cacti relishing as much of our watery sunshine as they can get. In more sunny climes shading seems to be the rule.

Temperature

With a few exceptions most cacti are remarkably tolerant of temperatures down to near freezing – provided that they are dry at the root – although there is less danger of losing them if a minimum of 40° F(5° C) is maintained, and less still at 45° F(8° C) or 50° F(10° C). Some need still more warmth, notably some *Cephalocereus*, and almost all *Melocactus* and *Discocactus*, which, to be sure of keeping should be at a minimum of 55° F(12° C). This can be achieved in a glasshouse heated at bench level to 45° F(8° C) if the more tender plants are kept at a high level, so that the rising heat gives them its main benefit all the time.

At the other extreme there is increasing awareness that species which, in habitat, survive temperatures of below freezing point, seem to prefer the equivalent in cultivation. Having suffered in the icy blast in New Mexico looking for *Toumeya papyracantha*, *Echinocereus viridiflorus*, *Mammillaria wrightii* and some *Thelocactus* (*Echinomastus* and *Sclerocactus*) species, I am well aware of the hardiness of these sometimes difficult plants. Hence perhaps their difficulty, since to provide such temperatures coupled with the necessary low humidity is not possible in England. More work is needed on this subject.

Propagation – seed-raising

With improved methods of seed-raising in the last few years, many species considered nigh impossible to raise from seed in the past are appearing on the market as seedlings; *Ariocarpus*, *Strombocactus*, *Discocactus*, *Pelecyphora*, *Epithelantha* and the like, helping reduce the activities of the slave-trade in wild-collected plants so damaging in the past. And many more of the choice newcomers of less difficult genera are often offered as seed before they appear commercially as plants – again reducing the need or demand for wild-collected plants.

Methods of seed-raising recommended in the past have been hit and miss or amateurish, not soundly based and leading to more loss of life among the cacti than one cares to think about. They enabled the seed-raiser following their recommendations to achieve only modest success, and often only with species which are so ready to oblige anyway that they frequently appear around a parent plant from seed that has trickled down from above – achieving independent life without any assistance (or interference) from the cultivator.

The most successful raisers of the more choice species of cacti keep their seedlings completely enclosed in polythene covering for six months or more, and almost all cacti seem to relish this Turkish bath treatment. I favour the use of small pots, one for each species, rather than sowing in a seed tray divided into strips like a seed-trial ground (which as you sow the seed gives them the chance to get thoroughly out of place by emulating Barnes Wallis's bouncing bomb). It also avoids the problem of different growth rates leading to overcrowding or the need to prick out some plants before the others are ready. Each pot can be placed in its own small polythene bag, or a tray of pots can be covered with thin polythene, enabling the whole tray to be watered from below when it is needed. Deep trays leaving an inch or so (3 cm) clearance above the surface of the pots should be used to allow room for the seedlings to develop.

Soil-less compost or *good* John Innes seed compost (rare these days) can be used, with the addition of 30% sharp gritty sand, although this is not entirely necessary. A light covering of gritty sand on the soil surface (limestone chippings for lime-loving plants) helps keep down the growth of algae and mosses, and seems to prevent caking of the top layer of soil.

After sowing on the surface of the compost a thorough watering, incorporating a fungicide, and, if Sciara fly are a pest for you, an insecticide, should be carried out from the base, until the surface shows signs of being reached. Then drain off and cover with polythene, only rewatering when the condensation (which will certainly appear every day on the covering) begins to be patchy – showing that the pots are drying out.

The seedlings can with advantage be left for a year before pricking-out into trays for growing on, but if they demand moving sooner a similar covering with a tent of polythene over the pricked-out seedlings will ensure they do not receive a check through being too dry. Do not water pricked-out seedlings for at least a week after pricking-out, to give any damaged roots a chance to heal. Again fungicides should be used to combat damping-off, and insecticides if Sciara fly or other pests are around.

Once seedlings are $\frac{1}{2}$ in (1 cm) or more across the covering can be removed and the plants treated as adult. But at no time during the first year should they be allowed to dry out completely at the root if best results are to be obtained. Light allowed should be strong, but avoid direct sunlight for the first few months, then accustom gradually.

Propagation – cuttings

Species with offsets can be readily propagated by severing with a sharp knife at the narrowest point of attachment, being careful to dust lightly the cut tissue of both offset and parent plant with a fungicide powder; most hormone rooting powders contain a fungicide. Be careful to shake off excess powder, or callousing will be impaired. Leave dry for a few days, a week or more if the cut surface is more than $\frac{1}{2}$ in (1 cm) or so, out of direct sunlight, but

not in darkness – an empty seed tray is ideal. When you are satisfied that the cut surface is dry and calloused (quite hard to the touch), place the cutting gently on the surface of almost dry compost for a further week or more, gradually bringing the cuttings into stronger light, but still not unshaded, direct sunlight. Within a few more weeks tiny root nodes should start appearing and pushing out of the base of the cuttings; then watering can commence to encourage root development. If roots do not appear for some time they can sometimes be encouraged by soaking the compost and leaving to dry out before soaking again. Check frequently to detect the start of rooting. Cuttings seem to do better once rooted if left in the seed trays to develop a good root system, before potting up individually.

Propagation – grafting

There is no doubt that some of these plants are so difficult to grow successfully on their own roots that grafting often the only answer; rather than watch plant after plant die a lingering death, while you talk encouragingly to it, curse it, or just pray in vain. If the grafted plant is grown in conditions equating to the rest of the collection it will often blow up, inflated out of all proportion with the character of the plant, or elongate excessively, or offset so prolifically as to resemble a monstrose form. This is because the grafting stocks used are generally very vigorous in growth. To slow down this effect the grafted plant can be held back by growing hard, i.e. using a small pot, very gritty compost, and keeping watering down to just sufficient to keep the plant going without encouraging it to grow excessively. Or, alternatively, less vigorous grafting stocks can be used, like *Lobivia, Notocactus* or similar, slower-growing genera.

Methods of grafting have been expounded in the past in book after book on the subject of cactus culture, and each grower develops his own preference. For most cacti flat grafting is the easiest and most successful. This involves the bringing together of two flat surfaces, that of the beheaded stock plant and the base of a cutting taken from the plant it is desired to graft. The stock should be in active growth, so that the cut surface is sappy, and the cut made within the current year's growth, so that soft, young tissues will form that part of the union. Similarly the scion should preferably be in active growth and sappy, with enough of the base removed to reveal a clearly distinguishable vascular bundle, the differently coloured ring towards the centre of the plant. No time should be wasted in getting the two freshly cut surfaces together, ensuring that their respective vascular bundles are in contact, not necessarily trying to line them up precisely, since they are often of different sizes, but ensuring they at least overlap each other, so that at two points

the rings make contact; a slight offsetting of the two should achieve this end. Light pressure is needed for a few days to facilitate the union of the tissue, which can best be done with elastic bands looped over the top of the scion and beneath the base of the pot. The bands should not be thin or tightly placed so as to cut into the tissue, but broader and tighter bands should be used if either stock or scion is not as sappy as it might be, when, for instance, trying to graft a piece of collapsing plant that has got somewhat dried out through losing its roots.

The bands may be removed after about two weeks, after which it should be only a matter of a few weeks before the scion starts to swell and indicate that the graft has been successful. Sometimes a false graft is achieved with a minimum connection of vascular tissue, which keeps the plant going until it forms roots which push out between the stock and scion. In this case carefully remove the scion, dust the cut surface and treat as for a cutting – see above. Cristate cacti are often grafted, as their habit makes them difficult to grow on their own roots.

Pests and diseases

Collectors of these plants soon become aware of the pests which interfere with their successful cultivation. A constant battle has to be fought, and the result of one

1. Group of cristate cacti on grafts, showing ribbon-like development compared with normal growth

season's lapse in the fight has a similar effect to the gardening adage 'one year's seeding, seven years' weeding', since they mostly make even rabbits appear monogamous, so prolifically do they multiply. By far the most common pest is the mealy-bug, a creature covered with a meal-like, powdery coating further enclosing itself in cottonwool-like tufts in which it settles down to suck the life out of your plants and raise a family. If unchecked, plants quickly become covered with the offspring, a springboard for the infestation of your whole collection. Regular spraying with a rotation of insecticides, whether or not the pests are seen, is advisable, and if an infestation has occurred it is as well to isolate the plants affected, so that the spread may be checked. The infested plants should be continuously treated, so that as the eggs that the pests will have laid hatch out, they are further bombarded with insecticide.

The companion form of mealy-bug to that found on your plants is the one found below ground on the roots, which is even more insidious and difficult to eradicate. In fact, the only sure cure is to perfect your rooting technique, cut off all the roots from infested plants, brush away any soil adhering to the base of the plant which may be harbouring these pests or their eggs, and re-root in clean pots and fresh compost. Carefully dispose of the discarded compost, which will rapidly reinfect your plants if left around in the glasshouse.

If you are too faint of heart to do this, then the next surest method is to wash off all the soil and the pests, dry off the roots, dust with an insecticide to catch any lurking pests in the crannies, and repot in fresh compost and clean pots. And don't forget the staging where the pots have been standing, particularly underneath, where both top and root mealy bugs have a habit of leaving a deposit for the future well-being of their kind in the form of patches of wool containing eggs; for these a good strong disinfectant brushed on is effective.

The next most common pest, and some would say bitterly the most common, is red spider mite – a tiny, barely visible, spider-like creature, red or red-brown in colour, whose presence is sometimes realized only when the plants start turning yellow-brown from its attentions. If such discoloration is viewed through a × 10 lens the tiny creatures may be seen together with the fine webbing that they exude between the spines. The damage they do is irreparable, and they are difficult pests to eradicate. Frequent sprayings with an insecticide specifying their control are needed, with the same after-treatment to catch the emerging offspring recommended for mealy-bugs. Regular spraying as advocated above will take care of, in a preventative manner, most other pests. Do not wait for them to be seen; it should be assumed that they always are there, just waiting for you to relax long enough for them to gain a foothold. Top-spraying and occasional soil-drenching will also take care of that more recent newcomer to the pest scene, brought in with peat com-posts – the Sciara fly or mushroom fly, a tiny gnat-like creature that will lay eggs in the compost, from which will develop tiny larvae, white with black heads, with a voracious appetite for cactus flesh. They usually start at the roots, and can be devastating in a pan of seedlings, but will tackle mature plants with equally disastrous results. Almost daily spraying with insecticide when the flies are seen, to knock them down and prevent them breeding, seems to be effective.

Most fungal attacks come about when the plants are damaged, either in repotting, from taking cuttings, or from overwatering causing loss of roots and the resultant creeping invasion of rot from the decaying roots into the plant body. Dusting lightly with fungicidal powder (as contained in hormone rooting powders) when taking cuttings (both offset and parent) helps prevent attack from this area. Care to let broken roots dry well after repotting, by using nearly dry compost and withholding water for at least a week or so, will help avoid an attack from below. An unsightly but not usually fatal fungus that is a bother mainly to European collectors at least is called 'sooty mould', which forms a black, soot-like coat-ing on plants with glands exuding a sugary solution, e.g. *Thelocactus, Ferocactus, Coryphantha*. Various remedies are proffered, among them frequent spraying during the growing period to dilute the sugars, encouragement of ants in the glasshouse to feed on the sugar, or regular spraying with a fungicide to kill off the mould as it forms. I saw a remarkable recovery from a plant covered with this mould, which was frequently sprayed with a fungicide and then lightly brushed to remove the mould once it had been killed.

CLASSIFICATION

For most collectors classification of the whole family is, I suspect, the most boring and potentially annoying aspect of the hobby. What most require and would be content with is a firm idea of what to write on their plant labels. But with differing opinions among the taxonomists who have been busy with the Cactaceae in the last few decades, confusion at present reigns. Current thinking favours the broader concepts of both genera and species, but the only comparatively modern, general, comprehensive work accessible to collectors is Curt Backeberg's *Cactus Lexicon*, favouring fine divisions to the extreme.

Although reminding collectors that what is most recent is not necessarily most right, I would advocate bending their thoughts towards the more broad approach, since that seems to be the way things are moving. This is largely what I have favoured in this book, with a few reservations on the more unacceptable amalgamations. In particular I have taken Gordon Rowley's concept of the scheme of classification of the Cactaceae, as set out admirably in his book *Name that Succulent*, with only one or two divergences. With the more drastic amalgamations, such as *Borzicactus, Echinopsis, Cephalocereus* and *Neoporteria*, there is a lot to be said for including on the label the subgeneric or former name as a more informative way of labelling your plants, e.g. *Borzicactus (Matucana) haynei, Echinopsis (Trichocereus) fulvilanus, Cephalocereus (Pilosocereus) estevesii, Neoporteria (Islaya) islayensis.*

Gordon Rowley's classification, as modified herein, is set out below for reference purposes; in the *Commentary on Genera* section of the book I have listed all the cactus genera and referred them where necessary to their synonymy. In this respect at least this book will serve as a guide to current taxonomic thinking. For readers who might have reservations in implementing this scheme of things I have shown previous allegiances, so they can be conservative if they wish.

Family CACTACEAE

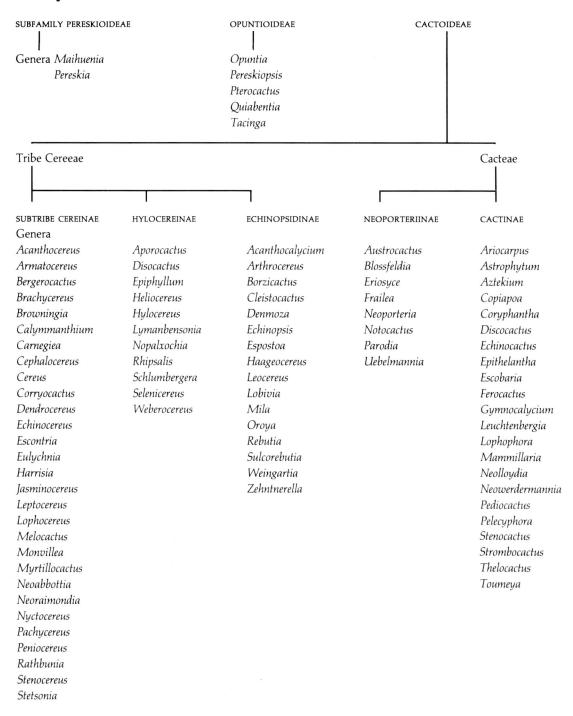

SUBFAMILY PERESKIOIDEAE	OPUNTIOIDEAE	CACTOIDEAE

Genera *Maihuenia*
Pereskia

Opuntia
Pereskiopsis
Pterocactus
Quiabentia
Tacinga

Tribe Cereeae   Cacteae

SUBTRIBE CEREINAE	HYLOCEREINAE	ECHINOPSIDINAE	NEOPORTERIINAE	CACTINAE
Genera				
Acanthocereus	*Aporocactus*	*Acanthocalycium*	*Austrocactus*	*Ariocarpus*
Armatocereus	*Disocactus*	*Arthrocereus*	*Blossfeldia*	*Astrophytum*
Bergerocactus	*Epiphyllum*	*Borzicactus*	*Eriosyce*	*Aztekium*
Brachycereus	*Heliocereus*	*Cleistocactus*	*Frailea*	*Copiapoa*
Browningia	*Hylocereus*	*Denmoza*	*Neoporteria*	*Coryphantha*
Calymmanthium	*Lymanbensonia*	*Echinopsis*	*Notocactus*	*Discocactus*
Carnegiea	*Nopalxochia*	*Espostoa*	*Parodia*	*Echinocactus*
Cephalocereus	*Rhipsalis*	*Haageocereus*	*Uebelmannia*	*Epithelantha*
Cereus	*Schlumbergera*	*Leocereus*		*Escobaria*
Corryocactus	*Selenicereus*	*Lobivia*		*Ferocactus*
Dendrocereus	*Weberocereus*	*Mila*		*Gymnocalycium*
Echinocereus		*Oroya*		*Leuchtenbergia*
Escontria		*Rebutia*		*Lophophora*
Eulychnia		*Sulcorebutia*		*Mammillaria*
Harrisia		*Weingartia*		*Neolloydia*
Jasminocereus		*Zehntnerella*		*Neowerdermannia*
Leptocereus				*Pediocactus*
Lophocereus				*Pelecyphora*
Melocactus				*Stenocactus*
Monvillea				*Strombocactus*
Myrtillocactus				*Thelocactus*
Neoabbottia				*Toumeya*
Neoraimondia				
Nyctocereus				
Pachycereus				
Peniocereus				
Rathbunia				
Stenocereus				
Stetsonia				

DISTRIBUTION AND MORPHOLOGY

Cacti, except for one or two intriguing strays into Africa and Sri Lanka, come exclusively from the New World, from southern parts of Canada in the north, through a proliferation in the southern United States, Mexico and tropical America, along the Andean chain in South America as far as Patagonia in Argentina.

They are found wherever there is a paucity of moisture available to plants. This can occur because of long, rainless periods, as in the Sonora, Mojave and Chihuahua deserts, with regular downpours in only short periods of the year followed by long periods of drought, or where the precipitation is rapidly dispersed or locked up for long periods through being frozen, as in mountainous areas, or the extreme, where only condensation from sea-mists is available with no rainfall at all, as in the Atacama desert in Chile.

In addition to these desert or semi-desert cacti, there are the jungle or forest cacti, which grow on or are supported by trees or shrubs, not parasitically but epiphytically, rooting into detritus in tree crotches and crannies or using trees or shrubs for support to enable them to clamber from where they are rooted in the floor litter or among rocks into the sunlight. These mainly occur in Central America and the tropical zone of South America.

The distribution of individual cactus genera is sometimes extremely localized, within a few square miles, or even hundreds of yards or metres, but the more successful genera occur over a wide area of thousands of square miles, with different genera overlapping. With this overlapping, there are occasional, rare, intergeneric hybrids, which have overcome nature's barriers to inter-pollination, such as different flowering times, different pollinators, or just plain incompatibility. But these intergeneric hybrids are very often sterile, and eventually die off without issue. A general idea of the countries in which genera occur is given in the main part of this book, the *Commentary on Genera*.

The forms that cacti adopt suit their locality and its conditions, and, except for the epiphytic genera, which often do not want for water, are primarily designed to get them through the dry period that they suffer to a greater or lesser degree. Most inhabit semi-desert areas with annual rainfall of more than 10 in (25 cm) rather than the true, really dry deserts, where it is 10 in or less, or even none at all. The semi-desert cacti are on the whole adaptable to cultivation in glass houses, and tolerate, or even enjoy the more favourable conditions they find themselves in. The true desert cacti on the other hand do present much more difficulty in cultivation, and their drought tolerance should constantly be borne in mind.

There are various ways in which cacti combat this potential threat to their well-being in the wild, and this adaptation has led to the variety of forms they adopt. The most obvious means of water conservation is the reduction of leaves to spines, and transferring the job of photosynthesis (the use of light to promote growth) to the stem of the plants – which are usually therefore green from the chlorophyll necessary for this process. Most cacti have a waxy covering on the epidermis, to cut down moisture loss, and of course the spines filter the light falling on them and control the immediate temperature around the plant by breaking down the air currents, and in cold areas insulate the plants from the worst of low temperatures. The structure of the plant too lends itself to this end, being composed of ribs or nipples (delicately called tubercles in England), which enable the plants to contract at times of drought, to cut down the surface area exposed to the drying effects of the sun and wind, and expand when water becomes available to allow maximum take-up of moisture. The root system incorporates either swollen, tuber-like development to store water below ground, or thick roots capable of withdrawing the top of the plant into the soil, the better to prevent transpiration at times of drought. The fibrous roots of cacti often spread far and wide just below the surface, to take the maximum advantage of even light rainfall. The flowers are wasteful of moisture, and perhaps for this reason often appear after the first uptake of water following the local rains, lasting only a day or two, or seldom more than a week. But in that short time they will have fulfilled their purpose, attracted with their bright colours or perfume their pollinators, and set seed. The fruits will quickly form, to dry and spill their contents on to the sandy surface, or go winging their way to dispersal via a co-operating bird's gut, for the future continuation of the species.

CACTUS PLANTS UNDER COLLECTORS' NUMBERS

Many plants are acquired with the enigmatic label including just the generic name followed by a collection number, e.g. *Mammillaria* 'Lau 777'. Such labels should not be looked down upon, since they contain in the name and number, if correctly applied, more information than is often the case with named plants. Lau, or WR, or P, or other abbreviations refer to the field-collector who collected the plant in the first place, and from which, hopefully, such material bearing its number has been vegetatively propagated. Such collectors usually publish from time to time their lists of collection numbers with details of the place that they collected the various plants, and their opinion as to what they are. Some turn out to be new species, and when such species are described the collection number is usually nowadays quoted. The lists are obtainable from the collectors themselves, or from the cactus society in their home country. Some of these collectors' names and their abbreviations are as follows:

FR   Friedrich Ritter
G & F   Charles Glass & Robert Foster
H   David Hunt
HS   Heinz Swoboda
HU   Horst Uebelmann
KK   Karel Knize
L or Lau   Alfred Lau
MLV   Michael Vereb
P   Jorg Piltz
R or WR   Walter Rausch
Rep.   Walter Reppenhagen
SB   Steven Brack
V   Roberto Vasquez
WK or Kr   Wolfgang Krahn
WM   Woody Minnich

BROAD VIEW OF GENERA

In the following commentary only passing reference is made to genera considered superfluous because of the broad genera concepts followed in this book, and their resting place is indicated. Explanations of the thinking behind the various combinations should be sought elsewhere as indicated, since the proposals are often long and detailed. Suffice it to say here that the concepts followed have been studied and accepted as cogently argued by the author concerned, but the governing factor tends to be acceptance by the cactus fraternity as a whole, either tacitly or otherwise. In some instances where genera are particularly large and complex it is recommended that if a subgeneric system is indicated, that the subgenus or even lower ranking might usefully and informatively be included in the labels of plants as a clearer indication of their standing and their affinities, e.g. *Rebutia (Mediolobivia) pygmaea, Mammillaria (Cochemiea) poselgeri,* or *Borzicactus (Matucane) haynei.*

The list of named species for each genus is as full as possible, taking account of declared synonymies where considered appropriate, and based on validly described names. Names without descriptions (e.g. catalogue names) are not included, unless commonly in use or misuse. The descriptions of the recommended species for each genus are brief, merely supplementing the photographs, and the choice of those recommended is based largely on the author's preferences, although it must be said that those chosen almost chose themselves and would probably be very near such a list chosen by other enthusiasts with a wide knowledge of the available species in a particular genus. The final selection (the 'connoisseur's choice') is rather like *Desert Island Discs* presenter Roy Plomley's dictum: 'if you had to choose only one ...', and again, I think would be a popular consensus among the cognoscenti. With a few large genera, 'only one' has been somewhat expanded.

COMMENTARY ON GENERA

Acanthocalycium Backeb., *Kaktus ABC* 412 (1935)

Although moves have been made to include this genus within the concept of *Lobivia*, opinion has tended to keep it separate, and it is so treated here. It is a genus of spiny budded species (hence the name) from northern Argentina, mostly slow growing, globular species, with strong or flexible spines, with flowers varying from yellow through pinks and reds to white and lilac. They are of easy culture, although quite slow growing, producing flowers at about four or five years from seed when they are about 3–4 in (8–10 cm) wide.

Species named are: *A. aurantiacum, A. brevispinum, A. catamarcense, A. chionanthum, A. glaucum, A. griseum, A. klimpelianum, A. peitscherianum, A. spiniflorum, A. thionanthum, A. variiflorum, A. violaceum.*

Recommended species: *A. brevispinum* is a slow growing, solitary species with blue-green body colour, short, stiff, brown spines and yellow flowers. *A. catamarcense* is similar in habit, with longer black to grey spines and yellow flowers.
A. peitscherianum makes clusters of heads after several years, with clearly defined vertical ribs, and short dark brown spines, producing pale pink to white coloured flowers freely.
A. violaceum is the most popular of the genus, and the most rewarding in its dense, brownish-yellow, bristle-like spines and lilac flowers. If potted on and grown well it will flower at about 5 years from seed, when it is small apple sized, staying globular and solitary. The blooms are particularly beautiful and unusually coloured for cacti, in being lilac.

Connoisseur's choice: *A. violaceum.*

2. *Acanthocalycium brevispinum*

3. *Acanthocalycium peitscherianum*

Acanthocereus (Bgr.) B. & R., *Contrib. U.S., Nat. Herb.* 12:432 (1909)

A small group of sprawling, cylindrical-stemmed cacti from the south-eastern United States and Central America. They are little seen in cultivation because of their untidy habit of growth and lack of flowers until they reach a size which makes their presence in the collection intrusive, although seed is regularly offered of some species.

Species named are: *A. acutangularis, A. albicaulis,* A. baxaniensis, A. brasiliensis, A. chiapensis, A. colombianus, A. floridanus, A. griseus, A. horridus, A. maculatus, A. occidentalis, A. pentagonus, A. princeps, A. sicariguensis, A. subinermis.*

They are not recommended.

Acantholobivia Backeb. (1942)

Referred to *Lobivia.*

Acanthorhipsalis B. & R. (1923)

Referred to *Rhipsalis*, except for *A. micrantha* which is referred to *Lymanbensonia.*

Akersia Buining (1961)

Referred to *Borzicactus.*

Ancistrocactus B. & R. (1923)

Referred to *Thelocactus* in accordance with Rowley's thinking, although Nigel Taylor places this genus as well as *Thelocactus* and others beneath his broad concept of *Ferocactus.*

Anisocereus Backeb. (1938)

Referred to *Stenocereus.*

Aporocactus Lem. *Illustr. Hort.* 7:Misc.67 (1860)

Sprawling or pendant cacti from Mexico, the commonest, *A. flagelliformis* still undiscovered (or rather unrediscovered) in the wild since its original description in 1860. Other than this commonly grown species the others tend to have springy, invasive stems, making their accommodation more difficult than the obligingly limply-hanging stems of *A. flagelliformis.*

Species named are: *A. conzattii, A. flagelliformis, A. flagriformis, A. leptophis, A. martianus.*

*See also the genus *Mirabella.*

Recommended species: the first three mentioned are occasionally seen in cultivation or on nurserymen's lists, but I am not aware of the last two named being available at all. *A. conzattii* is seen in photographs occasionally festooning trees in its native habitat and hanging down stems many feet long. In cultivation it makes a sprawling, untidy hanging plant, launching itself sideways for 1 ft (30 cm) or more, before sagging downwards under its own weight. The orange-red flowers are more intensely coloured if kept out of full sunshine.

A. flagelliformis as indicated above is deservedly popular, and not always grown to its full potential. I well remember a magnificent plant of this species, which had been grafted on to a 6 ft (2 m) stem of a Cereus, completely covering the stock and covered with flowers in abundance. Grafting is one way to achieve a good-sized plant, but it will grow well on its own roots in a hanging pot if repotted at least every other year, otherwise the compost is likely to become exhausted to the detriment of the continuing good growth of this rampant plant. Too much sunlight can cause it to turn yellow and stunt its growth, and it is significant that good specimens are often seen in dwelling houses on windowsills, where the light levels are lower. The flowers are bright purple-pink.

A. flagriformis is usually identified as a similar plant to the previous species, but with slightly stronger, more bristly spines and more red-coloured flowers.

Connoisseur's choice: *A. flagelliformis.*

Arequipa B. & R. (1922)

Referred to *Borzicactus.*

Ariocarpus Scheidw., *Bull. Acad. Sci. Brux.* 5:491 (1838); E. F. Anderson, *Amer. Journ. Bot.* 47:582 (1960); *l.c.* 49:615 (1962); *l.c.* 50:724 (1963)

This genus from the Chihuahuan desert in southern Texas and northern Mexico is highly adapted to harsh conditions in the wild, growing flush with the soil level (or even below in dry periods), with no spines, and a rhinocerous-like upper epidermis. Often still seen in collections as wild-collected plants, and often consequently of great age, since they grow extremely slowly, the traffic has lessened somewhat in recent years now that it is illegal to collect such plants in the USA, and many seedling plants are finding their way into collections as seed-raising techniques have improved.

They fall broadly into two categories by size, the larger group consisting of *A. fissuratus, A. furfuraceus, A. retusus* and *A. trigonus*, getting to about 6 in (15 cm) or more in diameter; the smaller growing species, up to about 2–3 in

4. *Ariocarpus fissuratus* (in habitat on limestone ridges, in Texas, USA)

15 cm, and lacks the fissure on the lower edge of the tubercles.

A. kotschoubeyanus is a small, beautiful species often no more than an inch or so (2–3 cm) wide, flat-topped, with neatly fitting, triangular tubercles, each with a prominent woolly furrow, surmounting a fat, tuberous root. Often seen solitary it will form small clumps in time. Flowers are freely produced, and are purple-pink, or white (var. *albiflorus*). The smaller growing form has been named as *A. kotschoubeyanus* var. *macdowellii*, rarely more than an inch wide and with smaller tubercles than the type.

A. retusus, together with the smaller tubercled *A. retusus* var. *furfuraceus*, makes large flat topped plants to about 10 in (25 cm) wide, sometimes clustering, and producing its large white flowers from a mass of brownish-yellow wool at the growing point in the centre. It is made up of three-sided pyramid shaped tubercles, with a tuft at the upper surface tip on *A. retusus* var. *furfuraceus*, and as with the others has a large, turnip root.

A. scapharostrus is perhaps the most difficult to cultivate successfully, and is the most uncommon in cultivation because of this. It makes most of its growth underground, and pushes up from this thick rootstock small, incurving, keeled, round-ended tubercles, quite unlike any other species, rarely achieving more than about 3 in (8 cm) wide in the wild or in cultivation. Flowers are large and purple-pink. It grows on steep, limestone ridges in Nuevo Leon, Mexico.

A. trigonus is similar to *A. retusus*, but with long, incurving tubercles and yellow flowers. It makes plants up to about 10 in (25 cm) wide, coming also from Nuevo Leon in Mexico.

Connoisseur's choice: *A. scapharostrus*.

Armatocereus Backeb., *Blatt. fur Kakteenf.* 1938 pt. 6: unpaged (21) (1938)

This is a peculiar columnar genus from Colombia, Ecuador and Peru, which makes spurts of growth each year and then 'necks' in a somewhat unsightly way, giving the impression of jointed stems.

It is seldom seen in cultivation, although *Cereus* enthusiasts no doubt find room for at least one.

Species named are: *A. arduus*, *A. balsasensis*, *A. cartwrightianus* (& var. *longispinus*), *A. ghiesbreghtii* (& var. *oligogonus*), *A. godingianus*, *A. humilis*, *A. laetus*, *A. mataranus* (& var. *ancashensis*), *A. procerus*, *A. rauhii*, *A. rupicola*.

Rejected names and synonymies are:
A. arboreus = *A. ghiesbreghtii*
A. armatus = *A. procerus*
A. churinensis = *A. ghiesbreghtii*
A. matucanensis = *A. ghiesbreghtii*
A. nazasensis & var. *armatus* = *A. procerus*

(5–8 cm), are quite delightful miniatures, and do present somewhat more difficulty in cultivation than the larger ones, which are difficult enough. These are *A. agavoides*, *A. kotschoubeyanus* and *A. scapharostrus*.

Species named are: *A.* (syn. *Neogomesia*) *agavoides*, *A.* (syn. *Roseocactus*) *fissuratus* (& var. *lloydii*) *A.* (syn. *Roseocactus*) *kotschoubeyanus* (& var. *albiflora*, var. *macdowellii*), *A. retusus* (& var. *furfuraceus*), *A. scapharostrus*, *A. trigonus*.

Rejected names and synonymies are:
A. furfuraceus = *A. retusus* var. *furfuraceus*
A. intermedius = *A. fissuratus* var. *lloydii*
A. lloydii = *A. fissuratus* var. *lloydii*.

Recommended species: *A. agavoides* differs from the others, and indeed for some time insisted on its own monotypic genus (*Neogomesia*), because of its elongated tubercles, reminiscent of *Leuchtenbergia* in miniature, with a tuft on the end of each. It forms a large underground stem or root, and produces large, purple-pink flowers from the centre point. It rarely gets to more than about 2 in (5 cm) tall and wide, and stays solitary, although the occasional ancient plant in cultivation is seen consisting of several heads.

A. fissuratus is named for the fissured upper part of the tubercles, with a deep crack along the lower edges, which fit together like some ancient pavement of rough, grey-brown, weathered stone. The plants will grow to about 10 cm in time, or a little more, but will take many years to do so. The root is thick and turnip-like. Flowers are a deep rose-pink and produced in late summer in England. *A. fissuratus* var. *lloydii*, from further south, in Coahuila, Durango and Zacatecas, Mexico, gets a little larger, to

A. oligogonus = A. ghiesbreghtii var. oligogonus
A. riemajensis = A. ghiesbreghtii

They are not recommended

Arrojadoa B. & R., (1920)

Referred to *Cephalocereus*.

Arthrocereus (Bgr.) Backeb. & Knuth, *Kaktus ABC*, 211 (1935)

The concept of this genus has been expanded to include *Pygmaeocereus* and *Setiechinopsis*, which, although they do not sit comfortably together, fit as well here as anywhere else, with enough points of similarity to justify the amalgamation. They are miniature members of the Cereus group, with stems no more than about 6 in (15 cm), forming clusters and freely producing their nocturnal, white flowers – with one exception, *A. rondonianus*, which has diurnal, pink flowers.

Species named (with former generic names, where they were different, abbreviated and in brackets): *A. (Pygm)bylesianus, A. campos-portoi, A. itabiriticola, A. mello-barretoi, A. microsphaericus, A. (Set)mirabilis, A. odorus, A. rondonianus, A. spinosissimus.*

Rejected names and synonymies are:
A. (Pygm)akersii = A. bylesianus
A. (Pygm)densiaculeatus = Haageocereus lanugispinus
A. (Pygm)familiaris = A. bylesianus
A. (Pygm)rowlevanus = A. bylesianus
A. (Pygm)vespertianus = A. bylesianus.

Recommended species: *A. bylesianus*, as might be gleaned from the synonymous names above is a variable species, mainly in the density and coloration of the spines, from dark brown overall colouring in *A. akersii* to almost entirely creamy-white in *A. rowleyanus*, but with the same overall shape and flower characteristics, i.e. short stems, about 4–6 in (10–15 cm) long and an inch or so (2–3 cm) wide, densely covered with spines so as to completely obscure the stem beneath, the spines fairly short and bristle-like. Flowers are nocturnal, but last 2 to 3 nights, long-tubed and white, highly scented.

A. mirabilis seems to be short-lived, and to see a plant of more than one stem about 4 in (10 cm) is unusual. The stems are little finger size, dark purplish-brown in colour, with vertical ribs of slender, black spines. Flowers are freely produced and open to a delightful ball of spiky, white petals at dusk, fading by the next morning. They are worth staying up for.

A. rondonianus makes stems to about 8–9 in (20 cm), narrow and densely clothed with red-brown spines. The flowers last several days and are deep pink, fading as they age.

Connoisseur's choice: *A. bylesianus.*

Astrophytum Lem., *Cact. Gen. Nov. Sp. Nov. Hort. Monv.* 3 (1839)

This is a small genus from Mexico and Texas in the USA

5. *Arthrocereus mirabilis*

6. *Astrophytum myriostigma* var. *potosinum* fa. *nudum*

of generally low-growing species, although *A. ornatum* will get columnar with age, and old specimens get several feet tall (to 2 m in cultivation).

With the exception of *A. asterias*, they present little difficulty in cultivation, although overwatering is a danger at any time, and an open compost with up to 40 or 50% grit content is recommended to ensure rapid drainage.

Species named are: *A. asterias*, *A. capricorne* (& fa. *aureum*, fa. *crassispinum*, fa. *minus*, fa. *niveum*), *A. coahuilense*, *A. myriostigma* (& var. *columnare*, var. *glabrum*, var. *potosinum* & fa. *nudum*, var. *strongylogonum*, fa. *quadricostatum*, fa. *tulense*), *A. ornatum* (& fa. *glabrescens*, fa. *mirbelii*), *A. senile*.

Recommended species: *A. asterias*. This needs care with watering. It is a slow growing species, solitary, to about 4 in (10 cm) wide with up to 10 flat ribs, commonly 8, with round, tufted areoles down the rib centres. Flowers are a dusky yellow with reddish throat. A gritty compost to ensure good drainage is essential, and a late start for watering in spring. It is found in south-eastern Texas, USA and in north-eastern Mexico.

A. capricorne grows eventually to about 9 in (25 cm) tall and about 4–5 in (10–13 cm) wide, but it is slow growing and more often is seen at half or less than this size. The distinguishing feature is the heavy covering of brown or black twisting and interlacing spines, up to 3–4 in (7–10 cm) long. White tufted flocking on the body is variable and often sparse. Flowers are large, to about 3 in (7 cm) long and wide, bright yellow with red throat. The forms

listed above are minor variants. Reported from northern Mexico.

A. myriostigma is such a variable species that it has given rise to several varietal names most of which hardly represent more than slight variation. Characteristically this species has usually 5 ribs, edged more or less prominently with tufted areoles and with no spines. The body is more or less covered with white tufted flecks, sometimes so dense as to give the plant a completely white or greyish-white aspect, but sometimes completely absent so that the green body colour is apparent. Flowers are usually smaller than other species, all yellow, to about 2 in (6 cm) wide, with black tipped outer petals.

Reported from Mexico, in the central to northern highlands.

A. ornatum is the giant of the genus, growing to 9 feet (3 m) tall and a foot (30 m) wide, but in cultivation rarely seen more than a foot or so (30 cm) tall and wide. Usually there are 8 ribs, acute and sometimes wavy, spiralling, with well separated, tufted areoles bearing 5 to 11 strong, 1–1½ in (3–4 cm) long, brown or yellow spines. The white flecking varies, but is seldom as dense as seen in *A. myriostigma*, and often patchy, giving rise to the two forms: fa. *glabrescens*, for nearly fleckless forms, and fa. *mirbelii*, for heavily-flecked yellow-spined forms. Flowers are up to 9 cm wide, all yellow.

Reported from Mexico, Hidalgo to Queretaro.

A. senile has similar spines to *A. capricorne*, but less dense, and with little flecking on the body. Otherwise there is

7. Astrophytum senile

8. Astrophytum asterias × myriostigma (hybrid)

little difference.

There are also in cultivation numerous hybrids between the species, particularly involving *A. asterias*, and some of them are very handsome.

Connoisseur's choice: all species are well worth growing, and fall comfortably within the 'connoisseur' category, but the doyen of the genus is undoubtedly the smallest, and the most difficult to cultivate well – *A. asterias*.

Austrocactus B. & R., *The Cact.* 3:44, fig. 56 (1922)

This genus is high in Debrett's 'Aristocacti'. It comes from Patagonia in Argentina, and presents some difficulty in cultivation. In the past, imported plants have been difficult to establish, often drying up without ever forming roots, but seed is often offered these days, and with care seedlings may be brought to maturity and flowered. Grafting is sometimes resorted to, and such plants grown 'hard', i.e. with a lean compost of high grit content and not overwatered, will develop their strong spines and grow into attractive plants. Temperature is no problem, except perhaps that growers may sometimes keep them warmer than they need to be. They come from southern Argentina, and southern upper Chile. All species are columnar, tuberculate, and very spiny, the central spines often hooked.

Species named are few, dubiously distinct: *A bertinii, A. coxii, A. gracilis, A. hibernus, A. patagonicus, A. phillippii, A. spiniflorus.*

Connoisseur's choice: any that can be obtained are worth growing – *A. patagonicus* is the name most frequently seen offered.

Austrocephalocereus Backeb. (1938)

Referred to *Cephalocereus.*

Austrocylindropuntia Backeb. (1938)

This is a name coined by Backeberg for a group of about 20 cylindrical stemmed *Opuntia* species coming from south America, in Ecuador, Peru, Chile, Bolivia, northern Argentina and Paraguay. While *Cylindropuntia* as a subgenus distinguishes for collectors the cylindrical rather than the disc shaped jointed species in the large, widespread genus *Opuntia*, it is doubtful whether a further division for the more southerly growing species is necessary or desirable, and it is here regarded as synonymous with subgenus *Cylindropuntia* beneath the overall genus *Opuntia*.

Aylostera Speg. (1923)

This genus has been generally accepted for some time as part of the wide view of the genus *Rebutia*, see under that name.

Aztekium Boed. *Monatsschr. Deutsche Kakt. Gesell.* 1:52 (1929)

There has been little, if any, suggestion of merging this very individual species with any other genus, although it is the only one in the genus. Its unique form sets it apart, spineless (except in very young growth), wrinkly-ribbed, slow growing in the extreme, and small (to about 2 in/5 cm) tall and wide. It is not easy to cultivate successfully, although once its nature is accepted (it grows embedded in near vertical cliff faces), and an open gritty compost provided, with carefully spaced out watering, it will settle down to flower and grow imperceptibly each year, eventually offsetting around the base to form a small clump. Grafted plants should be treated very harshly if anything like the typical form is to be maintained, otherwise they become green and bloated and smother themselves with offsets – keep them in a smallish pot with an open, gritty compost in maximum light, and water sparingly. Propagation from seed is almost impossible. Reported from Nuevo Leon in Mexico.

Recommended species and ***connoisseur's choice*** (the only one): *Aztekium ritteri.*

Azureocereus Akers & Johnson, (1949)

Referred to *Browningia.*

Backebergia Bravo (1954)

Because of its distinct, very attractive yellow cephalium like a colourful busby produced at the top of stems several metres tall in Michoacan, Mexico, this monotypic genus (*Backebergia militaris*) has resisted submerging in Hunt's wider concept of *Cephalocereus*, and is still commonly listed and referred to under this name. But however individual the species the separation has no merit – see under *Cephalocereus.*

Bartschella B. & R., (1923)

This is a monotypic genus (*Bartschella schumannii*) set up by Britton and Rose, and differentiated from *Mammillaria* in the way the fruit splits on ripening. It has long been regarded and accepted by most as submerged in *Mammillaria* – see under *Mammillaria.*

Bergerocactus B. & R., *Contr. U.S. Nat. Herb.* 12.435 (1909)

A monotypic genus (*Bergerocactus emoryi*) from south-west California, USA and Baja California, Mexico in the north-west, which Hunt (1967) submerged in *Echinocereus*, but which has been maintained separately from that genus and any other since that time. This is a good example of a plant which looks very well in the wild but grows unsatisfactorily in cultivation. It has an untidy, sprawling habit, with stems about 2–4 ft (a metre or so) long, an inch or two (4–5 cm) wide, densely yellow spined, and producing small yellow flowers, about an inch or so (3 cm) long and wide. In cultivation it grows reluctantly or untypically and rarely does well.

It is not recommended.

Blossfeldia Werderm., *Kakteenk.* 11:162 (1937)

This is the smallest cactus, with heads no more than about ½–¾ in (2–3 cm) across, clustering, but rarely seen on its own roots in cultivation for any length of time. It comes from northern Argentina and southern Bolivia.

It is possible to grow *Blossfeldia* species on their own roots, and a great deal of folklore surrounds their successful cultivation – varying from keeping the soil constantly damp to not watering the soil at all but just spraying the plants overhead daily. I have grown a small cluster successfully for a few years by striking the balance between these two extremes, watering thoroughly about once fortnightly in late spring and summer, and spraying quite heavily, as for Bromeliads, weekly throughout spring and summer and well into the autumn. But a better proposition is to graft on to a *Cereus*, or better a globular *Echinopsis* stock, growing the stock in a poor soil with sparse watering, so that the grafted *Blossfeldia* does not romp away and form a large, jostling clump of bloated heads – as is so often seen. Plants on *Echinopsis* are more easily sunk so that just the scion is above the soil level. Offsets from the stock should be removed rigorously as they appear to prevent their taking over or even pushing the scion off its graft.

There are numerous names, but probably only one variable species, the type, *B. liliputana*.

Species named are: *B. atroviridis* (& var. *intermedia*), *B. campaniflora*, *B. cyathiformis*, (*B. fechseri* = *B. liliputana* var. *fechseri*), *B. flocculosa*, *B. liliputana* (& var. *fechseri*, var. *formosa*), *B. minima*, *B. pedicellata*.

Recommended species and *connoisseur's choice* (there is little point in growing more than one): *B. liliputana* (or any other name), grafted, or, if you want a real challenge, on its own roots.

9. *Bergerocactus emoryi* (in habitat in northern Baja California, Mexico)

Bolivicereus Card. (1951)

Still popularly grown and listed as such by nurseries, the combination with *Borzicactus* is here accepted, see under that name.

Bonifazia Standley & Steyermark (1944)

Referred to *Disocactus*.

Borzicactella Ritt. (1981)

This is a small genus proposed by Ritter for species segregated by him from *Borzicactus*. Here regarded as *Borzicactus*.

Borzicactus Riccobono, *Boll. R. Ort. Bot. Palermo* 8:261 (1909); Kimnach, *Cact. Amer.* 32:8 et seq. (1960)

The admirably cogent, painstaking revision of *Borzicactus* by Kimnach is compulsory and compulsive reading for anyone interested in the taxonomy of cacti. It must also be read by anyone who doubts the wisdom of his combining in *Borzicactus* the several genera which fall into synonymy and, perhaps more importantly, his exclusion of other members of the subtribe *Borzicactinae*, i.e.

Borzicactus

Denmoza, Cleistocactus and *Oroya*. The main obstacle to acceptance of the amalgamation in collectors' minds is, I think, the diversity of form of species in such genera as *Matucana* and, say, *Bolivicereus*. But no such doubts, to quote Kimnach's parallels, are felt about comparable species in *Mammillaria* or *Echinocereus*, for instance.

The constant character of the revised concept of *Borzicactus* is the diurnal flower, which has an expanded, zygomorphic limb, the tepals on one side of the tube being almost erect, while those on the other side are more or less recurved.

The genera sunk beneath *Borzicactus* then and since, are: *Akersia, Arequipa, Arequipiopsis, Bolivicereus, Clistanthocereus, Eomatucana, Hildewintera* (and the synonymous *Winteria* and *Winterocereus*), *Loxanthocereus, Maritimocereus, Matucana, Morawetzia, Oreocereus, Seticereus, Submatucana.*

Species named (with more familiar allegiances abbreviated in brackets) are: *B. (Lox)acanthurus, B. (Subm)aurantiacus* (& var. *calvescens*), *B. (Subm)aureiflorus, B. (Hild)aureispinus, B. (Areq)australis, B. (Lox)bicolor, B. (Bol)brevicaulis, B. (Lox)brevispinus, B. cajamarcensis, B. (Mat)callianthus* (& var. *prolifera*), *B. (Mat)calocephalus, B. (Clist)calviflorus, B. (Lox)camanaensis, B. (Lox)canetensis, B. (Oreo)celsianus* (& var. *fossulatus*, var. *hendriksenianus*, var. *maximus*, var. *ritteri*, var. *trollii*, var. *variicolor*), *B. (Set)chlorocarpus, B. (Lox)convergens, B. (Bol)croceus, B. (Lox)cullmannianus, B. (Lox)deserticola, B. (Mor/Oreo)doelzianus* (& fa. *calvus*), *B. (Lox)erectispinus B.(Lox)eremiticus, B. (Lox)erigens, B. (Lox)eulalianus, B. (Lox)faustianus, B. (Lox)ferrugineus, B. (Clist) fieldianus* (& var. *tessellatus*), *B. (Mat/Subm)formosus, B. (Mat)fruticosus, B. (Lox)gracilius B. (Mat)hastifera, B. (Mat)haynei* (& var. *atrispinus*, var. *breviflorus*, var. *perplexus*), *B. (Lox)hoffmannii, B. huagalensis, B. (Lox)hystrix* (& var. *brunnescens*), *B. (Set)icosagonus* (& var. *aurantiaciflorus*, var. *ferrugineus*, var. *oehmeanus*), *B. (Subm) intertextus* (& var. *celendinensis*), *B. (Lox)jajoianus, B. (Lox)keller-badensis, B. knizei, B. (Mat)krahnii, B. (Areq) leucotrichus* (& var. *hempelianus*, var. *rettigii*, var. *spinosissimus*, var. *weingartianus*), *B. (Subm)madisoniorum* (& var. *pujupatii*), *B. (Mat)megalanthus, B. (Areq)mirabilis, B. (Lox)montanus, B. (Lox)multifloccosus, B. (Mat)myriacanthus, B. (Lox)neglectus* (& var. *chimbotensis*), *B. neoroezlii, B. (Eom)oreodoxus, B. (Lox)otuscensis, B. (Lox)pacaranensis, B. (Lox)pachycladus, B. (Mat)pallarensis, B. (Lox)parvitessellatus, B. (Subm)paucicostatus* (& fa. *robustispinus*), *B. (Lox)peculiaris, B. (Bol)-pisacensis, B. (Lox)piscoensis, B. pseudothelegonus, B. (Lox)-puquiensis, B. (Mat)purpureoalbus, B. purpureus, B. (Subm)ritteri, B. (Ak)roseiflorus, B. (Bol)rufus, B. (Bol) samaipatanus, B. (Clist)samnensis, B. sepium* (& var. *morleyanus*), *B. (Mor/Oreo)sericatus, B. (Bol)serpens, B. (Lox)sextonianus, B. (Bol)soukupi, B. (Lox)sulcifer, B. (Mat)supertextus, B. (Oreo) tacnaensis, B. (Bol)tenuiserpens,* *B. (Lox)trujilloensis, B. (Mat)tuberculosus, B. (Lox)variabilis, B. (Mat)winteri, B. (Lox)xylorhizus, B. (Lox)yauyosensis*

Rejected names and synonymies:

B. aequatioralis = B. sepium
B. (Lox)aticensis = B. sextonianus
B. aurivillus = B. icosagonus
B. (Mat)blancii & var. *nigriarmata = B. haynei* var. *perplexus*
B. (Mat)breviflorus = B. haynei var. *breviflorus*
B. (Subm)calvescens = B. aurantiacus var. *calvescens*
B. cantaensis = B. peculiaris
B. (Lox)casmaensis = Haageocereus pacalaensis
B. (Subm)celendinensis = B. intertextus var. *celendinensis*
B. (Mat)cereoides = B. haynei
B. (Lox)clavispinus = Haageocereus pacalaensis
B. (Mat)comacephalus = B. haynei var. *perplexus*
B. (Oreo)crassiniveus = B. celsianus var. *trollii*
B. (Lox)crassiserpens = B. serpens × B. icosagonus
B. (Mat)criniferus = B. haynei var. *perplexus*
B. (Subm)currundayensis = B. aurantiacus var. *calvescens*
B. (Mat)elongatus = B. haynei var. *atrispinus*
B. (Areq)erectocylindricus = B. leucotrichus var. *rettigii*
B. (Lox)eriotrichus = B. acanthurus
B. (Mat/Subm)formosus var. *minor = B. formosus*
B. (Oreo)fossulatus = B. celsianus var. *fossulatus*
B. (Marit/Lox)gracilis = B. sextonianus
B. (Lox)gracilispinus = B. acanthurus
B. (Lox)granditessellatus = B. sulcifer
B. (Mat)haynei var. *erectipetalus = B. haynei*
B. (Areq)hempelianus = B. leucotrichus var. *hempelianus*
B. (Oreo)hendriksenianus = B. celsianus var. *hendriksenianus*
B. (Mat)herzogianus & var. *perplexus = B. haynei* var. *perplexus*
B. (Set)humboldtii = B. icosagonus
B. (Mat)hystrix & vars. *= B. haynei* var. *atrispinus*
B. (Oreo)maximus = B. celsianus var. *maximus*
B. morleyanus = B. sepium var. *morleyanus*
B. (Mat)multicolor = B. haynei var. *atrispinus*
B. (Lox)nanus = B. sextonianus
B. (Oreo)neocelsianus = B. celsianus
B. (Set)oehmianus = B. icosagonus
B. plagiostomus = B. icosagonus
B. (Lox)pullatus & vars. *= B. acanthurus*
B. (Areq)rettigii = B. leucotrichus var. *rettigii*
B. (Oreo)ritteri = B. celsianus var. *ritteri*
B. (Set)roezlii = B. neoroezlii
B. (Clist)samnensis var. *fuscatus = B. variabilis*
B. (Areq)soehrensii = B. leucotrichus var. *rettigii*
B. (Areq)spinosissimus = B. leucotrichus var. *spinosissimus*
B. (Lox)splendens = B. gracilis
B. (Clist)tessellatus = B. fieldianus var. *tessellatus*
B. (Oreo)trollii = B. celsianus var. *trollii*
B. (Mat)variabilis = B. haynei

10. *Borzicactus (Oreocereus) celsianus* var. *hendriksenianus*

B. *(Areq/Oreo)variicolor* = B. *celsianus* var. *variicolor*
B. *ventimigliae* = B. *sepium*
B. *(Mat)weberbaueri* = B. *aurantiacus*
B. *websterianus* (& var. *rufispinus*) = B. *sepium*
B. *(Areq)weingartianus* & var. *carminanthinus* = B.
    leucotrichus var. *weingartianus*
B. *(Mat)yanganucensis* = B. *haynei* var. *perplexus*.

Recommended species: B. *(Hildewintera)aureispinus*
makes a magnificent hanging plant if planted in a large
container and placed so that the arching semi-pendant
stems, a little thicker than a man's thumb, can hang
unobstructed in good light, when it will produce a succession of the pale orange coloured flowers on each stem
throughout the spring and summer months. The stems
have the added attraction of being thickly clothed with
soft, bristly spines in deep golden-yellow. Old stems that
have gone brown are best cut out to encourage more
young stems to develop; although this will mar them as
show plants.
B. *(Oreocereus) celsianus* in any of its varieties is among
the best of columnar plants seen in collections, densely
covered with long, silky, protective, hair like spines twisting this way and that, through which the strong, long
spines of its armament protrude erratically from the hidden areoles. It is slow growing, and if quicker, more
regular growth is desired, it can with advantage be grafted
on to a good sized piece of grafting stock of a more quick
growing nature. Flowers are rare in England for this or
similar ex-Oreocereus species. B. *celsianus* var. *trollii* is
smaller growing than most other varieties, and conse-

quently clusters at a smaller size to make an attractive
clump of hairy stems with usually red central spines. B.
celsianus var. *hendriksenianus* or var. *maximus* are both
strong growing potential giants if you prefer to go for
the big ones, with variably coloured central spines from
yellow to brown.
B. *(Seticereus) icosagonus*, if room can be found to accommodate its feet long ($\frac{1}{2}$ m or so) sprawling, 2 in (5 cm)
thick stems, is a lovely, golden spined plant to grow, and
will readily produce its orange flowers at the ends of
stems once they get to about a foot (30 cm) or more long,
and produce the more bristly area from which they arise,
a sort of pseudo-cephalium.
B. *(Matucana) haynei*: the *Matucana* species in the narrow
sense had boiled down to barely one or two species
(Ritter's recent erections of *Matucana* species have yet to
be assessed for merit), under the prior name 'haynei',
beneath which many names were reduced. It is a globular
to short columnar species, densely covered with incurving, white to pale yellow spines, more or less tipped
brown. Flowers are fiery red, pushing out through the
basket of spines at the apex, and not too readily produced
in England, except where a sunny position can be provided.
B. *(Arequipa)leucotrichus* var. *rettigii*: the former *Arequipa*
species have been reduced to one variably spined species:
B. *leucotrichus* makes slow, columnar plants to about 6–
8 in (15–20 cm) tall in 10 years or so, and will in age
produce basal offsets. A good sunny position is needed
to produce the deep red flowers at the apex, usually late
summer in England. B. *leucotrichus* var. *rettigii* is darker
spined than most other varieties.
B. *(Submatucana) madisoniorum*: the *Submatucana* species
had not enjoyed such wide acceptance as some of the
other genera submerged here, and were already combined
by some authorities with *Matucana*, or rather the split
away from *Matucana* was not accepted. Unlike the *Matucana* species in the narrow sense, they more readily produce flowers, and are immediately distinguishable by their
more open bodies with less spination. In this species it is
taken to its extreme, as the few spines it does produce
are lightly attached and easily fall, leaving a spineless,
globular, grey-green plant getting to about 3–4 in (8–
10 cm) tall and wide, eventually offsetting to form clumps,
gloriously surmounted by several bright red flowers at
the growing point.
B. *(Submatucanus) paucicostatus* is a smaller growing species, with persistent curving, brownish-yellow spines, and
similar freely produced red flowers, making quite large
clumps of stems to about 8–10 in (20–25 cm) eventually.
B. *(Akersia)roseiflorus* is a columnar, sprawling, narrow-
stemmed species, with golden yellow spines and beautiful
pink flowers. It is seldom seen as a well-grown plant, but
pays for patience.

11. *Borzicactus (Submatucana) paucicostatus*

B. (Bolivicereus)samaipatanus has such wonderful flowers, so often featured on book covers and in general books in the past, bright red with pink edged petals, that one can forgive its space–invading nature, the thick, sprawling stems taking up yards of room given half a chance. It is best treated as a subject for a hanging pot, so that the weight of its stems encourages it to make less use of the air space around it than if left on the bench, when it will wander among some of your less strenuous fellow plants with gay abandon. The stems are quite heavily spined, but not so densely as in the similar sort of plant, *B. aureispinus*, described above. The colour is usually yellow or yellowish-brown.

Connoisseur's choice: *B. aureispinus, B. icosagonus, B. haynei, B. madisoniorum.*

Brachycalycium Backeb. (1942)

Although still listed by some devoted Backebergian continental nurseries as such, this monotypic genus (*B. tilcarense*) is usually regarded as synonymous with *Gymnocalycium* – see under that name.

Brachycereus B. & R. *The Cact.* 2:120, figs 179, 180 (1920)

A rare, monotypic genus (*B. nesioticus*) from the Galapagos Islands in the Pacific Ocean, of Darwinian fame, rarely seen offered for sale. It is a slow growing shortly columnar cactus with dense brown spines, with little appeal, except for its rarity, to any but the *Cereus* enthusiast. It is not recommended.

Brasilicactus Backeb. (1942)

There is some illogicality in the general acceptance of this genus and *Eriocactus* as synonymous with *Notocactus*, as they are such different looking plants in many ways.

But this *is* the general opinion as well as that of most taxonomists concerned with the Cactaceae, and so they are herein included under *Notocactus*.

Brasilicereus Backeb. (1938)

Referred to synonymy with *Monvillea*.

Brasilopuntia (K. Schum.) Bgr. (1926)

The four species erected in this genus are tree-like Opuntias with very thin, leaf-like segments, occurring in Brazil, Paraguay, Peru, eastern Bolivia and eastern Argentina, and are regarded herein as synonymous with the broad concept of the genus *Opuntia*. Their vigorous growth and requirements for somewhat warmer conditions than most *Opuntia* species makes them unsuitable for most collectors, although they are among the few Opuntias which will flower without too much trouble. See under *Opuntia*.

Brasiliparodia Ritt. (1979)

This is a generic name set up by Ritter for a fine-spined group of *Notocactus* species with affinities to *Parodia*. See under *Notocactus*.

Brittonia Houghton ex C. A. Armstrong (1934)

Referred to *Thelocactus*.

Brittonrosea Speg. (1923)

See under *Stenocactus*.

Browningia B. & R. *The Cact.* 2:63, figs 92–94 (1920)

The original concept of this genus has been expanded to embrace *Azureocereus, Castellanosia, Gymnanthocereus, Gymnocereus* and *Rauhocereus*. While *Azureocereus* is often seen in cultivation (seldom as yet labelled *Browningia*) the others (including *Browningia* in the narrow sense) are seldom grown at all, as their attraction is primarily as mature plants of considerable size in the wild.

Named species are: *B. albiceps, B. (Gymno)altissimus, B. (Gymno)amstutziae, B. (Cas)caineana, B. candelaris, B. cillisquama, B. columnaris, B. (Azur)hertlingianus, B. icaensis, B. macracantha, B. (Gymno)microsperma, B. (Gymno)pilleifera, B. (Rauh)riosaniensis (& var. jaenensis) B. (Azur) viridis.*

Recommended species: the only one of note really, except for *Cereus* enthusiasts, is *B. hertlingianus*, which will make attractive, blue columns to 3 ft (1 m) or so tall

12. *Carnegiea gigantea* (in Arizona, dwarfing two English cactus enthusiasts, Keith Grantham and Derek Bowdery)

13. Top of cristate *Carnegiea gigantea* in Arizona (about 10 ft/3 m across)

n eight to 10 years, with yellow to brown spines, and, if you are lucky, flowers may be produced from black, hairy buds after about 2 ft (60 cm) height is achieved.

Connoisseur's choice: B. (*Azureocereus*) *hertlingianus*.

Buiningia F. Buxb. in Krainz (1971)

A genus of fat-stemmed, shortly-columnar plants from Brazil, which fall under the wide concept of *Cephalocereus*.

Calymmanthium Ritter in Backeb. *Die Cact.* 2:886 1959), not validly published, and in *Kakt. u.a. Sukk.* 13:25, figs. 1–3 (1962)

Cephalocereus

A genus of two species (*C. fertile* and *C. substerile*) with three or four acutely angled ribs to the columnar stems, and with unusual, partly sheathed flowers. Found by Ritter in northern Peru, this genus is of interest only to *Cereus* enthusiasts. It is not recommended.

Carnegiea B. & R., *Journ. N. York Bot. Gard.* 9:187 (1908)

It may seem hard to dismiss this well-known epitome of the cactus family, the Giant Saguaro of the southern United States, but while in the wild it is magnificent, in cultivation it is painfully slow-growing from seed and takes 20 years to make 1–2 ft (to 60 cm) in height. It is of interest only to (young) *Cereus* enthusiasts, and is not recommended. The one species is *C. gigantea*.

Castellanosia Card. (1951)

Referred to *Browningia*.

Cephalocereus Pfeiff. *Allg. Gartenz.* 6:142 (1838)

This old generic name is now taken to embrace tropical and sub-tropical species of columnar cacti which form a cephalium from which the flowers emerge. Genera subsumed in *Cephalocereus* are: *Arrojadoa*, *Austrocephalocereus*, *Backebergia*, *Buiningia*, *Coleocephalocereus*, *Espostoopsis*, *Haseltonia*, *Micranthocereus*, *Mitrocereus*, *Neobuxbaumia*, *Neodawsonia*, *Pilocereus*, *Pilosocereus*, *Pseudopilocereus*, *Stephanocereus*, *Subpilocereus*.

This amalgamation makes a good deal of sense in what was a splintered group of separate genera with essentially similar flower characteristics. This ultra-splitting of genera of the Cactaceae does nothing to help the understanding of the relationships of the various species, and the broader generic concept has become much more widely accepted over the last few years by both the leading taxonomists concerned with the Cactaceae and by collectors looking for a more radical approach to nomenclature of these plants.

Species named (with other allegiances in brackets and abbreviated to the first few letters) are: *C.* (*Col/Aus/Mic*)-*albicephalus*, *C.*(*Arr*)*albiflorus*, *C.* (*Pilos*)*alensis*, *C.* (*Neod*)*apicephalium*, *C.* (*Pilos*)*arenicola*, *C.* (*Pilos/Pseud*)*arrabidae*, *C.* (*Pilos*)*atroflavispinus*, *C.* (*Sub*) *atroviridis*, *C.* (*Col/Pilos*)*aureispinus*, *C.* (*Col/Buin*)*aureus*, *C.* (*Mic*)*auri-azureus*, *C.* (*Pilos*)-*aurilanatus*, *C.* (*Pilos*)*azureus*,* *C.* (*Pilos*)*bahamensis*, *C.* (*Pilos*)-*barbadensis*, *C.* (*Pilos/Pseud*)*bradyi*, *C.* (*Pilos*)*brasiliensis*, *C.* (*Col*)*braunii*, *C.* (*Buin*)*brevicylindricus* (& var. *elongatus*, var.

* This is *C. azureus* as described by Ritter; for *C. azureus* Buining & Brederoo, see synonymies below.

longispinus), C. (Pilos)brooksianus, C. (Arr)canudosensis, C. (Pilos)catalinii, C. (Pilos)catingicola, C. (Pilos)chrysacanthus, C.Pilos/(Pseud)chrysostele, C.(Pilos)claroviridis, C.(Piloc/Pilos)-coerulescens, C. (Pilos)collinsii, C. (Pilos)colombianus, C. (Has)-columna-trajani, C. (Pilos)cometes, C. (Pilos)cuyabayensis, C. (Pilos)cyaneus, C.(Col)decumbens, C.(Pilos)deeringii, C.(Pilos)-densiareolatus, C. (Pseud)diersianus, C. (Arr)dinae, C. (Aus)-dolichospermaticus, C. (Aus/Col/Esp)dybowskii, C. (Arr)erio-caulis (& var. albicoronata), C. (Aus)estevesii, C. (Mic)flavi-florus, C. (Pseud/Pilos)flavipulvinatus (& var. carolinensis), C. (Col)flavisetus, C. (Pseud/Pilos)floccosus, C. (Aus/Col)-fluminensis (& var. braamhaari), C. (Mit)fulviceps, C. (Pseud/Pilos)fulvilanatus, C. (Pilos)gaturianensis, C.(Pilos)gaumeri, C. (Pilos)gironensis, C. (Piloc/Pilos/Pseud)glaucescens, C. (Pilos/Pseud)glaucochrous, C.(Col) goebelianus, C.(Pilos)gounellii, C. (Sub)grenadensis, C. (Pilos)gruberi, C. (Pilos)guerreronis, C. (Mic)haematocarpus, C.(Pilos/Pseud)hapalacanthus, C.(Pilos)-hermentianus, C. (Sub)horrispinus, C. (Arr)horstianus, C. (Pilos)houlletii, C. (Pilos)lanuginosus, C. (Pilos)leucoce-phalus, C. (Steph) leucostele, C. (Pilos/Col)luetzelbergii, C. (Pilos/Pseud)magnificus, C. (Pilos)maxonii, C. (Pilos/Pseud)-medirisii, C. (Neob)mexcalensis, C. (Back)militaris, C. (Pilos)-millspaughii, C. (Pilos)monoclonus, C. (Mic)monteazulensis, C. (Pilos)moritzianus (& var. backebergii), C. (Pilos)mortensis, C. (Pseud/Pilos)mucosiflorus, C. (Neob)multiareolatus, C. (Pilos)multicostatus, C. (Arr)multiflorus, C. (Neod)nizandensis, C. (Pilos/Pseud)nobilis, C. (Pilos/Pseud)oligolepis, C. (Pilos)-oreus, C. (Pilos/Sub)ottonis, C. (Pilos)pachycladus, C. (Pilos)-palmeri, C. (Pilos)paraguayensis, C. (Pseud)parvus, C. (Col)-paulensis, C. (Arr)penicillatus (& var. decumbens, var. spino-sior), C. (Piloc/Pilos/Pseud)pentaedrophus, C. (Pilos)pernam-bucoensis (& var. caesius, var. montealtoi), C. (Pilos/Pseud)-piauhyensis, C. (Col)pluricostatus, C. (Mic)polyanthus, C. (Pilos)polygonus, C.(Neob)polylophus, C.(Aus/Mic)purpureus, C. (Pilos)purpusii, C. (Pilos)quadricentralis, C. (Pilos)quadri-costatus, C. (Sub)remolinenais, C. (Sub)repandus, C. (Arr)rho-danthus (& subsp. reflexus, & var. occibahiensis), C. (Pilos)-robustus, C. (Pilos)rosae, C. (Pilos)royenii, C. (Mit)ruficeps,* C. (Pilos/Pseud)rupicolus, C. (Pseud)ruschianus, C. (Sub)russel-ianus (& var. microanthus), C. (Pilos/Aus)salvadorensis, C. (Pilos)sartorianus, C. (Pilos)saudadensis, C. (Neob)scoparius C. (Pseud/Pilos)sergipensis, C. (Pilos)splendidus, C. (Pilos) sub-lanatus, C. (Pilos)supthutianus, C. (Pilos)superbus (& var. gaca-paensis, var. lanosior, var. regius), C. (Pseud/Pilos)superflocco-sus, C. (Pilos)swartzii, C. (Pilos)tehuacanus, C. (Neob)tetetzo, C. (Arr)theunissenianus, C. (Pilos)tillianus, C. (Neod)totoralen-sis, C. (Pilos/Pseud)tuberculatus, C. (Pilos/Pseud)tuberculosus, C. (Pilos)tweedyanus, C. (Mic)uilianus, C. (Pilos/Pseud)ulei, C. (Pilos/Pseud)urbanianus, C.(Pseud)vilaboensis, C.(Mic)vio-laciflorus, C. (Pseud/Pilos)werdermannianus (& var. densila-natus var. diamentinensis), C. (Pilos)zehntneri.

* Because of this prior name *Micranthocereus ruficeps* on transfer here needs a new name.

Rejected names and synonymies:

C. (Pilos/Pseud)aurisaetus = C. coerulescens
C. (Pseud)azureus Buin. & Bred. = C. cyaneus
C. (Aus/Col/Mic)lehmannianus = C. purpureus
C. (Col/Pilos)minensis = Cipocereusminensis

It must be said that there seems to be a superfluity of names of species in this genus, but rationalization needs such lengthy and laborious study over a vast area, that it is unlikely to be reduced to any significant extent for many years.

Recommended species: many of the more recent intro-ductions are worth a try, especially those with blue col-oured stems, which make most attractive additions to a collection. Even as young plants many species develop this colouring, and after about 2 feet (60 cm) in height they begin to show more wool on the new growth, which ultimately becomes the cephalium, a thick woolled area from which the flowers emerge, when they get to about 5–6 feet (2 m) in height. In some species the cephalium develops at smaller sizes, since the plants are smaller anyway, and flowers may be expected after they reach about 18 in (45 cm) in height; former *Arrojadoa* and *Mic-ranthocereus* species fall into this category, and the former genus *Buiningia* contain species which get to no more than about a foot tall, being squatter, thick stemmed growers, developing cephalium at about 6 in (15 cm) tall. But these species, coming as they do from tropical areas in the main, require extra warmth in the winter months and a minimum temperature of 55° F (13° c) is safest to prevent any marking of the stems through chilling.

C. auri-azureus makes short, arching, blue, branching stems to about 2 feet (60 cm) long, and about 1 ½ in (4 cm) thick, covered with dense yellow to yellowish-brown spines and will produce a cephalium and dozens of its small reddish-pink flowers after it gets to about a foot or so (30 cm).

C. dolichospermaticus is one of the most attractive of the blue stemmed, tall growing species, looking marvellous in its young growth as well as in maturity.

C. estevesii has variably coloured spines, densely clothing the columnar stem, from yellowish-brown to red-brown the stem becoming blue at an early stage, contrasting well with the spines.

C. militaris is not an attractive plant in its youth, but its stunning beauty as a mature plant must be acknowledged with tall, 12 feet (4 m) or more stems crowned with a golden busby or bearskin of bristles through which the creamy white flowers emerge. Hopes of producing a cephalium from seed grown plants are remote and it would take many years. One or two very good growers have managed to keep rooted topcuts of this species most imported died without forming roots, and many of those which did for a brief period grow, did so as new green stem emerging through the cephalium, producing some odd looking plants.

C. palmeri is a better proposition to get to flowering size from seedlings, and the process can be hastened by grafting on to a more robust stock. The densely woolly growth produced is a glorious sight on a greyish blue stem, and even in youth the seedling plants start to develop a more hirsute aspect at about 6 in (15 cm) in height.

C. penicillatus, like others of the former genus *Arrojadoa*, makes narrow stems, requiring support after they get to a foot (30 cm) or so tall. At this height flowers may be expected, developing from the tuft of bristles which appear at the top of the stem when the plant is mature enough. Subsequent growth is made through the bristly cephalium, which remains as a collar marking the end of the previous year's growth, and from which flowers will develop as well as at the current year's cephalium. The flowers themselves are to be marvelled at in their waxy structure, pink becoming black as they fade and fall. In other species they are also red or white. These species need 55° F (13° c) for safety.

C. senilis is so well known that few can be unfamiliar with it, familiarly called 'the Old Man of the Andes', because of the white hair produced in youth having the distinct appearance of a white-haired old man. As a young plant it presents few problems, and will grow quite quickly to several inches tall without trouble. After this it seems

more difficult to persuade to behave itself, being prone to go off its roots at the least excuse, or develop unsightly black, corky patches. Some old-fashioned treatment in clay pots and with very gritty compost has given me best results; too much root room is not advisable, and not too much water at any time.

Connoisseur's choice: *C. estevesii, C. palmeri, C. penicillatus.*

Cephalocleistocactus Ritt. (1959)

The few species named under this genus, separated from *Cleistocactus* because of the production of a more densely bristled area when flowering, are regarded as insufficiently distinct to warrant separation. See under *Cleistocactus*.

Cereus Mill., *Gard. Dict.* abr. ed., 4 (1754)

It is sometimes surprising with the wealth of prefixes to this name that have appeared over the last half century, to come across the plain unadorned name *Cereus*. But there are about 50 species from the West Indies and east tropical south America and down to Argentina, which still bear the name without prefix, although most are of little interest to collectors except for the enthusiast for columnar cacti.

Piptanthocereus is referred here.

14. *Cephalocereus leucostele* (seedling)   15. *Cephalocereus polylophus* (seedling)   16. *Cephalocereus senilis* (bedded out in California, USA)

Species named are: *C. aethiops* (& var. *landbeckii*, var. *melanacanthus*), *C. alacriportanus*, *C. argentinensis*, *C. azureus*, *C. bageanus*, *C. braunii*, *C. cabralens*, *C. caesius*, *C. calcirupicola* (& var. *pluricostatus*), *C. chacoanus*, *C. chalybaeus*, *C. childsii*, *C. cipoensis*, *C. colosseus*, *C. comarapanus*, *C. crassisepalus*, *C. dayamii*, *C. eriophorus* (& var. *fragrans*), *C. forbesii* (& var. *bolivianus*), *C. glaucus*, *C. goiasensis*. *C. gracilis* (& var. *aboriginus*, var. *simpsonii*), *C. grandicostatus*, *C. hankeanus*, *C. hertrichianus*, *C. hexagonus*, *C. hildmannianus*, *C. horridus* (& var. *alatosquamatus*), *C. huilunchu*, *C. huntingtonianus*, *C. insularis*, *C. jamacaru*, *C. jugatiflorus*, *C. lamprospermus*, *C. lanosus*, *C. lindenzweigianus*, *C. milesimus*, *C. neonesioticus* (& var. *interior*), *C. neotetragonus*, *C. obtusus*, *C. pachyrhizus*, *C. perlucens*, *C. pernambucensis*, *C. peruvianus* (& var. *monstrosus*, var. *ovicarpus*, var. *persicinus*, var. *proferrens*, var. *reclinatus*, var. *tortuosus*), *C. pseudocaesius*, *C. ridlei*, *C. robinii* (& var. *deeringii*), *C. roseiflorus*, *C. seidelii*, *C. sericifer*, *C. stenogonus*, *C. tacuaralensis*, *C. torulosus*, *C. trigonodendron*, *C. uruguayensis*, *C. validus*, *C. vargasianus*, *C. xanthocarpus*.

Recommended species: *C. aethiops*. A slender species making about 5–6 feet (2 m) of growth in cultivation without too much hesitation if potted on regularly in the early years, with stems to about 1–1 ½ in (3–4 cm) wide, fairly densely clothed with clusters of black or dark brown spines. It has the advantage of being about the only species which will produce flowers at a modest height, and they can be expected when it has reached about 1 ½– 2 ft (45–60 cm) tall. As with all this genus the flowers are white, opening in the evening and lasting two or three days at most; some species have white flowers flushed pale pink.

C. peruvianus must be mentioned if only for the very popular monstrose form, which can be grown to a magnificent heap of jostling, oddly shaped stems, with an attractive blue colouring to the body.

C. chalybaeus is another with attractive blue colouring and with black spines on quite sharply defined ribs. It makes a colourful column about 2 in (5 cm) or more thick.

Connoisseur's choice: *C. aethiops*.

Chamaecereus B. & R. (1922)

In spite of repeated sinking beneath *Lobivia* this name still surfaces for this very individual species. And although regarded herein as a *Lobivia*, it is worth mentioning the proliferation of hybrids with other *Lobivia* species, generally referred to as Chamaelobivias. Many do no credit to the raiser, and do not improve on either parent, but a few have been produced with typical *Chamaecereus* habit, but with thicker stems and are grown principally for their free and improved colour flowering capabilities. There are one or two good yellow flowered, and the names Chamaelobivia 'Pres. Calvinii' and Chamaelobivia

'Kent Sunrise' are attached to two of the best, with respectively pure yellow flowers, and yellow inner and pink outer petals; there is too a good purple flowered one called Chamaelobivia 'Peclard' and a scarlet flowered one with purple flush to the inner petals called Chamaelobivia 'Shot Scarlet'; Chamaelobivia 'Satsuma' is a clear orange flowered hybrid.

Chiapasia B. & R. (1923)

This is a monotypic genus (*C. nelsonii*) referred to *Disocactus*.

Chileorebutia Ritt. (1959)

Referred to *Neoporteria*.

Chilita Orcutt (1926)

Referred to *Mammillaria*.

Cinnabarinea Fric ex Ritt., *Kakt. Sudamer.* 2:633 (1980)

This is a recent genus set up for species of *Lobivia* and *Sulcorebutia*. The separation has not generally been accepted, nor yet properly evaluated by others, and in this book the species are left in their former genera. For interest the species so named, with their allegiances in brackets and abbreviated are as follows: *C. (Lob)-acanthophlegma* (& var. *laneosiphus*), *C. (Lob)boedekeriana*, *C. (Lob)cinnabarina*, *C. (Lob)neocinnabarina* (& var. *microthelis*), *C. (Sulc)purpurea*, *C. (Sulc)torotorensis*, *C. (Lob)-walterspielii* (& var. *sanguiniflora*), *C. (Lob)zudanensis*. See under *Lobivia* and *Sulcorebutia*.

Cipocereus Ritt., *Kakt. Sudamer.* 1:54 (1979)

This genus was set up by Ritter for two columnar, cephalium-less species from Brazil, close to *Cephalocereus* in the broad sense, but in view of their lack of cephalium, Ritter's placing is recognized for the present at least.

Species named are: *C. (Col/Pilos)minensis*, *C. pleurocarpus*. They are little known at present, but the first may be found listed, as indicated, as a *Coleocephalocereus* or *Pilosocereus*.

Cleistocactus Lem., *Illustr. Hort.* 8:Misc.35 (1861)

Species of this popular, but paradoxically neglected genus, are upright, clambering or decumbent, mostly narrow-stemmed, cylindrical plants, widespread in an area including the countries of Peru, Bolivia, Paraguay, Uruguay and northern Argentina. The 60 or so species could probably be rationalized to a smaller number, but with such a widespread genus there is little chance of that for some time to come. They are generally underrated as collectors' plants, with the exception of the very popular *C. strausii*, but most will flower at a modest size compared with most columnar genera of cacti, and are often densely clothed in yellow and brown spines of some attraction. They should be regularly potted on for the first few years to encourage rapid growth to flowering size when their full beauty will be realized. For many this is achieved at only one or two feet (30 to 60 cm) tall.

Species named are: *C. angosturensis*, *C. anguinus*, *C. apurimacensis*, *C. ayopayanus*, *C. azerensis*, *C. baumannii* (& var. *flavispinus*), *C. brevispinus*, *C. brookei* (& var. *flavispinus*), *C. bruneispinus*, *C. buchtienii* (& var. *flavispinus*), *C. candellila*, *C. capadalensis*, *C. chacoanus* (& var. *santacruzensis*), *C. chrysocephalus*, *C. clavicaulis*, *C. compactus*, *C. crassicaulis* (& var. *paucispinus*), *C. croceiflorus*, *C. dependens*, *C. flavescens* (& fa. *wendlandiorum*), *C. flavispinus*, *C. fusiflorus*, *C. glaucus* (& var. *plurispinus*), *C. granjaensis*, *C. grossei*, *C. hildegardiae*, *C. horstii*, *C. hyalacanthus*, *C. ianthinus*, *C. jugatiflorus*, *C. jujuyensis* (& var. *fulvus*), *C. laniceps* (& var. *plurispinus*), *C. luminosus*, *C. luribayensis*, *C. mendozae*, *C. micropetalus*, *C. morawetzianus* (& var. *arboreus*), *C. muyurinensis*, *C. orthogonus*, *C. palhuayensis* (& var. *camachoensis*), *C. pallidus*, *C. paraguayensis*, *C. parapetiensis*, *C. parviflorus* (& var. *comarapanus*, var. *herzogianus*), *C. piraymirensis*, *C. pojoensis*, *C. pungens*, *C. pycnacanthus*, *C. reae*, *C. ressinianus*, *C. ritteri*, *C. santacruzensis*, *C. schattatianus*, *C. smaragdiflorus* (& fa. *rojoi*, & var. *gracilior*), *C. strausii* (& var. *fricii*), *C. tarijensis*, *C. tominensis*, *C. tupizensis* (& var. *sucrensis*), *C. vallegrandensis*, *C. variispinus*, *C. villaazulensis*, *C. villamontesii* (& var *longiflorior*), *C. viridialabastri*, *C. viridiflorus*, *C. vulpis-cauda*.

Rejected names and synonymies:

C. rojoi = *C. smaragdiflorus* fa. *rojoi*
C. sucrensis = *C. tupizensis* var. *sucrensis*
C. wendlandiorum = *C. flavescens* fa. *wendlandiorum*.

Recommended species

(any which become available are worth trying, and few will disappoint, but the following selection is worth seeking out): *C. ritterii*, with inch-wide (2–3 cm) 3–5 feet long (1–1.5 m) arching stems densely clad with stiff, thin white spines, and freely producing its tubular yellow flowers; *C. santacruzensis*, surely the species flowering at the smallest height (about 6–9 in/15–20 cm), with pencil thin stems at this size, later to about 1½ in (4 cm) wide, and long spines standing straight out from the stems, the flowers red and yellow; *C. strausii*, the best known, producing arm thick straight columns up to 6 ft (2 m) or more tall, completely covered with thin, glassy white spines and producing its thick, tubular, deep red flowers after getting to about 1½ feet (45 cm) tall; *C. vulpis-cauda* with thick (1½ in/4 cm) pendant stems to about 3–4 feet (1 m or so) long, covered with soft, bristly

17. *Cleistocactus ritteri*

18. *Cleistocactus strausii*, bedded out in Lotusland, a private garden in California, USA

yellowish or reddish-brown spines, and producing its angled orange-red flowers throughout the growing season for six months or more.

Connoisseur's choice: *C. strausii*, *C. vulpis-cauda*.

Clistanthocereus Backeb. (1937)

Referred to *Borzicactus*.

Cochemiea

Cochemiea (K. Brandegee) Walton (1899)

Referred to *Mammillaria.*

Cochiseia Earle (1976)

This is a monotypic genus (*C. robbinsorum*), referred to *Escobaria.*

Coleocephalocereus Backeb. (1938)

This is a slow-growing genus of columnar plants now referred to consideration beneath the broad concept of *Cephalocereus.*

Coloradoa Boissevain (1947)

Referred to *Thelocactus.*

Copiapoa B. & R., *The Cact.* 3:85, t.10, figs 98–100 (1922); N.P. Taylor, *Cact. GB.* 43(2/3):49–60 (1981)

The magnificent plants of the larger-growing *Copiapoa* species in the wild can never be matched by their seed-grown counterparts in cultivation, and, although after some 10 or 15 years sizable, often non-flowering plants can be attained (in themselves extremely attractive) the better proposition for collectors is the smaller-growing species, which will mostly flower readily, and at a modest size of 2–3 in (5–8 cm) tall and wide.

Broadly Copiapoas fall into two categories as far as collectors are concerned: large and small. The large-growing species have mainly come into collectors' hands over the last 20 years or so as imported, wild plants, with all their native beauty from survival in the exposed coastal deserts of Chile, where they rely heavily, it is said, on coastal mists for their moisture supply. Some have survived and have produced their yellow, Hypericum-like flowers with fanned, prominent stamens, from the pad of yellow-brown wool at the growing point, but for every one that has lived, many have perished. Much more commonly collectors rely on seedling plants now, and in time they will make as beautiful, if not so weather-worn, plants, but I know of no one who has managed to flower such species grown from seed. Flowering can be achieved from the smaller growing species quite easily, and may be expected at only two or three years old, when they are barely more than about 1–2 in (3–5 cm) across.

Species named are: *C. alticostata, C. atacamensis, C. bridgesii, C. calderana, C. chaniaralensis, C. cinerascens* (& var. *intermedia*), *C. cinerea* (& var. *albispina,* var. *columna-alba,* var. *dealbata,* var. *haseltoniana*), *C. conglomerata, C. coquimbana* (& var. *wagenknechtii*), *C. cuprea, C. cupreata, C.*

19. *Copiapoa cinerea* (20 year old seedling, 4 in/10 cm in diameter)

20. *Copiapoa coquimbana*

21. *Copiapoa krainziana*

desertorum, C. dura, C. echinata (& fa. *pulla*), *C. echinoides,*
C. eremophila, C. esmeraldana, C. fiedleriana, C. grandiflora,
C. hornilloensis, C. humilis, C. hypogaea, C. krainziana, C.
laui, C. longispina, C. malletiana, C. marginata, C. megarhiza
(& var. *microrhiza*), *C. melanohystrix, C. mollicula, C.*
montana, C. olivana, C. paposoensis, C. pendulina, C. pepi-
niana, C. pseudocoquimbana (& var. *chaniarensis,* var. *domey-*
koensis, var. *vulgata*), *C. rarissima, C. rubriflora, C. rupestris,*
C. serenana, C. serpentisulcata, C. solaris, C. taltalensis, C.
tenebrosa, C. tenuissima, C. tocopillana, C. variispinata.

Rejected names and synonymies are:

C. applanata = C. cinerascens var. intermedia
C. barquitensis = C. hypogaea
C. boliviana = C. echinoides, but as applied by Ritter = C.
   atacamensi
C. calderana var. spinosior = C. calderana
C. carrizalensis = C. cinerea var. dealbata
C. columna-alba = C. cinerea var. columna-alba
C. columna-alba var. nuda = C. cinerea var. columna-alba
C. coquimbana var. armata = C. coquimbana var.
   wagenknechtii
C. dealbata = C. cinerea var. dealbata
C. ferox = C. solaris
C. gigantea = C. cinerea var. haseltoniana
C. haseltoniana = C. cinerea var. haseltoniana
C. hypogaea var. barquitensis = C. hypogaea
C. krainziana var. scopulina = C. krainziana
C. lembckei = C. calderana
C. longistaminea = C. cinerea
C. scopulina = C. krainziana

C. serpentisulcata var. castanea = C. serpentisulcata
C. streptocaulon = C. marginata
C. totoralensis = C. echinata
C. vallenarensis = C. fiedleriana
C. wagenknechtii = C. coquimbana var. wagenknechtii.

Recommended species: *C. cinerea* is perhaps the epitome of the beauty of the genus, and most collectors will have seen pictures of the superb clumps of this large-growing species grouped like strange beached sea-dwellers on the gradual slopes of the Chilean coastal area of Antofagasta. It is slow-growing, but makes a beautiful plant at any stage of its development; flowering is unlikely to be achieved with seedling plants, except with considerable age and in favoured sunny glasshouses, and imports of such plants are only obtainable nowadays from old collections, since the dubious 'slave-trade' in them has been outlawed.

C. hypogaea (often seen labelled as *C. barquitensis*) has a completely brown epidermis, with sparse, short black spines, and a prominent tuberculate structure in spirals. It forms small clumps of stems each about 5 cm or so tall and wide, and produces its yellow flowers readily, and at an early age.

C. krainziana is one of the most handsome of the larger growing types, and is popular with collectors even though its flowering is almost unknown, certainly in England. It forms clumps of globular, apple sized stems, with a brown epidermis and dense rows of flexible, bristlelike, white spines down the ribs, which are set at a slight angle from the vertical. It is prone to brown, disfiguring marking on the stems, perhaps caused by too low temperatures.

C. humilis, reckoned by Nigel Taylor to embrace among others the diminutive *C. tenuissima,* is a small-growing free-flowering species worth a place in any collection, with densely tubercled globular to short-columnar stems, getting to about 1.5–2 in (3–5 cm) wide, with short dark bristly spines, and brown epidermis; the flowers are produced as with all species at the crown and are pale, bright yellow.

Connoisseur's choice: *C. krainziana, C. tenuissima.*

Corryocactus B. & R., *The Cact.* 2:66, figs 99–103 (1920); Ritter, *Kakt. Sudamer.* 4-:1279, fig. 1136 et seq. (1981)

Very few mature species of this genus from Bolivia, Chile and Peru are seen in cultivation. They are usually erect, occasionally procumbent, narrow-cylindrical, branching plants, and will flower in cultivation at about 2–3 ft (75 cm–1 m) tall, or less. Their form and spination is not very appealing, but one or two are worth a place in a general collection, if only for their ability to flower, given

sunny conditions; more than this would be of interest only to *Cereus* enthusiasts. They are undemanding, and almost indestructible, but better results, as always, will be obtained if they are potted on frequently in the early years, to encourage quick growth and flowering capability. *Erdisia* and *Samaipaticereus corroanus* are referred hereunder (*Samaipaticereus inquisivensis* is referred to *Haageocereus inquisivensis*).

Species named (with former allegiances abbreviated in brackets) are:
C. acervatus, C. (Erd)apiciflorus, C. aureus, C. ayacuchoensis, C. brachycladus, C. brachypetalus, C. brevispinus, C. brevistylus (& var. *puquiensis*), *C. chachapoyensis, C. chavinilloensis, C.* (Sam)*corroanus, C. cuajonesensis, C.* (Erd)*erectus, C. gracilis, C. huincoensis, C. matucanensis, C. megarhizus, C. melaleucus, C. melanotrichus, C. odoratus, C. pilispinus, C. prostratus, C. pyroporphyranthus, C.* (Erd)*quadrangularis, C. quivillanus, C. serpens, C. solitarius, C.* (Erd)*squarrosus, C. tarijensis, C. tenuiculus.*

Rejected names and synonymies are:
C. apurimacensis = *C. ayacuchoensis*
C. (Erd) *aureispinus* = *C. erectus*
C. ayacuchoensis var. *leucacanthus* = *C. ayacuchoensis*
C. ayopayanus = *C. tarijensis*
C. charazanensis = *C. melanotrichus*
C. (Erd)*fortalazensis* = *C. tenuiculus*
C. heteracanthus = *C. ayacuchoensis?*
C. (Sam)*inquisivensis* = *Haageocereus inquisivensis*
C. krausii = *C. brevistylus*
C. (Erd)*maximus* = *C. apiciflorus*
C. melanotrichus var. *caulescens* = *C. melanotrichus*
C. (Erd)*meyenii* = *C. aureus*
C. otuyensis = *C. melanotrichus*
C. pachycladus = *C. brevistylus* var. *puquiensis*
C. perezianus = *C. tarijensis*
C. (Erd)*philippii* = *Austrocactus philippii*
C. pulquinensis = *C. melanotrichus*
C. puquiensis = *C. brevistylus* var. *puquiensis*
C. (Erd)*sextonianus* = *Borzicactus sextonianus*
C. (Erd)*spiniflorus* = *Austrocactus spiniflorus.*

Recommended species: few appear in cultivation, and they are little sought after, since neither the stems nor the spines have great appeal, but they will flower at about 18 in–2 ft (45–60 cm) tall, and for this perhaps warrant a place. *C. corroanus* and *C. erectus* are two that have appeared in cultivation from time to time, and obliged with blooms.

Corynopuntia F. M. Knuth (1935)

A group of *Opuntia* species separated for low-growing, ovoid-jointed species from southern USA and Mexico. With such a vast genus as the broad concept of *Opuntia*

22. *Copiapoa montana*

23. *Copiapoa tenuissima*

embraces, it is useful for collectors to have some sort of recognizable division into subgenera. Subgenus *Opuntia* is used for the flat, disc-shaped jointed species, *Cylindropuntia* for the Chollas with long cylindrical joints but also taking in *Corynopuntia*; and *Tephrocactus* for the southerly growing small, globular or short-ovoid species from Argentina and surrounds. This broad division into three subgenera is sufficient, and further division is really unnecessary. For *Corynopuntia* species, see under *Opuntia*, subgenus *Cylindropuntia*.

Coryphantha (Engelm.) Lem., *Les Cactees* 32 (1868)

This is an attractive genus of mainly low-growing, globular species from the south-west United States and Mexico. There is some taxonomic argument at present concerning the separation of the genus *Escobaria* from *Coryphantha*, and indeed in the past few years one or two species have crossed back and forth between these two genera, and some authorities take the view that *Escobaria* should be sunk completely beneath *Coryphantha*. Here the fringed and petalled flowered species with pitted seeds are taken to be *Escobaria* (including the well-known *Coryphantha vivipara* and its varieties), leaving *Coryphantha* for the more usual concept of *Coryphantha* species, mostly globular, many with prominent fat tubercles, and with few exceptions producing yellow flowers.

Species named are: *C. andreae, C. asterias, C. bergeriana, C. bernalensis, C. borwigii, C. bumamma, C. bussleri, C. calipensis, C. calochlora, C. chlorantha* (& var. *desertii*), *C. clava* (& var. *schlechtendalii*), *C. clavata* (& var. *ancistracantha*, var. *radicantissima*), *C. columnaris, C. compacta, C. conimamma, C. connivens, C. cornifera* (& var. *echinus*), *C. cornuta, C. cuencamensis, C. daimonoceras, C. delaetiana, C. delicata, C. densispina, C. difficilis, C. durangensis, C. echinoides, C. elephantidens* (& var. *barciae*), *C. erecta, C. exsudans, C. garessii, C. georgii, C. gladiispina, C. gracilis, C. grandis, C. grata, C. greenwoodii, C. guerkeana, C. indensis, C. jalpanensis, C. laui, C. longicornis, C. macromeris* (& var. *runyonii*), *C. maiz-tablasensis, C. maliterrarum, C. melleospina, C. neglecta, C. neoscheerii, C. obscura, C. octacantha, C. ottonis, C. pallida, C. palmeri, C. pectinata, C. pirtlei, C. poselgeriana* (& var. *saltillensis*), *C. potosiana, C. pseudoechinus, C. pseudonickelsae, C. pulleiniana, C. pusilliflora, C. pycnacantha, C. radians* (& var. *pectinoides*, var. *pseudoradians*), *C. ramillosa, C. recurvata, C. recurvispina, C. reduncuspina, C. retusa* (& var. *melleospina*, var. *pallidispina*), *C. roederiana, C. salm-dyckiana, C. scheerii* (& var. *robustispina*, var. *uncinata*, var. *valida*), *C. schwarziana, C. scolymoides, C. speciosa, C. sulcata* (& var. *nickelsae*), *C. sulcolanata, C. unicornis, C. valida, C. vaupeliana, C. villarensis, C. voghtherriana, C. werdermannii.*

Rejected names and synonymies are:

C. albicolumnaria = *Escobaria orcuttii*

C. alversonii = *Escobaria vivipara* var. *alversonii*
C. dasyacantha = *Escobaria dasyacantha*
C. duncanii = *Escobaria duncanii*
C. echinus = *C. cornifera* var. *echinus*
C. henricksonii = *Escobaria henricksonii*
C. hesteri = *Escobaria hesteri*
C. laredoi = *Escobaria laredoi*
C. marstonii = *Escobaria missouriensis* var. *marstonii*
C. minina = *Escobaria minima*
C. missouriensis = *Escobaria missouriensis*
C. nellieae = *Escobaria minima*
C. nickelsae = *C. sulcata* var. *nickelsae*
C. orcuttii = *Escobaria orcuttii*
C. organensis = *Escobaria organensis*
C. poselgeriana var. *valida* = *C. valida*
C. robbinsorum = *Escobaria robbinsorum*
C. robustispina = *C. scheerii* var. *robustispina*
C. runyonii = *C. macromeris* var. *runyonii*
C. sneedii = *Escobaria sneedii*
C. strobiliformis = *Escobaria strobiliformis*
C. vivipara = *Escobaria vivipara*.

Recommended species:

C. borwigii is a strongly spined, slow growing species making a slightly conical-shaped plant of prominent triangular tubercles and curving, short, white, brown tipped spines. Flowers are yellow.

C. calipensis is particularly noted for the copious wool produced in the growing area through which the thin curving dark brown spines protrude; flowers are yellow.

C. elephantidens is a low growing globular species with strong spines curving back on to the body; flowers are a good colour break, being deep pink with yellow throat.

C. georgii has appeared in the seed lists in the last several years, and resulting seedlings are strong growing plants, with long tubercles and clusters of strong, stiff, needle-like spines with dark tips. Flowers are whitish yellow, and smaller than most.

C. macromeris is unusual for its very long tubercles, and has been split off in the past to a separate genus, *Lepidocoryphantha*. It also has very long, thin, sharp spines, and bright pink flowers not readily produced except in sunny glasshouses in England.

C. maiz-tablasensis makes a slow cluster of globular heads, each about 2–3 in (5–8 cm) tall and wide, with solely radial spines, greyish-white in colour, and readily produces its smallish, yellow or whitish flowers after 3 or 4 years.

C. pycnacantha is another slow grower, making generally solitary stems to about 3 in (8 cm) tall and wide, with prominent tubercles, dark green in colour and with plenty of wool in between the tubercles especially in the younger, upper part of the plant. Spines are whitish with darker tips, the curved central spines almost black. Flowers are large and yellow.

C. recurvata is a large growing, globular stemmed species, making huge clusters eventually, but taking many years to do so. It is densely covered with recurving, yellow spines, but is not noted for flowering in England.

C. scheerii is very difficult to grow to any size in cultivation, forming in the wild large solitary, or sparingly clustering stems about 8 in (20 cm) tall and wide, with long, brownish-yellow spines.

C. werdermannii makes a tall, cone-shaped plant densely covered with white spines, with brown-tipped central spines standing out from the body. It is somewhat reluctant to produce its pale yellow flowers until it is about 3–4 in (8–10 cm) tall.

Connoisseur's choice: *C. elephantidens, C. scheerii, C. werdermannii.*

Cryptocereus Alex. (1950)

Referred to *Selinicereus.*

Cullmannia Dist, (1956)

Referred to *Peniocereus.*

Cumarinia Buxbaum (1951)

This monotypic genus (*C. odorata*) is referred to *Neolloydia.*

Cumulopuntia Ritter (1980)

A separate genus set up recently by Ritter for former species mostly under *Tephrocactus.* Here referred to *Opuntia.*

Cylindropuntia (Engelm.) Backeb. & Knuth (1935)

This is a useful name to distinguish the cylindrical-jointed and spheroid or ovoid jointed Opuntias from Central and North America, from the standard flat-padded Opuntias and from the low-growing spherical or ovoid-jointed Opuntias from South America known as *Tephrocactus.* Their fierce nature and generally invasive growth make them largely unsuitable for cultivation in glasshouses, except for the smaller, former *Corynopuntia.* But the name is recognized only at subgeneric level herein, and they are discussed under *Opuntia.*

Cylindrorebulia Fric & Kreuzr. (1938)

Referred to *Rebutia.*

Deamia B. & R. (1920)

Referred to *Selenicereus.*

Delaetia Backeb. (1962)

Referred to *Neoporteria.*

Dendrocereus B. & R., *The Cact.* 2:113, t. 14, figs 169, 170 (1920); Backeb., *Die Cact.* 4:1948, tt. 161–164, figs. 1854, 1871–1873 (1960)

This is a monotypic Cuban genus (*D. nudiflorus*), tree-like with stems having three to five narrow ribs, and is of interest only to *Cereus* enthusiasts.

Denmoza B. & R., *The Cact.* 3:78, t. 8, fig. 93 (1922)

The species usually seen of this small genus of large growing, barrel-shaped plants, is *D. rhodacantha,* an extremely handsomely spined, slow-growing, globular species from north-west Argentina, somewhat underrated because of its slow growth and the consequent difficulty in maintaining a good looking, unmarked plant to the size when it begins to look its best – about pineapple size. But if a young seedling is grafted, this sort

24. *Coryphantha borwigii*

25. *Coryphantha maiz-tablasensis*

of size can be achieved in five or six years, compared with about 12 or 15 on its own roots. The short-tubed, red flowers are seldom produced on plants less than 6 in (15 cm) tall and wide.

Species named are: *D. erythrocephala, D. rhodacantha.*

Recommended species and connoisseur's choice: the intense red colour of the spines of *D. rhodacantha* make it the usual and indeed the best choice of the two species.

Digitorebutia Fric & Kreuzr. ex Buining (1940)

Referred to *Rebutia.*

Discocactus Pfeiff. *Allg. Gartenz.* 5:241 (1837); Buining, *Discocactus* (1980); N. P. Taylor, *Cact. GB* 43:37 (1981)

This is a much underrated genus of low-growing, flat-globular cacti from Brazil, which collectors tend to be apprehensive about trying, since they require more winter warmth than many genera to ensure their safety. But if a high position can be found in a glasshouse in which a minimum of 45° F (7° C) is maintained in the body of the house, so that the benefit of the rising warmth keeps them at 50° F (10° C) or perhaps more safely at 55° F (13 °C) they will survive. Most form a cephalium in the centre of the plant after getting to about 4–5 in (10–12 cm) wide, although *D. horstii* will do so at about 2 in (5 cm) wide, after which the night-opening, large white flowers will be produced in succession over a period of a month or more, coming up and fading within 24 hours. They are slow-growing on their own roots, but if grafted grow well and not too untypically to produce a large, flowering size specimen within about three or four years; some have a tendency to offset prolifically when grafted, but I have not found this to be too much of a problem, and on those which do so the offsets can be removed early with

advantage.

Buining's beautifully illustrated book on the genus gives an excellent guide to the species, with many pictures of plants in the wild, but it should be seen in the light of Nigel Taylor's excellent rationalization of the genus (ref. above), which indicates that a reduction to only five (1. *D. hartmannii,* 2. *D. heptacanthus,* 3. *D. horstii,* 4. *D. placentiformis,* and 5. *D. zehntneri*) is probably right, taking a broad view of the variability of the species. Further fieldwork is needed to determine the standing of some of the species Taylor has sunk beneath these five species, but for the purposes of this book they are listed in full below, with an indication by means of a figure from 1 to 5 (referring to the five species above) by each one showing where Taylor places them.

Species named are: *D. albispinus*[5], *D. alteolens*[4], *D. araneispinus*[5], *D. bahiensis*[4], *D. boliviensis*[2], *D. boomianus*[5], *D. cangaensis*[2], *D. catingicola*[2], *D. cephaliaciculosus*[2], *D. crystallophilus*[4], *D. diersianus*[2], *D. estevesii*[2], *D. ferricola*[2], *D. flavispinus*[2], *D. goianus*[2], *D. griseus*[2], *D. hartmannii*[1], *D. heptacanthus*[2], *D. horstii*[3], *D. insignis*[4], *D. latispinus*[4], *D. lehmannii*[4], *D. lindaianus*[2], *D. linkii*[4], *D. magnimammus*[1], *D. mamillosus*[1], *D. melanochlorus*[2], *D. multicolorispinus*[4], *D. nigrisaetosus*[2], *D. pachythele*[1-2], *D. paranaensis*[2], *D. pugionacanthus*[4], *D. rapirhizus*[2], *D. semicampaniflorus*[2], *D. silicicola*[2], *D. silvaticus*[2], *D. spinosior*[2], *D. squamibaccatus*[2], *D. subterraneo-proliferans*[2], *D. subviridigriseus*[4], *D. tricornis*[4], *D. woutersiana*[3], *D. zehntneri.*

Recommended species: *D. araneispinus* is one of the small group of four named species which Taylor places under the prior name *D. zehntneri,* typified by long, creamy-white curling, interlacing, flexible spines, and making most attractive specimens in maturity, to about 6 in (15 cm) wide and about 2 in (5 cm) tall. *D. horstii* is a quite distinctive species, resembling no other, except for the

26. Coryphantha pycnacantha

27. Coryphantha werdermannii

strange *D. woutersiana*, which appears to be just a more spiny form of *D. horstii*, or perhaps a hybrid. *D. horstii* is smaller by far than all other known species, to about 2–3 in (5–8 cm) in maturity, the body colour dark purplish-brown, with 15–22 distinct, narrow, vertical ribs, beset with extraordinary, tiny clusters of spider-like spines, which, it has been speculated, are capable of absorbing water by way of their spongy make-up. It is probably safer to keep this species on a graft, as it is difficult to cultivate on its own roots successfully; it does not seem prone to cluster when grafted, or to grow untypically.

D. magnimammus is one of a handful of species, placed by Taylor under the prior name *D. hartmannii*, with prominent, long tubercles arranged in clearly defined vertical ribs, about 15 or so in number, growing to about 7 in (17 cm) wide and about 3 in (8 cm) tall.

The number of names in the group ascribed by Taylor to *D. heptacanthus* indicates its variability, but they are characterised by large, fat tubercles on about 12 ribs, which are arranged in slight spirals.

D. silicicola is typical of this group, forming a cephalium when it reaches about 4–5 in (10–12 cm) in diameter, and about 2 or 3 in (5–8 cm) wide.

D. subviridigriseus represents the group based on the prior name *D. placentiformis*. It has 13 to 15 low ribs, distinctly enlarged at the areoles into fat tubercles. Spines are strong and recurving, black or red at first, later grey. It forms a woolly cephalium after it reaches about 3 in (8 cm) in diameter.

Connoisseur's choice: *D. horstii.*

Disocactus Lindl., *Bot. Reg.* 31:t.9(1845); Kimnach, *Cact.Amer.*51:166 (1979)

This genus of about a dozen species, flat-stemmed, with tubular flowers and prominent berries, is of interest mainly to epiphyte enthusiasts, but contains some of the more colourful and larger flowered species of epiphytic cacti worthy of more general interest. They come from the West Indies and tropical and sub-tropical America, where they grow epiphytically or on rocks.

Species named are: *D. acuminatus, D. alatus, D. amazonicus, D. biformis, D. eichlamii, D. himantocladus, D. horichii, D. lankesteri, D. macranthus, D. nelsonii* (& var. *hondurensis*), *D. quezaltecus, D. ramulosus.*

Recommended species: few turn up in cultivation, but *D. nelsonii* is the most frequently encountered, and is

28. *Discocactus (araneispinus) zehntneri*

29. *Discocactus (subviridigriseus) placentiformis*

30. *Echinocactus horizonthalonius*, in habitat, Big Bend area, Texas, USA

probably the best for flowering, producing numerous, pink, trumpet-shaped flowers along the edges of the flat, leaf-like stems.

Connoisseur's choice: D. nelsonii var. *hondurensis.*

Dolichothele (not *Dolicothele* – a mis-spelling) (K. Schum.) B. & R. (1923)

Most authorities now place this genus within the broad concept of *Mammillaria*, as a subgenus. See under *Mammillaria*.

Ebnerella F. Buxb. (1951)

Referred to *Mammillaria.*

Eccremocactus B. & R. (1923)

Referred to *Weberocereus.*

Echinocactus Link & Otto *Verh. Ver. Beförd. Gartenb. Preuss. Staat.* 3:420, t.14 (1827)

The current concept of this genus (it was used as a catch-all a century ago) is of a handful of species from the south-west United States and Mexico. They are mostly of massive dimensions, reaching a yard (1m) across or more, globular or shortly columnar with age, but one or two are of more modest dimensions, and one or two more will take a long time to outgrow their welcome.

Species named are: *E. grusonii, E. horizonthalonius* (& var. *nicholii*), *E. ingens, E, palmeri, E. parryi, E. platyacanthus* (& fa. *grandis*, fa *visnaga*), *E. polycephalus, E. (Homolocephala) texensis, E. xeranthemoides.*

Rejected names and synonymies:
E. grandis = E. platyacantha fa. *grandis*
E. visnaga = E. platyacantha fa. *visnaga.*

Recommended species: the best known of the genus is *E. grusonii*, rightly popular, known as the 'golden-barrel cactus' or 'mother-in-law's armchair', covered with fierce, golden-yellow spines, and often seen bedded out in kinder climes than England, where it will get to about 3–4 ft (1 m or so), wide and tall, eventually offsetting to form massive clumps. In cultivation under glass, with a little extra heat (minimum 50° F/10° C) to prevent the brown marks it suffers from if kept below this temperature, it can grow to large football size in 10 or 15 years. There has recently been a white-spined form available commercially. *E. horizonthalonius* is another which collectors attempt to grow, but it defies many an effort to cultivate successfully, being prone to rot off, or reluctant to root if brought in as a collected wild plant. Seed is seldom offered, and if seedlings are obtained grafting at an early stage is probably the safest proposition unless you like a real challenge (in nearly 40 years cactus growing I have never seen a mature successfully grown seedling). But it is really worth the effort, by whatever means, as, with its blue-green epidermis, strong groups of spines arranged neatly on vertical ribs, and sumptuous pink flowers it is probably the best looking species in the genus.

E. polycephalus is even more of a problem to grow successfully, although I have seen it cultivated successfully in a collection with no protection at about 6000 ft altitude in New Mexico, where night temperatures frequently fell well below zero, so that it is not winter warmth that is needed, rather the dry atmosphere which in England is impossible to provide. It is worth trying for the strong spine covering alone, which with an overhead watering colours a deep intense red. I have never seen mature seed-grown plants in cultivation, but grafting at an early stage may make this a possible plant to grow as a seedling; certainly most plants in cultivation are imported from the wild, and sadly do not often last long.

E. (Homalocephala) texensis is well known and, although frequently imported in the past from wild collections, is now more available in the form of seed-raised plants. It is slow from seed, and is another plant that might well benefit from early grafting to bring it along more quickly to a size when it may be expected to produce its lovely, pink, fringed-petalled flowers – about 5–6 in (15cm) wide. Its strong spines are a delight to behold at any time, red in the new growth, then fading to brown and yellow.

Connoisseur's choice: E. horizonthalonius.

Echinocereus Engelm. in Wisliz., *Mem. Tour Northern Mexico* 91 (1848); N. P. Taylor, *The Genus Echinocereus* (1985)

This genus has recently had the full treatment by Nigel Taylor, a Kew Gardens taxonomist, who has produced an admirable monograph on the genus, reducing the 70 or so described species to 44, with 51 varieties, a rationalization well overdue. He has included in the genus three former *Wilcoxia* species (the remainder referred already to *Peniocereus*), and *Morangaya*, the latter genus recently erected separate from *Echinocereus* by Gordon Rowley, who considered it intermediate between *Echinocereus* and *Aporocactus*, a view I have some sympathy with.

Echinocereus species come from a wide area of the western United States and northern and central Mexico, varying considerably in shape from almost globular to short columnar, or pencil thin stems several feet long with thick tuberous roots (former *Wilcoxia* species), mostly clustering sooner or later, some to form large, yard wide (to 1m) clumps. Flowers are mostly large and sumptuous, bursting damagingly through the plant body to leave scars. In general they need plenty of exposure to light to induce the best flowering.

Echinocereus

Species named are: *E. adustus* (& var. *schwarzii*), *E. barthelowianus*, *E. berlandieri*, *E. brandegeei*, *E. bristolii* (& var. *pseudopectinatus*), *E. chisoensis* (& var. *fobeanus*), *E. chloranthus* (& var. *cylindricus*, var. *neocapillus*, var. *russanthus*), *E. cinerascens* (& var. *ehrenbergii*) *E. delaetii* (& var. *freudenbergeri*), *E. engelmannii* (& var. *acicularis* var. *armatus*, var. *chrysocentrus*, var. *howei*, var. *munzii*, var. *nicholii*, var. *purpureus*, var. *variegatus*), *E. enneacanthus* (& var. *brevispinus*), *E. fendleri* (& var. *bonkerae*, var. *boyce-thompsonii*, var. *fasciculatus*, var. *kuenzleri*, var. *ledingii*, var. *rectispinus*), *E. ferreirianus* (& var. *lindsayi*), *E. grandis*, *E. knippelianus* (& var. *kruegeri*), *E. laui*, *E.(Wil)leucanthus*, *E. longisetus*, *E. maritimus* (& var. *hancockii*), *E. nivosus*, *E. palmeri*, *E. pamanesiorum*, *E. papillosus* (& var. *angusticeps*), *E. pectinatus* (& var. *dasyacanthus*, var. *wenigeri*), *E. (Mor)pensilis*, *E. pentalophus* (& var. *leonensis*), *E. polyacanthus* (& var. *densus*, var. *pacificus*), *E. (Wil)poselgeri*, *E. primolanatus*, *E. pulchellus* (& var. *amoenus*, var. *weinbergii*), *E. reichenbachii* (& var. *armatus*, var. *baileyi*, var. *fitchii*, var. *perbellus*), *E. rigidissimus* (& var. *rubispinus*), *E. scheerii* (& var. *gentryi*), *E. (Wil)schmollii*, *E. sciurus* (& var. *floresii*), *E. scopulorum*, *E. spinigemmatus*, *E. stoloniferus* (& var. *tayopensis*), *E. stramineus*, *E. subinermis* (& var. *ochoteranae*), *E. triglochidiatus* (& var. *arizonicus*, var. *gonacanthus*, var. *gurneyi*, var. *melanacanthus*, var. *mojavensis*, var. *neomexicanus*, var. *paucispinus*), *E. viereckii* (& var. *morricalii*), *E. viridiflorus* (& var. *correllii*, var. *davisii*), *E. websterianus*.

Rejected names and synonymies
(for full list see Nigel Taylor's *The Genus Echinocereus*; the list below takes account of the more recently circulating names):

E. acifer (& var. *durangensis*, var. *trichacanthus*) = *E. polyacanthus*

E. albatus = *E. nivosus*

(Wilcoxia) albiflorus = *E. leucanthus*

E. amoenus = *E. pulchellus* var. *amoenus*

E. angusticeps = *E. papillosus* var. *angusticeps*

E. arizonicus = *E. triglochidiatus* var. *arizonicus*

E. armatus = *E. reichenbachii* var. *armatus*

E. baileyi = *E. reichenbachii* var. *baileyi*

E. blanckii (Poselger)Ruempler = *E. enneacanthus*

E. blanckii Hort. = *E. berlandieri*

E. bonkerae = *E. fendleri* var. *bonkerae*

E. boyce-thompsonii = *E. fendleri* var. *boyce-thompsonii*

E. caespitosus = *E. reichenbachii*

E. castaneus = *E. rigidissimus*

E. chiloensis = *E. chisoensis*

E. chloraphthalmus = *E. cinerascens*

E. chrysocentrus = *E. engelmannii* var. *chrysocentrus*

E. coccineus = *E. triglochidiatus*?

E. conglomeratus = *E. stramineus*

E. ctenoides = *E. pectinatus*

E. cucumis = *E. scheerii*

E. dasyacanthus = *E. pectinatus* var. *dasyacanthus*

E. davisii = *E. viridiflorus* var. *davisii*

E. dubius = *E. enneacanthus*

E. durangensis = *E. polyacanthus*

E. ehrenbergii = *E. cinerascens* var. *ehrenbergii*

E. fasciculatus = *E. fendleri* var. *fasciculatus*

E. fitchii = *E. reichenbachii* var. *fitchii*

E. floresii = *E. sciurus* var. *floresii*

E. fobeanus = *E. chisoensis* var. *fobeanus*

E. freudenbergeri = *E. delaetii* var. *freudenbergeri*

E. gentryi = *E. scheerii* var. *gentryi*

E. gonacanthus = *E. triglochidiatus* var. *gonacanthus*

E. hancockii = *E. maritimus* var. *hancockii*

E. hempelii = *E. fendleri*

E. huitcholensis = *E. polyacanthus* var. *densus*

E. knippelianus var. *reyesii* = *E. knippelianus* var. *kruegeri*

E. ledingii = *E. fendleri* var. *ledingii*

E. leeanus = *E. polyacanthus*?

E. leonensis = *E. pentalophus* var. *leonensis*

E. lindsayi = *E. ferreirianus* var. *lindsayi*

E. luteus = *E. subinermis*

E. mamillatus = *E. brandegeei*

E. marksianus = *E. polyacanthus*

E. matthesianus = *E. scheerii*

E. matudae = *E. enneacanthus*

E. melanocentrus = *E. reichenbachii*

E. merkeri = *E. enneacanthus*

E. mojavensis = *E. triglochidiatus* var. *mojavensis*

E. morricalii = *E. viereckii* var. *morricalii*

E. munzii = *E. engelmannii* var. *munzii*

E. neomexicanus = *E. triglochidiatus* var. *neomexicanus*

E. ochoteranae = *E. subinermis* var. *ochoteranae*

E. oklahomensis = *E. reichenbachii*

E. pacificus = *E. polyacanthus* var. *pacificus*

E. pectinatus var. *castaneus* = *E. reichenbachii*

E. pectinatus var. *neomexicanus* = *E. pectinatus*

E. pectinatus var. *rigidissimus* = *E. rigidissimus*

E. pectinatus var. *rubispinus* = *E. rigidissimus* var. *rubispinus*

E. perbellus = *E. reichenbachii*

E. procumbens = *E. pentalophus*

E. purpureus = *E. reichenbachii*

E. radians = *E. adustus* var. *schwarzii*

E. reichenbachii var. *chisoensis* = *E. chisoensis*

E. robustus = *E. fendleri*

E. roemeri = *E. triglochidiatus*

E. roetteri = *E. pectinatus*

E. rosei = *E. triglochidiatus*

E. russanthus = *E. chloranthus* var. *russanthus*

E. salm-dyckianus = *E. scheerii*

E. salmianus = *E. scheerii*

E. schwarzii = *E. adustus* var. *schwarzii*

E. triglochidiatus var. *acifer* = *E. polyacanthus*

E. triglochidiatus var. *inermis* = *E. triglochidiatus*

E. triglochidiatus var. *pacificus* = *E. polyacanthus* var. *pacificus*

31. *Echinocactus texensis*

32. *Echinocereus adustus*

33. *Echinocereus berlandieri*

34. *Echinocereus chloranthus* var. *russanthus*

E. tulensis = *E. pentalophus*
E. uspenkii = *E. triglochidiatus*
E. weinbergii = *E. pulchellus* var. *weinbergii*.

Recommended species: *E. berlandieri* is Taylor's favoured name for the weakly-spined, sprawling, soft stemmed species, known usually hitherto as *E. blanckii* although both names have been freely misapplied. The untidy habit is tolerable when the flowers appear, a silken purple. It comes from Tamaulipas in Mexico.

E. chloranthus is a fine-spined species making small clusters of stems to 10 in (25 cm) or so tall, and producing many small, greenish flowers. *E. chloranthus* var. *russanthus* has wonderfully coloured, wine-red to rusty red flowers. It comes from Texas, USA.

E. delaetii is one of the most difficult species to grow well for any length of time, with long, white, hair like spines, reminiscent of *Cephalocereus senilis*, and stems to about 6–8 in (20 cm) long or more, an inch or so (3 cm) wide.

35. *Echinocereus engelmannii*, in habitat, northern Baja California, Mexico

36. *Echinocereus ferreirianus* var. *lindsayi*

37. *Echinocereus grandis*

Flowers are an event when produced in England, pink with white throat. It comes from Coahuila, Mexico.

E. engelmannii, a widespread species in south western USA and northern Mexico, makes magnificent clumps to 2–3 ft wide (1 m) in fully exposed positions in the wild, but is rarely seen well grown to any size in cultivation, although good sized plants with strong spines are possible in sunny positions, and with regular potting on in the early years, as it is a vigorous grower. The spines are long and needle like, in reds or yellows, densely covering the stem, flowers are purple-pink.

E. fendleri is widespread in Arizona and New Mexico, USA, and strays well into Sonora and Chihuahua, Mexico. It makes small, dark bodied clumps of stems, each about 5–6 in (15 cm) or so, and 2 or 3 in (5–8 cm) wide, fairly sparsely spined, and with deep pink flowers.

E. ferreirianus from around Bahia de Los Angeles in Baja California, Mexico, has only fairly recently been described, and even more recently the rare *E. lindsayi*, reduced by Taylor to a variety of *E. ferreirianus*, was described, but is now reckoned to be wiped out in habitat from roadworks and overcollecting. The type of the species is still to be found on steep rocky hillsides, where it gets to about a foot (30 cm) tall, sparingly off-setting. Both are well spined in dark red-brown, the variety *lindsayi* more heavily so, and squatter growing; flowers vary from pale pink in the type to deep pink in the variety.

E. grandis is an island species in the Gulf of California, on San Esteban Island and others, growing thick columnar stems to a foot (30 cm) or more tall and to 4 in (10 cm) thick, neatly close spined, the spines cream coloured. Flowers oblige on 2–3 in (8 cm) tall plants in cultivation and are pale, whitish pink with deeper coloured throat.

E. knippelianus is slow growing, shortly columnar or globular, and forms clusters in time. It is practically without spines, although each areole has about two or three weak bristles, easily falling or knocked off. The flowers are usually produced in quantity and are pale pink. In the wild this species withdraws almost completely into the soil when at rest. It comes from Coahuila, Mexico.

E. laui is another recent discovery, found by that explorer of remote areas in Mexico and elsewhere, Alfred Lau. It is already popular in cultivation, making small clumps of stems densely clad in white spines and producing freely its delicate shell-pink flowers.

E. palmeri makes a thick tuberous root, and, in cultivation, slow columns to about 6 in (15 cm) or so tall, and an inch (2.5 cm) or so thick, with dark spines intermingled with white in neat rows down the vertical ribs. Flowers are large and pink. In the wild it is much less columnar, growing in Chihuahua in northern Mexico.

38. *Echinocereus leucanthus*

39. *Echinocereus pentalophus*

40. *Echinocereus polyacanthus* var. *pacificus*, in Bob Kent's private
    collection, near San Diego, California, USA

E. papillosus var. *angusticeps* has a wonderful colour break
for this genus, with wide-opening flowers in yellow with
a red throat. The plant makes small clumps of soft
textured, thin spined stems to about 4 in (10 cm) or so
long. It comes from western Texas, USA.

E. pectinatus in any of its varieties is worth growing for
the well ordered spination, from which it gets its name –
the variously coloured spines almost hiding the plant
body completely. Plants tend to stay solitary for some
time, making thick columns to 8 in (20 cm) or more tall.
Flowers are bright or pale pink, or, in *E. pectinatus* var.
dasyacanthus, a lovely yellow. This plant comes from a
wide area of southern United States and northern Mexico
in the Chihuahuan desert.

E. polyacanthus is not well known in cultivation, although
it has sometimes been mistaken for one of the spinier
forms of *E. triglochidiatus*. It is covered with long, needle-
like spines, and in the wild is an impressive sight when in
flower, splashing the hillsides of Chihuahua and Durango
bright red. *E. polyacanthus* var. *pacificus*, from northern
Baja California, Mexico, has been available in recent years,
and is more compact.

E. pulchellus is an outstanding, small growing species,
although large clumps of 20 or 30 stems are occasionally
seen in cultivation. More usually they remain solitary for
some time, and are flat-globular, no more than about 2–

3 in (5–8 cm) wide, with vertical ribs of short spines, and
covering themselves with pink, striped flowers every year
from an early age. It comes from Pachuca, Mexico. The
type of this species is in fact rare in cultivation, and what
is usually seen is *E. pulchellus* var. *amoenus*, as illustrated.
E. reichenbachii comes in a variety of coloured spines, and
is a slightly more shaggy version of *E. pectinatus*, with
similar habit, and freely produced flowers on all varieties. *E. reichenbachii* var. *baileyi* is particularly attractive
with its pinkish-brown spines and lilac, silken sheen
flowers. The species comes from a wide area of southern
United States, embracing Oklahoma, New Mexico and
Texas.

E. rigidissimus has been separated by Taylor from *E.
pectinatus*. It is noted for the bands of red, pink and cream
coloration of the spines. *E. rigidissimus* var. *rubispinus* is a
particularly deeply coloured version recently described,
and proving very popular with collectors, for its intense
colouring. Flowers are large and pink. It comes from west
Chihuahua, Mexico.

E. schmollii is one of the more modestly sized of the
former *Wilcoxia* species, with a large, tuberous root and
pencil thin, floppy, woolly spined stems, to about 10–12
in (to 30 cm) long, almost supporting themselves, but
needing a little help as they lengthen. Flowers are pink
with deeper throat, an inch or more wide (3 cm), and

finishing off the collapse of the stems with their weight if not supported. The species comes from Queretaro, Mexico.

E. sciurus is a delightful, densely white-spined species from southern Baja California, Mexico – the extreme southern tip of that peninsula. It makes small clumps and has huge, pink flowers.

E. stramineus from Chihuahua, Mexico and the southern United States, in particular the Big Bend region of Texas, makes massive clumps a yard (1 m) or more wide and a foot (30 cm) tall, with fierce, white to yellow-brown, long, needle like spines densely clothing the plants. Flowers, freely produced in the wild, are not so forthcoming in cultivation, but are possible in a good sunny position, which is also desirable for best spine development.

E. subinermis is another small growing species, although it will form clumps in time, with globular to short columnar stems, and very little spination – the green, five to 11 ribbed plants little resembling most other *Echinocereus* species. Flowers are large, freely produced and yellow. It is native to Chihuahua, Mexico.

E. triglochidiatus and its several varieties are worth growing for the brilliant red, goblet shaped flowers which most have, although in cultivation good sunny conditions are needed to induce them to come anywhere near the sort of display they put on in the wild, where, at a distance of a hundred yards, they can stop a vehicle full of keen-eyed cactus enthusiasts in its tracks. *E. triglochidiatus* var. *gurneyi* comes from the Big Bend area of Texas, USA, and has paler flowers in salmon pink.

E. viridiflorus is a low-growing, clumping species from high in Colorado and New Mexico, USA where it tolerates temperatures well below freezing at times. It has short, fine spines in a mixture of red, black and white colours, and small, green flowers produced prolifically.

E. viridiflorus var. *davisii*, from a much lower elevation near Marathon, Texas, USA, is the miniature of the genus, in the wild attaining stems no bigger than the end of a little finger, set out of sight in the cracks of rocks on one or two hilltops, visible easily only when it thrusts up its green flowers from the cracks. In cultivation it does present some difficulty in growing, but if treated with the respect it commands, in the way of a gritty compost, and careful watering, it will grow slowly to form a small clump, freely covering itself with its green flowers in the spring.

E. websterianus, from an island in the Gulf of California, San Pedro Nolasco, makes magnificent, neatly-spined

41. *Echinocereus poselgeri*

42. *Echinocereus pulchellus* var. *weinbergii*

43. *Echinocereus scheerii*

clumps of stems to about 10 in (25 cm) long and 2–3 in (5–8 cm) wide. Flowers are deep pink.

Connoisseur's choice: *E. delaetii, E. laui, E. palmeri, E. pectinatus* var. *dasyacanthus, E. pulchellus, E. reichenbachii* var. *baileyi, E. rigidissimus* var. *rubispinus, E. subinermis, E. viridiflorus* var. *davisii.*

Echinofossulocactus Lawrence in Loudon, *Gard. Mag.* 17:317 (1841); D. R. Hunt, *Cact. GB* 42(4):105 (1980); N. P. Taylor, l.c.108 (1980) D. R. Hunt, l.c. 43(1): 12 (1981)

When Nigel Taylor decided to combine this genus with *Ferocactus*, he faced the difficulty of the unwieldy name *Echinofossulocactus* having priority over the more acceptable name *Ferocactus*. David Hunt came to the rescue, and in the same issue of the journal of the *Cactus and Succulent Society of Great Britain*, Hunt declared the name *Stenocactus* a conserved name taking precedence therefore over the prior *Echinofossulocactus*, and Taylor promptly combined it with Ferocactus over which it did not take precedence. This was as neat a piece of connivance (sorry – co-operation) as I have seen. Collectors and nurserymen have steered a middle course, however, and have welcomed the return of the name *Stenocactus*, which many had never discarded, keeping it as a generic name, rather than accept the combination with *Ferocactus*. See under *Stenocactus*.

Echinomastus B. & R. (1922)

Referred to *Thelocactus*.

Echinopsis Zucc., *Abh.Bayer.Akad.Wiss.München* 2:675 (1837)

As formerly defined and popularly regarded, this genus consists of globular plants, mostly producing white, night-flowering, long tubed blooms. But the genus now embraces the former, uncomfortably separate, day flowering Pseudolobivias, which have red, pink or yellow flowers, and several more columnar genera, whose flowers are similar, viz. *Trichocereus, Helianthocereus, Lasiocereus, Leucostele* and *Roseocereus*. While acceptance of these amalgamations is increasing, the latest move, to amalgamate *Lobivia* here as well, will take some time to be accepted; for the present it is regarded separately here.

There is a certain mystique surrounding some of the

44. *Echinocereus stoloniferus* var. *tayopensis*

45. *Echinocereus stramineus*, in habitat, Big Bend area, Texas, USA

46. *Echinocereus triglochidiatus*

47. *Echinocereus viridiflorus* var. *viridiflorus*

48. *Echinopsis ancistrophora* subsp. *arachnacantha* var. *arachnacantha*

hybrids produced over the years between *Echinopsis* and *Lobivia*, with an *Echinopsis* habit of growth (although less prolifically offsetting than many species) and flowers with long tubes, though taking colour from their *Lobivia* genes, usually in pink and peach-pink shading to orange. For me they do not rival some of the better species of *Echinopsis*.

The list of species below is revised according to Walter Rausch's recent work on this and the genus *Lobivia*, beautifully illustrated with colour photographs, many of plants in habitat from Rausch's extensive travels in South America. It is also expanded to include the amalgamation of the columnar genera mentioned above.

Species named are: *E. adolfo-friedrichii*, *E. albispinosa* (& var. *fauxiana*), *E. ancistrophora* (& var. *hamatacantha*, var. *kratochviliana*, var. *polyancistra*; subsp. *cardenasiana*, & var. *rubriflora*; subsp. *pojoensis*, & var., *grandiflora*, var. *megalocephala*; subsp. *arachnacantha*, & var. *densiseta*, var. *sulphurea*, var. *torrecillasensis*, var. *vallegrandensis*), *E. (Hel)*-

antezanae, *E. arebaloi*, *E. (Hel)atacamensis*, *E. ayopayana*, *E. baldiana*, *E. (Hel). bertramiana*, *E. brasiliensis*, *E. bridgesii*, *E. cajasensis*, *E. (Trich) calliantha*, *E. calochlora* (& var. *albispina*), *E. (Trich)candicans* (& fa. *rubriflora*, var. *gladiatus*, var. *nitens*, var. *tenuispinus*), *E. (Trich)carmarguensis*, *E. (Trich) catamarcensi*, *E. (Trich)cephalomacrostibas*, *E. (Trich)chalaensis*, *E. (Trich)chilensis* (& var. *borealis*, var. *conjungens*, var. *eburneus*), *E. (Trich)clavata*, *E. cochabambensis*, *E. (Trich)coquimbana*, *E. cordobensis*, *E. cotacajesii*, *E.(Trich)courantii*, *E. (Trich)cuzcoensis*, *E. dehrenbergii* (& var. *blossfeldii*), *E. (Trich) deserticola*, *E. (Trich)eremophila*, *E. (Hel)escayachensis*, *E. eyriesii*, *E. (Las)fulva*, *E. (Trich)fulvilana*, *E. hammerschmidii*, *E. (Hel)herzogiana*, *E.(Hel)huascha* (& var. *andalgalensis*, var. *auricolor*, var. *rubriflorus*), *E. huotii*, *E. (Hel)hyalacantha*, *E. ibicuatensis*, *E. intricatissima*, *E. klingeriana*, *E. (Trich)knuthiana*, *E. (Trich)lamprochlora*, *E. leucantha* (& var. *brasiliensis*, var. *volliana*), *E. (Trich)litoralis*, *E. luteiflora*, *E. (Trich)macrogona*, *E. mamillosa* (& var. *flexilis*, var. *histrichoides*, var. *kermesina*), *E. (Trich)manguinii*, *E. melanopotamica*, *E. meyeri*, *E. minuana*, *E. modesta*, *E. multiplex*, *E. (Hel)narvaecensis*, *E. (Trich)nigripilis*, *E. obrepanda* (& var. *aguilari*, var. *calorubra*, var. *mizquensis*, var. *purpurea*), *E. (Hel)orurensis* (& var. *albiflora*), *E. oxygona* (& fa. *brevispina*), *E. (Trich)pachanoi* (& fa. *peruviana*), *E. pamparuizii*, *E. paraguayensis*, *E. (Hel) pasacana*, *E. (Hel) pecheretiana* (& var. *viridior*), *E. pereziensis*, *E. (Hel)pseudocandicans* (& var. *flaviflora*, var. *roseoflora*), *E. pudantii*, *E.(Trich)puquiensis*, *E. (Trich)purpureopilosa*, *E. (Trich)quadratiumbaccata*, *E. (Hel)randallii*, *E. rhodotricha* (& var. *argentiniensis*, var. *brevispina*, var, *chacoana*, var. *robusta*), *E. (Trich)riomizquensis*, *E. (Leuc)rivierei*, *E. robinsoniana*, *E. (Trich)rowleyi*, *E. (Trich)rubinghiana*, *E. (Las)rupicola*, *E. (Trich)santaensis*, *E. (Trich)santiaguensis*, *E. (Trich)schickendantzii*, *E. (Trich)schoenii*, *E. schwantesii*, *E. schaferi*, *E. (Trich)scopulicola*, *E. shaferi*, *E. silvatica*, *E. silvestrii*, *E. (Trich)skottsbergii* (& var. *breviata*), *E. (Trich)smrziana*, *E. (Trich)spachianoides*, *E. (Trich)spachiana*, *E. spegazziniana*, *E. (Trich)strigosa* (& var. *flaviflora*), *E. subdenudata*, *E. sucrensis*, *E. (Trich)tacaquirensis*, *E. (Trich)tacuaensis*, *E. (Trich)taquimbalensis*, *E. (Hel)tarijensis* (& var. *densispina*, var. *orurensis*, var. *poco*), *E. (Trich)tarmaensis*, *E. (Trich)tenuispina*, *E. (Trich)terscheckii* (& var. *montana*), *E. (Trich)terscheckioides*, *E. (Trich)thelegona*, *E. (Trich)thelegonoides*, *E. (Trich)torataensis*, *E. (Trich)totorensis*, *E. (Trich)totorillana*, *E. (Trich)trichosa*, *E. tubiflora*, *E. (Trich)tulhuayacensis*, *E. (Trich)tunariensis*, *E. turbinata*, *(Trich)uyupampensis*, *E. (Trich)valida*, *E. vallegrandensis*, *E. (Trich)volcanensis*, *E. (Trich)volliana*, *(& var. rubrispina)*, *E. (Trich)werdermanniana*, *E. yungasensis*

Rejected names and synonymies:
E. aguilari = *E. obrepanda* var. *aguilari*
E. arachnacantha = *E. ancistrophora* subsp. *arachnacantha*
E. aurea = *Lobivia aurea*

E. boyuibensis = *E. obrepanda*

E. calliantho-lilacina = *E. obrepanda*

E. callichroma = *E. obrepanda* var. *purpurea*

E. calorubra = *E. obrepanda* var. *calorubra*

E. carmineoflora = *E. obrepanda* var. *calorubra*

E. cerdana = *Lobivia ferox* var. *potosina*

E. chacoana = *E. rhodotricha* var. *chacoana*

E. chacoana var. *spinosior* = *E. rhodotricha* var. *spinosior*

E. chrysantha = *Lobivia chrysantha*

E. coronata = *E. obrepanda*

E. cristata = *E. obrepanda*

E. eyriesii var. *grandiflora* = *E. oxygona* fa. *brevispina*

E. ferox = *Lobivia ferox*

E. fiebrigii = *E. obrepanda*

E. frankii = *E. obrepanda*

E. hamatacantha = *E. ancistrophora* var. *hamatacantha*

E. herbasii = *E. mamillosa*

E. hossei = *Lobivia chrysantha*

E. kermesina = *E. mamillosa* var. *kermesina*

E. korethroides = *Lobivia formosa* subsp. *bruchii* var. *nivalis*

E. kratochviliana = *E. ancistrophora* var. *kratochviliana*

E. lecoriensis = *Lobivia ferox* var. *longispina*

E. leucorhodantha = *E. ancistrophora*

E. lobivioides = *E. ancistrophora*

E. longispina = *Lobivia ferox* var. *longispina*

E. mamillosa var. *ritteri* = *E. mamillosa*

E. mamillosa var. *tamboensis* = *E. mamillosa*

E. marsoneri = *Lobivia chrysantha* subsp. *marsoneri*

E. mataranensis = *E. obrepanda*

E. mizquensis = *E. obrepanda* var. *mizquensis*

E. nigra = *Lobivia ferox* var. *longispina*

E. obrepanda var. *fiebrigii* = *E. obrepanda*

E. orozana = *E. mamillosa*

E. peleccyrhachis = *E. ancistrophora*

E. peruviana = *E. pachanoi* fa. *peruviana*

E. pojoensis = *E. ancistrophora* subsp. *pojoensis*

E. polyancistra = *E. ancistrophora* var. *polyancistra*

E. potosina = *Lobivia ferox* var. *potosina*

E. pseudomamillosa = *E. obrepanda*

E. rauschii = *E. ancistrophora* subsp. *pojoensis*

E. ritteri = *E. mamillosa*

E. riviere-de-caraltii = *E. obrepanda*

E. rojasii = *E. albiflora*

E. roseo-lilacina = *E. obrepanda*

E. tapecuana = *E. obrepanda*

E. toralapana = *E. obrepanda* var. *purpurea*

E. torrecillasensis = *E. ancistrophora* subsp. *arachnacantha*
    var. *torrecillasensis*

E. werdermanniana = *E. oxygona* fa. *brevispina*

E. wilkeae = *Lobivia ferox* var. *longispina*.

Recommended species: *E. ancistrophora* contains many worth bench space, but two are really outstanding. *E. ancistrophora* subsp. *cardenasiana* (also seen labelled *E.*

49. *Echinopsis mamillosa* var. *kermesina*

50. *Echinopsis obrepanda* var. *calorubra*

cardenasiana and *Lobivia cardenasiana*), which at about 2–3 in (10–12 cm) will produce several of its long tubed, magnificent, violet-pink flowers. *E. ancistrophora* subsp. *arachnacantha*, also frequently labelled *Echinopsis* or *Lobivia arachnacantha*, has neat, spider-like clusters of wispy spines on shining bronze or green stems, heavily clustering, and produces its display of fairly short-tubed clear yellow flowers freely, starting to do so when the stems are no more than an inch or so (2–3 cm) wide.

E. *mamillosa* var. *kermesina* (also seen labelled *Echinopsis* or *Pseudolobivia kermesina*) is a justifiably popular species, growing quite quickly to a globular, solitary plant about 4–5 in (8–10 cm) tall and wide, when it will produce several of its long-tubed, reddish-pink flowers, from a bright green stem with yellowish-brown, strong spines.

For the nocturnal, white flowered species few can better E. *subdenudata*, with unobtrusive, short spines, a purple flushed stem and long-tubed pure white flowers, or the old and well-known E. *eyriesii*, with very short spines in star clusters and white, long-tubed flowers flushed a delicate shade of pink.

Connoisseur's choice: *E. ancistrophora* subsp. *cardenasiana*.

Encephalocarpus Bgr. (1929)

Referred to *Pelecyphora*.

Eomatucana Ritt. (1965).

Referred to *Borzicactus*.

Epiphyllanthus Bgr. (1905)

Referred to *Schlumbergera*.

Epiphyllopsis (Bgr.) Backeb. & Knuth (1935)

Referred to *Rhipsalis*.

Epiphyllum Haw. *Syn. Pl. Succ.* 197 (1812)

Although commonly applied to plants which are the result of extensive hybridizing between this and related epiphytic genera, the true *Epiphyllum* species, from tropical and sub-tropical America and the West Indies, are seldom seen in cultivation to any great extent, and are sought out only by enthusiasts for epiphytic cacti. The aforementioned 'Epiphyllum' hybrids, of which there are many hundreds of names, most of them of no significance and little differentiated from each other, produce a range of different flower colours from white, through yellow,

orange, all shades of pink and red to purple, as well as some combinations of these colours. The range is tremendous, but many are just variations of the commonly seen cottage plant, so-called 'Epiphyllum ackermannii', determined probably to be a hybrid itself, between *Nopalxochia phyllanthoides* and *Heliocereus speciosus*.

The best choice of these is your own fancy, and a visit to a nursery that carries a long list of hybrids round about May or June in England, will enable you to pick out what appeals to you personally, but note the dimensions of the leaf-like stems, as some can get very large, with stems to several feet long (1 m, or so).

Species named (not the hybrids) are: E. *anguliger*, E. *cartagense*, E. *caudatum*, E. *caulorhizum*, E. *chrysocardium*, E. *crenatum* (& var. *kimnachii*), E. *darrahii*, E. *gigas*, E. *grandilobum*, E. *lepidocarpum*, E. *macrocarpum*, E. *macroptera*, E. *oxypetalum* (& var. *purpusii*), E. *phyllanthus* (& var. *boliviense*, var. *columbiense*, var. *guatemalense*, var. *hookeri*, var. *paraguayense*, var. *pittieri*, var. *rubrocoronatum*), E. *pumilum*, E, *ruestii*, E, *thomasianum* (& var. *costaricense*).

Rejected names and synonymies are:

E. *costaricense* = E. *thomasianum* var. *costaricense*
E. *guatemalense* = E. *phyllanthus* var. *guatemalense*
E. *hookeri* = E. *phyllanthus* var. *hookeri*
E. *pittieri* = E. *phyllanthus* var. *pittieri*
E. *stenopetalum* = E. *phyllanthus* var. *hookeri*
E. *strictum* = E. *phyllanthus* var. *hookeri*.

They are not recommended.

Epithelantha Weber ex B. & R. *The Cact.* 3:92, fig.102 (1922); Glass & Foster, *Cact.Amer.* 50:184 (1978)

This is a genus of small-stemmed, densely white-spined species found on limestone in Texas, USA and Mexico. Various species have been described, but the genus has been rationalized and reduced by Glass and Foster to only one species, E. *micromeris*, with the former species reduced to varieties. They are all slow growing, but will make a step towards maturity at a very early stage by producing their small pink flowers and bright red Mammillaria-like fruits, when they are only $\frac{1}{2}$ in (1cm) or so tall and wide; they all eventually cluster to form small clumps, although one or two stay solitary for some time.

Recommended species: all the varieties of the one species are recommended. E. *micromeris* var. *micromeris*, the type, from south eastern Texas, USA and nearby in Mexico, the most commonly seen in cultivation, forming rounded, white small mushroom like stems, $\frac{1}{2}$–$1\frac{1}{2}$in (1 to 4 cm) wide and a little taller, rounded with a slightly depressed centre at the growing point, becoming more

elongated in age and clustering to form densely packed clumps of small stems to about 5–6 in (15 cm) across, taking many years to do so. *E. micromeris* var. *bokei*, from the Big Bend area of Texas, where it is found usually solitary, and difficult to discern among the broken limestone it inhabits, tends to stay solitary or reluctantly produce odd offsets in cultivation. The creamy white or white spines lie close to the body to give a smooth appearance to the globular stem, which has a depressed crown with a tuft of new white bristles giving it the appearance of a turban.

E. micromeris var. *greggii*, has stems 2 in (5 cm) or more

51. *Epithelantha micromeris* var. *bokei*, in habitat on limestone ridges, Texas, USA

52. *Epithelantha micromeris* var. *pachyrhiza*

53. *Epithelantha micromeris* var. *polycephala*

wide, more or less globular, usually clustering quite heavily, with irregularly arranged spines, giving a slightly unkempt appearance, off white or grey, slate-blue or brownish, the upper spines much longer in youth, breaking off partly later. It comes from Mexico, at Saltillo and southern Coahuila, at Sierra de la Paila, Parras, where it is quite common. *E. micromeris* var. *pachyrhiza* (& fa. *elongata*) is named for its thick, tuberous roots. It is solitary, or sparingly clustering, globular, to about 1 ½ in (3 cm) tall, the colour a steely blue grey enhanced by off white, bluish-grey spines. It comes from Coahuila, Mexico.

E. micromeris var. *polycephala* is a small-stemmed, heavily clustering variety, the stems about ¾ in (2 cm) wide, becoming about three times taller, differently shaped from others in being columnar and more rounded at the apex. Spines are dense, not lying flat to the body, white with orange brown tips. It is found in Mexico, in Coahuila, north of Saltillo. *E. micromeris* var. *unguispina* has globular stems 1–2 in (3–5 cm) in diameter, clustering heavily around the base, and characterized by longish central spines, standing out somewhat, greyish-white with black tips. It is found in Mexico, Nuevo Leon.

Connoisseur's choice: *E. micromeris* var. *bokei*

Erdisia B. & R. (1920)

Referred to *Corryocactus*.

Eriocactus Backeb. (1942)

This name is used less and less these days, although Backeberg devotees still use it for a readily distinguishable group of species generally regarded as *Notocactus* now, with fine, hair like spines and all yellow flowers. See under *Notocactus*.

Eriocereus Riccobono (1909)

Referred to *Harrisia*.

Eriosyce Philippi, *Anal. Univ. Chile* 41:721 (1872); Ritter, *Kakt. Sudamer.* 3:911 to 918, figs. 769 to 778 (1980)

This name precedes *Neoporteria*, otherwise it might well by now have been swept into synonymy with that all-embracing genus; if it had, of course, it would have taken precedence, and so, in the same way that *Leuchtenbergia* is left embarrassingly separate from the wide concept of *Ferocactus*, *Eriosyce* has been upheld. Long regarded, for lack of knowledge, as one species with several varieties,

Ritter has recently sorted out the genus into seven species and one variety, reducing his unvalidated genus *Rodentiophila* here too. They come from Chile, making massive, foot wide (30 cm) or more, flat globular, eventually short columnar plants on the hillsides, covered with stiff, yellowish-brown to brown, incurving spines. It is rarely seen in cultivation except as an imported plant, which will usually take some years to die, but almost invariably will do. Seedlings are painfully slow unless grafted, and even then seem in no rush to emulate their achieved size in the wild. I have heard of only one flowering 'in captivity' in England.

Species named are: *E. algarrobensis, E. ihotzkyanae, E. lapampaensis, E. megacarpa, E. rodentiophila* (& var. *lanata*), *E. sandillon, E. spinibarbis.*

Rejected names and synonymies:
E. aurata = *E. sandillon*
E. ausseliana = *E. ihotzkyanae* or *E. algarrobensis*
E. ceratistes = *E. sandillon*
E. ceratistes var. *combarbalensis* = *E. ihotzkyanae*
E. ceratistes var. *jorgensis* = *E. ihotzkyanae*
E. ceratistes var. *mollensis* = *E. sandillon*
E. ceratistes var. *tranquillaensis* = *E. sandillon*
E. ceratistes var. *vallenarensis* = *E. ihotskyanae* or *E. algarrobensis*
E. ceratistes var. *zorillaensis* = *E. ihotzkyanae.*

Recommended species: any obtainable are worth a try, better on a graft than on their own roots if seedlings, unless you are very young or very patient, preferably both.

Connoisseur's choice: *E. sandillon.*

Escobaria B. & R. *The Cact.* 4:53, tt 6,7, figs 51–54 (1923); N. P. Taylor, *Cact. GB* 40(2):31 (1978)

Britton and Rose's concept of *Escobaria* has been widened in recent years to take in the genus *Neobesseya*, as well as some species named as *Coryphantha*, but having fringed petals and pitted seeds more in keeping with *Escobaria*, i.e. *Coryphantha vivipara*, *C. hesteri* and *C. minima*, the recently named *Cochisiea robbinsorum* and the more controversial *Ortegocactus macdougalii*. Opinion is divided among the experts, as at least two others class all the *Escobaria* species within the genus *Coryphantha*. Here Taylor's revision is followed with the addition of *Ortegocactus*, according to Rowley.

They come from a wide area of Mexico and the United States extending (in the case of *E. vivipara*) into Canada, (Alberta).

Species named are: *E. bella, E. chaffeyi, E. chihuahuensis, E. cubensis, E. dasyacantha* (& var. *varicolor*), *E. duncanii, E. emskoetteriana,* (& var. *muehlbaueriana,* var. *runyonii*), *E.*

54. *Escobaria bella*

55. *Escobaria chaffeyi*

56. *Escobaria cubensis*

57. *Escobaria dasyacantha* var. *varicolor*

guadalupensis, E. *henricksonii*, E. *hesteri*, E. *laredoi*, E. *lloydii*, E. *macdougalii*, E, *minima*, E. *missouriensis* (& var. *asperispina*, var. *caespitosa*, var. *marstonii*, var. *notesteinii*, var. *robustior*), E. *orcuttii* (& var. *albicolumnaria*, var. *koenigii*, var. *macraxina*), E. *organensis*, E. *robbinsorum*, E. *sandbergii*, E. *sneedii* (& var. *leei*), E. *strobiliformis* (& var. *durispina*), E. *villardii*, E. *vivipara* (& var. *alversonii*, var. *arizonica*, var. *bisbeeana*, var. *bisbeeana* fa. *sonorensis*, var. *buoflama*, var.

desertii, var. *kaibabensis*, var. *neomexicana*, var. *radiosa*, var. *rosea*), E. *zilziana*.

Rejected names and synonymies

E. *aggregata* = E. *vivipara*
E. *albicolumnaria* = E. *orcuttii* var. *albicolumnaria*
E. *arizonica* = E. *vivipara* var. *arizonica*

58. *Escobaria emskoetteriana*

59. *Escobaria laredoi*

60. *Escobaria missouriensis*

61. *Escobaria orcuttii* var. *albicolumnaria*

E. asperispina = *E. missouriensis* var. *asperispina*
E. bisbeeana = *E. vivipara* var. *bisbeeana*
E. chlorantha = *E. vivipara*
E. desertii = *E. vivipara* var. *desertii*
E. leei = *E. sneedii* var. *leei*
E. muehlbaueriana = *E. emskoetteriana*
E. nellieae = *E. minima*
E. neomexicana = *E. vivipara* var. *neomexicana*
E. oklahomensis = *E. vivipara*
E. radiosa = *E. vivipara* var. *radiosa*

E. rigida = *E. laredoi*
E. roseana = *Neolloydia roseana*
E. runyonii = *E. emskoetteriana* var. *runyonii*
E. tuberculosa = *E. strobiliformis*
E. varicolor = *E. dasyacantha* var. *varicolor*.

Recommended species: *E. cubensis* from the environs of Havana, Cuba, is a delightful miniature, with wispy, yellowish spines and greenish-yellow flowers, the stems getting in cultivation to no more than about an inch or so (2–3 cm) wide. It is difficult on its own roots, and is a better proposition on a graft, where it will offset to form a small cluster after a few years.

E. hesteri is another small growing species from Texas, where it grows in the elite company of *E. minima* and *Echinocereus viridiflorus* var. *davisii*, near Marathon. In cultivation it will make small clusters, to about 3–4 in wide (10 cm), of stems each only about an inch or so (2–3 cm) wide and tall, with wispy white spines and bright pink flowers freely produced. An open, gritty soil is needed, as with its companion in this genus, *E. minima* (see below). It is sensitive to overwatering.

E. laredoi, often seen offered by the invalid name *E. rigida*, is a fairly recent discovery, now getting into cultivation, with dense, fine, glassy-white spines completely obscuring the stem, and deep purple-pink flowers. It comes from Coahuila, Mexico.

E. macdougallii, often seen by the more familiar name *Ortegocactus macdougallii*, is a grey-green bodied, clustering species, with few, dark spines, and yellow flowers appearing at the centre. It is somewhat reluctant to flower in England in cultivation, and suffers from a brown-orange, unsightly marking, which seems to be a natural occurrence and not caused by pests or disease. It is from Oaxaca, Mexico.

E. minima (syn. *E.* or *Coryphantha nellieae*) is a charming, tiny species, better grown on its own roots. It takes 10 years or more to need more than a 3 inch pot, by when it will have developed a dozen or more stems in a flat cluster of creamy coloured spines tipped red or pink, and flowering each year prolifically from the centre of each stem with deep pink flowers. On a graft, unless grown rather hard, it will develop a top-heavy large cluster of tightly packed stems. It comes from near Marathon, Texas, where it grows in the select company of *E. hesteri* and *Echinocereus viridiflorus* var. *davisii*.

E. sneedii var. *sneedii* or *E. sneedii* var. *leei*, very similar varieties to each other, are again miniatures, with individual stems of about $\frac{1}{2}$ inch or so (1–2 cm) wide and tall, forming dense, close-packed clusters a few inches across, somewhat reluctant to produce their brown or pinkish-brown flowers in England, but completely covered with dense, white spines making for most attractive plants. They are susceptible to overwatering. They come from New Mexico and Texas, USA.

E. vivipara, although widespread and variable in the wild, is not such an easy plant to grow well in cultivation, being intolerant of overwatering, or overpotting. The spination is variable, but is at its best in *E. vivipara* var. *alversonii* and *E. vivipara* var. *bisbeeana*. Flowers are more or less the same in each variety, quite large, fringe-petalled, deep pink to purple-pink. Their spread is vast from Alberta, in Canada to the southern United States in a wide belt. Most varieties are cold tolerant.

62. *Escobaria runyonii*

63. *Escobaria strobiliformis* var. *durispina*

Connoisseur's choice: *E. minima, E. sneedii* var. *leei, E. vivipara* var. *alversonii*.

Escobesseya Hester (1945)

Referred to *Escobaria*

Escontria Rose, *Contrib. U.S. Nat. Herb.* 10:125 (1906)

This monotypic genus (*E. chiotilla*) from southern Mexico has been maintained separately by most authorities. It is a branching, tree-like, columnar cactus of little interest except to *Cereus* enthusiasts.

Espostoa B. & R. *The Cact.* 2:60, figs 87–91 (1920)

64. *Escobaria vivipara* var. *vivipara*

65. *Escobaria zilziana*

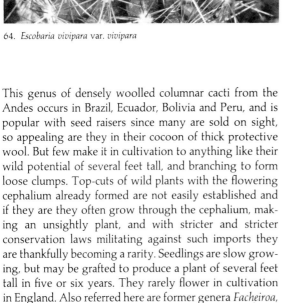

This genus of densely woolled columnar cacti from the Andes occurs in Brazil, Ecuador, Bolivia and Peru, and is popular with seed raisers since many are sold on sight, so appealing are they in their cocoon of thick protective wool. But few make it in cultivation to anything like their wild potential of several feet tall, and branching to form loose clumps. Top-cuts of wild plants with the flowering cephalium already formed are not easily established and if they are they often grow through the cephalium, making an unsightly plant, and with stricter and stricter conservation laws militating against such imports they are thankfully becoming a rarity. Seedlings are slow growing, but may be grafted to produce a plant of several feet tall in five or six years. They rarely flower in cultivation in England. Also referred here are former genera *Facheiroa*, *Pseudoespostoa*, *Thrixanthocereus* and *Vatricania*.

Species named (with former allegiances abbreviated in brackets) are: *E. baumannii* (& var. *arborescens*), *E.* (*Thrix*)-*blossfeldiorum*, *E. calva*, *E.*(*Fach*)*cephaliomelana*, *E.* (*Vat*)-*guentheri*, *E. haagei*, *E. huanucoensis*, *E. hylaea*, *E. lanata* (& var. *floridaensis*, var. *sericata*), *E. lanianuligera*, *E. laticornua* (& var. *atroviolacea*, var. *rubens*), *E.*(*Thrix*)*longispinus*, *E. melanostele* (& var. *inermis*, var. *rubrispina*), *E. mirabilis* (&

var. *primigena*), *E. nana*, *E.*(*Fach*)*pilosa*, *E. procera*, *E. ritteri*, *E. ruficeps*, *E.*(*Thrix*)*senilis*, *E.*(*Fach*)*ulei*.

Recommended species: *E. nana* is densely covered with creamy white wool, and will offset at about 15–18 in (30–40 cm) tall to make an attractive branched plant, with stems about 3 in (8 cm) thick, although flowers are rarely produced in England. *E. ritteri* has long, red-brown spines projecting out from red-brown tinted wool; *E. senilis* makes a densely white, spine covered stem, reminiscent of *Cleistocactus strausii*, but with denser, softer spines.

Connoisseur's choice: *E. melanostele.*

Eulychnia Philippi, *Flurula Atacamensis* 23, t.2 (1860)

This is a small genus of handsomely woolled, slow-growing, columnar plants from the Atacama desert in Chile, where the rainfall is as low or lower than anywhere in South America. The wool confines itself to the ribs and the long dark spines push through it. They are slow-growing plants and if a good-size plant is required grafting should be resorted to at an early age. On their own roots they will not tolerate too much dampness at the root, and a well-drained compost should be used.

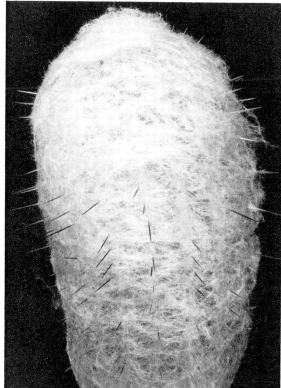

66. *Espostoa hylaea* seedling

67. *Espostoa melanostele* var. *rubrispina*

Species named are: *E. acida* (& var. *elata,* var. *procumbens*), *E. aricensis, E. barquitensis, E. breviflora* (& var. *taltalensis,* var. *tenuis*), *E. castanea* (syn. *Philippicereus castaneus*), *E. iquiquensis* (& var. *pullilana*), *E. morromorenoensis, E. saint-pieana.*

Rejected names and synonymies:

E. cephalophora = E. aricensis
E. longispina = E. breviflora
E. longispina var. *lanuginosior = E. barquitensis*
E. procumbens = E. breviflora
E. ritteri = E. saint-pieana
E. spinibarbis = E. breviflora.

Recommended species: few are available, but *E. saint-pieana* makes an attractive young seedling, with white wool down the vertical ribs, through which the spines in contrasting dark brown protrude for an inch (3 cm) or so.

Connoisseur's choice: *E. saint-pieana.*

Facheiroa B. & R. (1920)

Referred to *Espostoa.*

Ferocactus B. & R., *The Cact.* 3:123 (1922); N. P. Taylor, *Bradleya* 2:19 (1984)

In the last few years Nigel Taylor has published papers revising this genus and incorporating the genera *Stenocactus, Thelocactus, Hamatocactus* (in part), *Sclerocactus* and *Glandulicactus,* but leaving out *Leuchtenbergia,* probably as closely related but embarrassingly preceding *Ferocactus* and so the preferred name if incorporated. Gordon Rowley's view of these genera, as expounded in *Name that Succulent* (1980) is, however, followed here, with *Thelocactus* maintained and incorporating *Hamatocactus* (except for *H. hamatacanthus* and *H. sinuatus,* which have been transferred to *Ferocactus* in the narrower sense), *Sclerocactus, Glandulicactus* and *Echinomastus. Stenocactus* (syn. *Echinofossulocactus*) is also maintained separately.

This leaves Ferocactus largely as Britton and Rose saw it, consisting mostly of large-growing, solid, sentinels in the wild, several feet (1 to 3 m) or more tall and a foot or more thick, fiercely spined, as their name implies, the spines murderously hooked at the tips, and capable of tearing the flesh of any animal, including human ones, unwise enough to brush by too closely. But there are a few, smaller-growing, worthwhile species for the collector

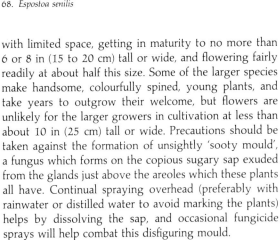

68. *Espostoa senilis*

69. *Eulychnia saint-pieana*

with limited space, getting in maturity to no more than 6 or 8 in (15 to 20 cm) tall or wide, and flowering fairly readily at about half this size. Some of the larger species make handsome, colourfully spined, young plants, and take years to outgrow their welcome, but flowers are unlikely for the larger growers in cultivation at less than about 10 in (25 cm) tall or wide. Precautions should be taken against the formation of unsightly 'sooty mould', a fungus which forms on the copious sugary sap exuded from the glands just above the areoles which these plants all have. Continual spraying overhead (preferably with rainwater or distilled water to avoid marking the plants) helps by dissolving the sap, and occasional fungicide sprays will help combat this disfiguring mould.

Ferocactus species are widespread in Mexico and the south western United States, where they often form a prominent feature of the desert landscape.

Species named are: *F. chrysacanthus, F. cylindraceus* (& var. *eastwoodiae,* var. *lecontei,* var. *tortulispinus*), *F. diguetii* (& var. *carmenensis*), *F. echidne, F. emoryi* (& var. *rectispinus*), *F. flavovirens, F. fordii* (& var. *grandiflorus*), *F. gatesii, F. glaucescens, F. gracilis* (& var. *coloratus*), *F. haematacanthus, F. hamatacanthus* (& var. *sinuatus*), *F. histrix, F. johnstonianus, F. latispinus* (& var. *spiralis,* var. *greenwoodii*), *F. lindsayi, F. macrodiscus, F. peninsulae* (& var. *santa-maria,* var. *townsendianus*), *F. pilosus, F. pottsii* (& var. *alamosanus*), *F. reppenhagenii, F. robustus, F. schwarzii, F. viridescens* (&

var. *littoralis*), *F. wislizenii* (& var. *herrerae,* var. *tiburonensis*).

Rejected names and synonymies:
F. acanthodes = *F. cylindraceus*
F. alamosanus = *F. pottsii* var. *alamosanus*
F. arizonicus = *F. wislizenii*
F. californicus = *F. viridescens*
F. coloratus = *F. gracilis* var. *coloratus*
F. covillei = *F. emoryi*
F. eastwoodiae = *F. cylindraceus* var. *eastwoodiae*
F. electracanthus = *F. histrix*
F. falconeri = *F. wislizenii*
F. guirocobensis = *F. pottsii*
F. herrerae = *F. wislizenii* var. *herrerae*
F. horridus = *F. peninsulae*
F. lecontei = *F. cylindraceus* var. *lecontei*
F. melocactiformis = *F. histrix*
F. nobilis = *F. latispinus* var. *spiralis*
F. orcuttii = *F. viridescens*
F. phoeniceus = *F. wislizenii*
F. pringlei = *F. pilosus*
F. rafaelensis = *F. echidne*
F. rectispinus = *F. emoryi* var. *rectispinus*
F. recurvus = *F. latispinus*
F. rhodanthus = *F. echidne*
F. rostii = *F. cylindraceus*
F. santa-maria = *F. peninsulae* var. *santa-maria*
F. stainesii = *F. pilosus*

F. tiburonensis = F. wislizenii var. tiburonensis
F. tortulospinus = F. cylindraceus var. tortulispinus
F. townsendianus = F. peninsulae var. townsendianus
F. victoriensis = F. echidne
F. viscainensis = F. gracilis var. coloratus.

Recommended species: *F. fordii* is the species which will flower at the smallest size, and I have seen flowers on plants no larger than 3 in (9 cm) in diameter, with flowers varying from plant to plant, purple to magenta; it comes from the northern part of Baja California, Mexico.

F. glaucescens needs to be about 8 in (20 cm) or more in diameter before the yellow flowers may be expected, but it makes a handsome, blue-bodied, yellow-spined plant while it is getting to this size, which will take, in England, 10 years or more; it is from eastern central Mexico over a wide area.

F. gracilis is unlikely to flower at all in captivity as a plant raised from seed – at least until it is small-football-size – but it is worth growing just for the magnificent red, long, hooked spines which adorn it, which after spraying it overhead are vividly coloured; it too comes from a wide area in northern Baja California, Mexico.

F. latispinus, with its broad, fiercely-hooked central spines is a favourite among collectors, and will grow slowly to form a flat-globular stem to about 6 or 8 in (15 to 20 cm) before the purplish-pink or yellow flowers may be looked for, which is liable to take ten years or more. But it is a wait well worthwhile for the lovely spines meanwhile. It comes from eastern central Mexico, near San Luis Potosi.

F. macrodiscus will flower at about 4 in (10 cm) or so in diameter, making a flat-globular stem to about 10 in (25cm) or more in ten or more years from seed, with short, recurving spines and purplish-pink, white margined flowers, which make very attractive, reticulated buds. It comes from southern Mexico in Oaxaca, and from further north in San Luis Potosi.

F. viridescens, with greenish flowers as the name implies, will produce them at about 4 or 5 in (10 to 12 cm) in diameter, which can be achieved in only about five or six years from seed in England; the spines are variable, but strong, with hooked central spines, coloured red or yellow; it comes from southern California, USA, around San Diego, and from northern Baja California, Mexico.

Connoisseur's choice: *F. macrodiscus, F. fordii, F. gracilis.*

Floresia Ritt., nom.nud.

Referred to *Haageocereus.*

Floribunda Ritt., *Kakt. Sudamer.* 1:58 (1979)

This is a monotypic genus set up by Ritter for a species

from Brazil related to *Cephalocereus*, but without cephalium. Its standing has yet to be determined.
Species named is: *F. pusilliflora.*

Frailea B. & R., *The Cact.* 3:208 (1922)

This is a genus of mostly small-stemmed, flat-globular, heavily clustering cacti from a wide area in Brazil, Paraguay, Colombia, Bolivia, Uruguay and Argentina. The small stems (to about 2 in/5 cm wide, often less) produce two different sorts of flowers. Firstly there are cleistogamous flowers, which do not open or even show any sign of petals, but which will produce seed. Secondly, there are normal flowers, invariably yellow, which seem to open briefly and then only on days of high temperature, i.e. 20°c/70°F or more, whether or not the sun is shining. Both sorts of flowers are self-fertile and set seed, which is reputedly short lived. Many of the species are fairly

70. *Ferocactus gracilis*, in habitat, northern Baja California, Mexico

71. *Ferocactus rectispinus*, planted out in Living Desert Museum, Phoenix, Arizona, USA

similar, weakly spined in brown or yellow, forming mounds of heavily clustering, small, globular stems, some forming loose clumps of finger-thin, cylindrical stems. There are a few species which are exceptional in their spination or their colouring.

Species named are: *F. alacriportana, F. albiareolata, F. albicolumnaris, F. albifusca, F. asperispina, F. asterioides* (& var. *backebergii,* var. *harmoniana*), *F. aureinitens, F, aureispina* (& var. *pallidior*), *F. carminifilamentosa* (& var. *windelmanniana*), *F. cataphracta* (& var. *duchii,* var. *tuyensis*), *F. cataphractoides, F. chiquitana, F. chrysacantha, F. colombiana, F. concepcionensis, F. curvispina, F. deminuta, F. friedrichii, F. fulviseta, F. gracillima, F. grahliana* (& var. *rubrispina*), *F. horstii, F. ignacionensis, F. knippeliana, F. lepida, F. magnifica* n.n. *F. mammifera, F. matoana, F. melitae, F. moseriana, F. perbella, F. perumbilicata* (& var. *spinosior*), *F. phaeodisca, F. pseudogracillima, F. pseudopulcherrima, F. pulcherrima, F. pumila* (& var. *maior*), *F. pygmaea* (& var. *antigibbera,*

72. *Ferocactus viridescens* (seedling, flowering at about 4 in/10 cm wide)

73. *Frailea cataphracta* (cristate plant)

74. *Gymnocalycium andreae*

75. *Gymnocalycium baldianum*

var. *atrofusca*, var. *aurea*, var. *curvispina*, var. *dadakii*, var. *lilalunula*, var. *longispina*, var. *maior*, var. *planicosta*), *F. schilinzkyana*, *F. uhligiana*, *F. ybatense*.

Rejected names and synonymies:

F. aurea = *F. pygmaea* var. *aurea*
F. castanea = *F. asterioides*
F. dadakii = *F. pygmaea* var. *dadakii*
F. pullispina = *F. chiquitana*.

Recommended species: *F. asterioides* has dark, purple-brown stems, usually solitary, to about 2 in (5 cm) wide and about the same in height or squatter, with neat vertical rows of short, black spines, sea-urchin-like in appearance. It is sensitive to overwatering.

F. cataphracta is also often single-stemmed, more or less globular, coloured purplish-brown, with a stem about 1.5 in (4 cm) wide and somewhat shorter in height, with indefinite, low ribs of short clusters of dark brown spines.

F. chiquitana is grey-green stemmed, with more definite ribs of blackish-brown spines contrasting well with the body-colour, tending to be slow-growing and often solitary. It too presents some sensitivity to overwatering.

F. curvispina has silvery-white spines curving back into the short, thick stems, about $\frac{3}{4}$ in (2 cm) wide and a little taller, and densely clothing them.

F. phaeodisca, has barely $\frac{3}{4}$ in (2 cm) wide globular, shining, stems, purplish-brown, with indefinite ribs and tiny brown spines.

F. magnifica n.n. has golden-yellow spines in neat rows on a short stemmed plant, sparingly clustering, the individual stems no more than $\frac{1}{2}$ to $\frac{3}{4}$ in (2 cm) wide and to about 2 in (5 cm) tall.

F. ybatense is fairly typical of the larger growing, clustering species, with stems about an inch (2.5 cm) or so tall and wide, usually a little less tall than wide, and with red-brown, short, weak spines.

Connoisseur's choice: *F. asterioides*

Glandulicactus Backeb. (1938)

Referred to *Thelocactus*.

Grusonia F. Reichenb, ex B. & R. (1919)

Referred to *Opuntia*.

Gymnanthocereus Backeb. (1937)

Referred to *Browningia*.

Gymnocactus Backeb. (1938)

Referred to *Neolloydia*.

Gymnocalycium Pfeiff., *Abbild.u.Beschr.Cact.* 2: under tt.1, 12 (1845); Swales, *The Chileans* 2(12):94 (1968); Putnam, *Gymnocalyciums* (1978)

This is a popular, widespread genus in the wild, covering an area equivalent to most of western Europe, intruding into Uruguay, Argentina, Paraguay, Bolivia, Chile and Brazil. The species are generally globular, or flat-globular, solitary or clustering, small – to 4–5 in (10 cm), or a little more – but rarely reaching a foot or more (30 cm) in the wild or in cultivation. They are noted for their ease of cultivation, except for one or two species, fierce spines in some, and their free flowering, with naked buds – from which the genus gets its name. In cultivation under glass they seem to prefer not to be in direct sun for too long in the day during the hot summer months. The most popular form of classification is based on seed characters, splitting the genus into five subgenera, according to the shape and size of the seed, for which a X10 magnifying glass is sufficient to differentiate. This system, devised in the 1930s by Fric and others is explained and amplified by Swales (see ref. above). Taken together with other factors, such as flower structure, stem characteristics, and spine characters it forms a useful basis for splitting the 80 or so species. Rowley lumps the genera *Neowerdermannia* and *Weingartia* with this genus, but they are treated separately herein.

Species named are: *G. achirasense*, *G. alboareolatum*, *G. ambatoense*, *G. andreae* (& var. *grandiflorum*, var. *svecianum*), *G. anisitsii*, *G. antherostele*, *G. armatum*, *G. artigas*, *G. baldianum*, *G. bayrianum*, *G. bicolor*, *G. bodenbenderianum*, *G. borthii*, *G. bozsingianum*, *G, bruchii* (& var. *hossei*), *G. buenekeri*, *G. calochlorum* (& var. *proliferum*), *G. capillaense*, *G. cardenasianum*, *G. carminanthum*, *G. castellanosii*, *G. chiquitanum*, *G. chubutense*, *G. damsii* (& var. *centrispinum*. var. *rotundulum*, var. *torulosum*, var. *tucavocense*), *G. deeszianum*, *G. denudatum*, *G. eurypleurum*, *G. ferrari*, *G. fleischerianum* (& var. *andersohnianum*, var. *heuschkelianum*, var. *meiklejohnianum*), *G. fricianum*, *G. friedrichii* (& var. *albiflorum*, var. *moserianum*, var. *pazoutianum*, var. *pirarettaense*), *G. gibbosum* (& var. *gerardii*, var. *leucodictyon*, var. *nigrum*, var. *nobile*), *G. glaucum*, *G. grandiflorum*, *G. griseo-pallidum*, *G. guerkeanum*, *G. hamatum*, *G. horridispinum*, *G. horstii*. *G. hossei*, *G. hyhopleurum* (& var. *breviflorum*, var. *centrispinum*, var. *euchlorum*, var. *ferocior*, var. *ferox*), *G. hyptiacanthum* (& var. *citriflorum*), *G. intertextum*, *G. joossensianum*, *G. kieslingii* (& fa. *alboareolatum*, fa. *castaneum*), *G. knebelii*, *G. kozelskyanum*, *G. leeanum* (& var. *brevispinum*, var. *netrelianum*, var. *roseiflorum*), *G. leptanthemum*, *G. marsoneri*, *G. matoense*, *G. mazanense*, *G. megalothelos*, *G. megatae* (& var. *bolivianum*), *G. melanocarpum*, *G. mesopotamicum*, *G. mihanovichii* (& var. *angusto-striatum*, var. *filadelfiense*, var. *melocactiformis* var. *roseiflorum*, var. *stenogonum*, var. *stenostriatum*), *G.*

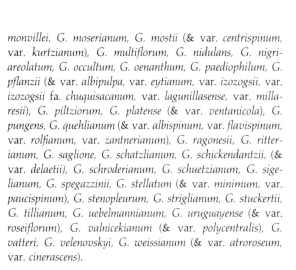

76. *Gymnocalycium bicolor*

77. *Gymnocalycium bodenbenderianum*

78. *Gymnocalycium calochlorum* var. *proliferum*

79. *Gymnocalycium damsii*

monvillei, G. moserianum, G. mostii (& var. *centrispinum*, var. *kurtzianum*), *G. multiflorum, G. nidulans, G. nigriareolatum, G. occultum, G. oenanthum, G. paediophilum, G. pflanzii* (& var. *albipulpa*, var. *eytianum*, var. *izozogsii*, var. *izozogsii* fa. *chuquisacanum*, var. *lagunillasense*, var. *millaresii*), *G. piltziorum, G. platense* (& var. *ventanicola*), *G. pungens, G. quehlianum* (& var. *albispinum*, var. *flavispinum*, var. *rolfianum*, var. *zantnerianum*), *G. ragonesii, G. ritterianum, G. saglione, G. schatzlianum, G. schickendantzii*, (& var. *delaetii*), *G. schroderianum, G. schuetzianum, G. sigelianum, G. spegazzinii, G. stellatum* (& var. *minimum*, var. *paucispinum*), *G. stenopleurum, G. striglianum, G. stuckertii, G. tillianum, G. uebelmannianum, G. uruguayense* (& var. *roseiflorum*), *G. valnicekianum* (& var. *polycentralis*), *G. vatteri, G. velenovskyi, G. weissianum* (& var. *atroroseum*, var. *cinerascens*).

Rejected names and synonymies:

G. albispinum = *G. bruchii*
G. asterium = *G. stellatum*
G. brachyanthum = *G. monvillei*
G. brachypetalum = *G. gibbosum*
G. chlorostictum = *G. mihanovichii* var. *filadelfiense*
G. chuquisacanum = *G. pflanzii* var. *izozogsii* fa. *chuquisacanum*
G. comarapense = *G. pflanzii*
G. curvispinum = *G. valnicekianum*
G. eytianum = *G. megatae*
G. guanchinense = *G. mazanense*
G. hammerschmidii = *G. chiquitanum*
G. hennissii Hort. = hybrid
G. horstii var. *buenekeri* = *G. buenekeri*
G. izozogsii = *G. pflanzii* var. *izozogsii*

G. kurtzianum = *G. mostii* var. *kurtzianum*

G. lafaldense = *G. bruchi*

G. lagunillasense = *G. pflanzii* var. *lagunillasense*

G. marquesii = *G. pflanzii*

G. michoga = *G. pungens*

G. mihanovichii var. *albiflorum* = *G. friedrichii* var. *albiflorum*

G. mihanovichii var. *rysanekianum* = *G. friedrichii* var. *albiflorum*

G. millaresii = *G. pflanzii* var. *millaresii*

G. netrelianum = *G. leeanum* var. *netrelianum*

G. neumannianum = *Weingartia neumanniana*

G. ochoteranai = *G. stellatum*

G. onchyacanthum = *G. megatae*

G. paraguayense = *G. denudatum*

G. parvulum = *G. quehlianum*

G. pflanzii var. *riograndense* = *G. pflanzii* var. *albipulpa*

G. pflanzi var. *zegarrae* = *G. pflanzii* var. *albipulpa*

G. proliferum = *G. calochlorum* var. *proliferum*

G. pseudo-malacocarpus = *G. megatae*

G. pugionacanthum = *G. hybopleurum*

G. riograndense = *G. pflanzii* var. *albipulpa*

G. riojense = *G. bodenbenderianum*

G. tilcarense = *G. saglione*

G. triacanthum = *G. quehlianum*

G. tudae = *G. megatae*

G. tudae var. *bolivianum* = *G. megatae* var. *bolivianum*

G. venturianum = *G. baldianum*

G. westii = *Weingartia westii*

G. zegarrae = *G. pflanzii* var. *albipulpa*.

Recommended species: *G. andreae* is an old, popular species, making clusters of small globular stems about an inch (2.5 cm) or so across, with dark green colouring, and with weak, dark grey spines well spaced out and not significant; its crowning glory is its beautiful yellow flowers with darker edges to the petals outside, making a very pleasing show, and produced in succession sporadically as in many *Gymnocalycium* species. It comes from Cordoba in Argentina.

G. baldianum is similar in appearance but larger bodied and clustering later in life, and with red flowers. Many hybrids of this species have been produced with colours in the deep pink to pale salmon-pink range. It comes from Catamarca in Argentina.

G. bicolor from Cordoba, Argentina, makes a large, solitary, flat-globular stem, with strong spines in two colours, hence the name; radial spines are greyish, the centrals black. Flowers are large with long tubes, wonderfully coloured in shades of lilac-pink.

G. bodenbenderianum is worth the longer label needed to get the lengthy name on. It is one of the slower growing species, with many low ribs, a brownish body colour, short, recurving spines, and white flowers. It comes from

near La Rioja in Cordoba, Argentina.

G. buenekeri, from Rio Grande do Sul, has become one of the most popular species since its introduction some 10 years or so ago. It grows eventually into a large cluster of fat, healthy, matt green stems with very few ribs, small clusters of yellowish-brown spines well spaced out, and glorious salmon pink flowers.

G. calochlorum (& var. *proliferum*) are heavily clustering brothers of the very well known *G. bruchii*, with thin, wispy white spines close to the stems, which are globular and get to about an inch or $1\frac{1}{2}$ in (2.5 to 4 m) wide, with long tubed pale pink flowers, followed by long, sausage shaped, blue pods.

G. damsii from north west Paraguay and Bolivia, is one of the slow growing, small species, eventually making a cluster, but often solitary for some time. It has rounded barely discernible ribs, wispy spines, and purple-green body colour, producing its white flowers freely, with characteristic grey anthers.

G. denudatum is a very variable species, but in general is few-ribbed, flat-growing, with spider like clusters of yellow-brown spines flat to the stem, and long-tubed white flowers. It is widespread from southern Brazil to Argentina at Misiones.

G. friedrichii is invariably dark reddish-purple coloured, slow growing, with sharp vertical ribs, and wispy, short spines in small clusters. One of the features of this and the allied species *G. mihanovichii* is the more or less prominent banding across the ribs, making for most attractive looking plants. Flowers are white or pink. It is from Bolivia.

G. glaucum is one of the most challenging to grow. It is slow, making a solitary, grey-green stem, with strong, recurving spines. Flowers are not large, pale pink. It is from Catamarca, Argentina.

G. horridispinum is so heavily spined as to confuse its identification as a *Gymnocalycium* species, the strong, outstanding, red-brown spines of the young growth becoming dark brown to grey in age. Flowers vary in colour from almost white to deep lilac pink. It comes from Cordoba, Argentina.

G. leeanum (& var. *netrelianum*) is a handsome, clustering species, making a hand sized clump in four or five years of bright, shining green stems about $1\frac{1}{2}$–2 in (3–5 cm) tall and wide, with small clusters of yellow spines close to the body, most attractively decorating the plant. Flowers are yellow with brownish smudgy stripes on the outside of the petals. Like many yellow flowered species it comes from Uruguay.

G. megatae is the prior name for a species variously named for differing forms (syn. *G. tudae*, *G. pseudomalacocarpus*, *G. eytianum*, *G. onchyacanthum*), from a very hostile area between Paraguay and Bolivia, consisting of an area of salt flats (not a recommendation for inclusion in the

80. *Gymnocalycium denudatum*

81. *Gymnocalycium mihanovichii*

82. *Gymnocalycium oenanthum*

83. *Gymnocalycium quehlianum*

compost), known as the Grey Hell. The plants are highly coloured, reddish-brown or grey, with little hint of green in their make-up at all. Flowers are a dirty white, but the spines compensate, being strong and curved slightly, though not dense on the plants, which are flattish globular, strongly ribbed, clustering later in life in cultivation. As might be expected from their habitat they are slow growing and not the easiest to cultivate successfully; care is needed in avoiding too much water at any time. Surprisingly in view of their wild occurrence and colouring they do not respond to excessive light, preferring a limited amount of sunlight each day as do most species in this genus.

G. mesopotamicum is a very recently described species

66

84. *Gymnocalycium saglione*

85. *Gymnocalycium tillianum*

down the vertical ribs, brownish-green in body colour, the flowers pale pink.

G. ragonesii created a sensation when it first was discovered. The imported plants from Catamarca in Argentina were flat topped, desert brown, and with vestigial spines on the barely discernible ribs. And the seedlings now available from nurseries continue to show these characteristics, if to a slightly less severe extent. It is slow growing, solitary, and a handsome species, with long, narrow tubed, white flowers.

G. saglione, from northern Argentina and Bolivia, is one of the big boys, making a 9–10 in (to 25 cm) or more wide plant in time, although taking quite a few years to do so, covered with curving back, strong brown to yellowish-brown spines. The flowers are unusual, being short tubed, almost urn shaped, and white, sometimes flushed pale pink. *G. stellatum*, from Cordoba, Argentina, is a somewhat variable species, low growing, brown in colour with short, dark brown spines, and white flowers flushed pink.

G. tillianum is slow growing, with strong, curved spines and short tubed red flowers. It comes from a remote area of Argentina, in the Sierra Ambato.

G. weissianum has strong curving spines coloured red-brown at first, later grey, and seems to need to get to about 3 in (8 cm) tall and wide before it will flower freely, with lovely pink to deep pink (*G. weissianum* var. *atroroseum*) flowers, worth the delay. It is from Catamarca, in Argentina.

Connoisseur's choice: G. buenekeri, G. friedrichii, G. horridispinum. G. leeanum, G. megatae, G. oenanthum, G. pflanzii, G. weissianum.

Gymnocereus Rauh ex Backeb (1959)

Referred to *Browningia*

Haageocereus Backeb., *Blatter fur Kakteenf.* 3, 6 (1934); Ritter, *Kakt. Sudamer.* 3:1124, figs 1089, 1090 (1980) & 4:1387, figs 1266 et seq. (1981)

Apart from an attempt to sink this genus beneath *Trichocereus*, there has been little real effort to discredit it, and it is still commonly used by both collectors and nurserymen. The appeal of the species of this genus is in their dense spination, in all shades between yellowish-white, through yellows and browns to almost black, often with differing coloured spines on the same plant. As young, single stems, they are most attractive, but as they approach about a foot (30 cm) in height, they naturally defer from the vertical, start to offset and demand more space for their eventually decumbent stems, which in the wild often sprawl down slopes. The tubular flowers in

from Mercedes, Argentina, with shining green stems, thin, curving spines and relatively large pale pink flowers. *G. mihanovichii*, closely related to *G. friedrichii*, is a small growing species, with extremely attractive body colouring and marking in bands, wispy spines, sharp ribs and white or pink flowers.

G. oenanthum is a slow grower, with strong, curved brown to grey spines, and deep wine-red flowers, from Catamarca, in Argentina.

G. pflanzi has several synonyms and comes from a wide area of Bolivia, makes solitary, squat stems to about 5–6 in (15 cm) or more, green to olive green in colour, with clusters of curving spines and gloriously coloured flowers, varying in different plants, from pale pink, to shell pink to apricot pink.

G. quehlianum is a well-known, popular, free flowering species, with many ribs, globular to short columnar habit, with closely spaced, but quite short clusters of spines

red, yellow, orange or white are an event in this country at least, and usually plants have to be a foot or more in length before they may be expected to flower, and then only in sunny glasshouses.

The genera *Floresia*, *Peruvocereus*, *Weberbauerocereus* and *Yungasocereus* are referred here, as well as the former *Samaipaticereus inquisivensis*. Ritter's opinions on the inter-relationships of species are followed in the list below.

Species named (with former allegiances abbreviated in brackets) are: *H. albispinus*, *H. albus*, *H. ambiguus* (*nom. dub.*), *H. australis* (& fa. *nanus*, fa. *subtilispinus*), *H. (Web) cephalomacrostibas*, *H. chalaensis*, *H. chryseus*, *H. churinensis*, *H. cuzcoensis* (& var. *tenuiarboreus*), *H. decumbens* (& var. *brevispinus*, var. *spinosior*), *H. fascicularis*, *H. fulvus* (& var. *yautanensis*), *H. icensis*, *H. icosagonoides* (& fa. *heteracanthus*), *H. (Sam)inquisivensis*, *H. (Web)johnsonii*, *H. lanugispinus*, *H. limensis* (& var. *andicola*, var. *brevispinus*, var. *deflexispinus*, var. *metachrous*, var. *zonatus*), *H. litoralis* (*nom. dub.*), *H. longicomus*, *H. multangularis* (& var. *dichromus*, var. *pseudomelanostele*, var. *turbidus*), *H. pacalaensis* (& var. *pseudoversicolor*), *H. platinospinus* (& var. *pluriflorus*), *H. rauhii* (& var. *laticornua*), *H. (Web)seyboldianus*, *H. subtilispinus*, *H. tenuis*, *H. torataensis*, *H. versicolor* (& var. *fuscus*, var. *humifusus*), *H. vulpes*, *H. (Web)weberbaueri* (& var. *aureifuscus*, var. *horribilus*, var. *horridispinus*, var. *humi-*

lior), *H. (Web)winterianus* (& var. *australis*), *H. zangalensis*, *H. zehnderi* (*nom. dub.*).

Rejected names and synonymies:

H. acanthocladus = *H. multangularis*
H. achaetus = *H. limensis* var. *deflexispinus*
H. acranthus = *H. limensis* var. *andicola* & var. *brevispinus*
H. acranthus var. *crassispinus* = *H. limensis* var. *metachrous*
H. acranthus var. *fortalezensis* = *H. fulvus*
H. acranthus var. *metachrous* = *H. limensis* var. *metachrous*
H. akersii = *H. multangularis* var. *pseudomelanostele*
H. albisetatus = *Espostoa haagei* × *H. multangularis*
H. andinus = *Borzicactus montanus*
H. aticensis = *H. subtilispinus*
H. aureispinus = *H. multangularis*
H. bicolor = *Borzicactus bicolor*
H. chosicensis = *H. multangularis*
H. chosicensis var. *albispinus* = *H. albispinus*
H. chosicensis var. *marksianus* = *H. multangularis*
H. chosicensis var. *rubrospinus* = *H. albispinus* × *H. multangularis*
H. chrysacanthus = *H. multangularis* var. *pseudomelanostele*
H. clavatus = *H. multangularis* var. *pseudomelanostele*
H. clavispinus = *H. limensis*
H. comosus = *H. albispinus* × *Espostoa haagei*
H. convergens = *Borzicactus convergens*

86. *Haageocereus limensis* var. *zonatus*

87. *Haageocereus winterianus*

H. crassiareolatus = H. multangularis var. *dichromus*
H. deflexispinus = H. limensis var. *deflexispinus*
H. deserticola = Borzicactus deserticola
H. dichromus = H. multangularis var. *dichromus*
H. divaricatispinus = H. multangularis
H. elegans = H. icosagonoides
H. laradensis var. *pseudoversicolor = H. pacalaensis* var. *pseudoversicolor*
H. longiareolatus = H. multangularis
H. mamillatus = H. decumbens
H. multicolorispinus = H. decumbens var. *multicolorispinus*
H. olowinskianus = H. limensis
H. pachystele = H. multangularis
H. paradoxus = Borzicactus faustianus
H. peculiaris = Borzicactus peculiaris
H. peniculatus = H. albispinus
H. piliger = H. multangularis var. *pseudomelanostele*
H. pluriflorus = H. platinospinus var. *pluriflorus*
H. pseudoacranthus = H. limensis var. *deflexispinus*
H. pseudomelanostele & vars *= H. multangularis* var. *pseudomelanostele*
H. pseudoversicolor = H. pacalaensis var. *pseudoversicolor*
H. repens = H. pacalaensis
H. salmonoideus (& var. *rubrispinus*) *= H. albispinus* × *H. multangularis*
H. seticeps (& var. *robustispinus*) *= Haageocereus* × *Espostoa*
H. setosus = H. multangularis var. *pseudomelanostele*
H. smaragdiflorus = H. albispinus × *H. multangularis*
H. symmetros = H. multangularis var. *dichromus*
H. tenuispinus = H. multangularis var. *pseudomelanostele*
H. turbidus = H. multangularis
H. viridiflorus = H. multangularis
H. zonatus = H. limensis var. *zonatus.*

Recommended species: there is little to choose between the various species, and it is largely a matter of colour preference in choosing between anything from almost white spines to dark brown. *H. limensis* var. *zonatus* and *H. seyboldianus* are fairly typical of the form of the majority of species.
H. winterianus, recently combined here, is exceptional, with bright golden yellow spines, and a more tall columnar habit, making stems to five feet or more tall in a few years if grown on well.

Connoisseur's choice: *H. winterianus.*

Hamatocactus B. & R. (1922)

Although referred to *Ferocactus* by Taylor, Rowley's placing beneath *Thelocactus* (also referred to *Ferocactus* by Taylor) is preferred. See under *Thelocactus*. However, *H. hamatocanthus* (& var. *sinuatus*) are referred to *Ferocactus* in the narrower sense.

Harrisia Britton, *Bull. Torr. Bot. Club* 35:561 (1908)

This is a genus of erect, climbing or sprawling, narrow-stemmed, cylindrical, night-flowering cacti from a wide distribution in Argentina, Paraguay, Brazil, the West Indies and Florida, USA, of little interest except to *Cereus* enthusiasts, and for grafting stock.

Species named are: *H. adscendens, H. arendtii, H. bonplandii, H. brookii, H. crucicentra, H. deeringii, H. divaricata, H. earlei, H. fernowii, H. gracilis, H. guelichii, H. hurstii, H. jusbertii, H. martinii, H. nashii* (& var. *straminia*), *H. platygona, H. polyacantha, H. pomanensis* (& var. *uruguayensis*), *H. portoricensis, H. regelii, H. taetra, H. tarijensis, H. taylorii.*

Rejected names and synonymies:
H. aboriginum = Cereus gracilis var. *aboriginum*
H. eriophora = Cereus eriophorus
H. fragrans = Cereus eriophorus var. *fragrans*
H. simpsonii = Cereus gracilis var. *simpsonii*
H. tortuosa = H. arendtii
H. undata = H. gracilis.

They are not recommended.

Hatiora B. & R. (1923)

Referred to *Rhipsalis.*

Heliabravoa Backeb. (1956)

Referred to *Stenocereus.*

Helianthocereus Backeb. (1949)

Equated to *Trichocereus* by Hunt, and now referred to Rowley's broad concept of *Echinopsis*.

Heliocereus (Bgr.) B. & R., *Contrib. U.S. Nat. Herb.* 12:433 (1909)

Apart from being the source of many hybrid 'Epiphyllums', this genus is of little interest to all but epiphyte enthusiasts, unless you are prepared, and have plenty of room to accommodate the very long stems the species produce. Certainly the flowers are worth the struggle to contain the plant, in the style of the familiar, aforementioned Epiphyllum hybrids, but smaller.

If grown these Central American epiphytic cacti should be given a peat based compost, watered moderately throughout most of the year, and sprayed as frequently as convenient. They also benefit from having their feet in the shade and their heads in the sun – don't we all?

Hildewintera

Species named are: *H. aurantiacus, H. cinnabarinus, H. elegantissimus* (& var. *helenae,* var. *stenopetalus*), *H. heterodoxus, H. luzmariae, H. schrankii, H. speciosus* (& var. *amecamensis,* var. *serratus,* var. *superbus*).

Rejected names and synonymies:
H. amecamensis = *H. speciosus* var. *amecamensis*
H. serratus = *H. speciosus* var. *serratus*
H. superbus = *H. speciosus* var. *superbus*

They are not recommended.

Hildewintera Ritter (1966)

Referred to *Borzicactus.*

Homalocephala B. & R. (1922)

Referred to *Echinocactus.*

Horridocactus Backeb. (1938)

Referred to *Neoporteria.*

Hylocereus (Bgr.) B. & R., *Contrib. U.S. Nat. Herb.* 12:428 (1909)

The species of this genus are climbing or scrambling cacti from the West Indies, Venezuela, Colombia and central America. Most often they are seen as the triangular stock for grafted plants produced by nurserymen in kinder climates than England, since they are somewhat tender and will not take the sort of low temperatures most collectors keep in the winter months in English glasshouses. They are in themselves of little interest, except to epiphyte enthusiasts with plenty of room to accommodate the very long stems they produce in order to clamber amongst trees in the wild.

Species named are: *H. antiguensis, H. broxensis, H. calcaratus, H. costaricensis, H. cubensis, H. escuintlensis, H. estebanensis, H. extensus, H. guatemalensis, H. lemairei, H. microcladus, H. minutiflorus, H. monacanthus, H. napoleonensis, H. ocamponis, H. peruvianus, H. polyrhizus, H. purpusii, H. scandens, H. schomburgkii, H. stenopterus, H. triangularis, H. trigonus, H. trinitatensis, H. undatus, H. venezuelensis.*

They are not recommended.

Hymenorebutia Fric ex Buining (1939)

An old generic name resurrected by Ritter recently for a group of *Lobivia* species – not here accepted.

Islaya Backeb. (1934)

Referred to *Neoporteria.*

Isolatocereus Backeb. (1942)

Referred to *Stenocereus.*

Jasminocereus B. & R., *The Cact.* 2:146, figs 212–214 (1920)

This is a genus from the Galapagos Islands, rarely seen in cultivation, and of little interest except to *Cereus* or Darwin enthusiasts. In habitat they grow to tree size, but in cultivation they are extremely slow growing and to achieve three or four feet (a metre) is liable to take 10 years or more; the stems are very densely clothed with dark brown, thin, outstanding spines; flowers are unlikely to be produced.

Species named are: *J. howellii, J. thouarsii* (& var. *chathamensis,* var. *delicatus,* var. *sclerocarpus*)

They are not recommended.

Krainzia Backeb. (1938)

Referred to *Mammillaria.*

Lasiocereus Ritter (1966)

Referred to *Echinopsis.*

Lemairocereus B. & R. (1909)

Referred to *Stenocereus.*

Leocereus B. & R., *The Cact.* 2:108, figs 160, 162 (1920)

This is a small, thin-stemmed, many-ribbed, small white flowered columnar growing cactus from Brazil, little known in cultivation, and of little interest except to *Cereus* enthusiasts.

Species named are: *L. bahiensis, L. glaziovii, L. melanurus, L. paulensis, L. urandiensis.*

They are not recommended.

Lepidocoryphantha Backeb. (1938)

Referred to *Coryphantha.*

Lepismium Pfeiff. (1835)

Referred to *Rhipsalis.*

Leptocereus (Bgr.) B. & R., *Contrib. U.S. Nat. Herb.* 12:433 (1909)

This is a little known genus of thin stemmed, clambering or shrubby cactus species from the West Indies, of interest only to *Cereus* enthusiasts.

Species named are: *L. arboreus, L. assurgens, L. ekmannii, L. leonii, L. maxonii, L. prostratus, L. quadricostatus, L. sylvestris, L. weingartianus, L. wrightii.*

They are not recommended.

Leptocladodia F. Buxb (1954)

Referred to *Mammillaria.*

Leuchtenbergia Hook, *Curtis Bot. Mag.* 74: t. 4393 (1848)

This distinctive species (*Leuchtenbergia principis* is the only known one) comes from northern and central Mexico. The long, thin, grey-green angled tubercles have no real parallel in the rest of the cactus family, except perhaps for the diminutive *Ariocarpus agavoides*, and they are instantly recognizable. It will flower if given sufficient water in the growing season, and this will prevent the characteristic, unsightly dying back of the tubercle tips, so often spoiling this very handsome plant. Flowers are large, yellow and come from the growing centre of the plant. The spines are long, thin, flexible and somewhat twisted, unlike the strong spines of the related genus *Ferocactus*, with which there have been some interesting hybrids produced in cultivation, indicating their close relationship.

Connoisseur's choice: *L. principis.*

Leucostele Backeb. (1953)

Referred to *Echinopsis.*

Lobeira Alex. (1944)

Referred to *Nopalxochia.*

Lobivia B. & R., *The Cact.* 3:49:tt.4,5, figs 62–78 (1922); Rausch, *Lobivia* (3 parts) (1975–77)

This large genus from Bolivia, Peru and Argentina is generally low-growing, globular to short-cylindric, clustering or, more uncommonly, solitary, variously spined, with ribs somewhat broken into tubercles. The flowers are sumptuous, but short-lived, usually lasting one day or so.

Rausch's 3 volume work on the genus is not laid out for easy use, but is full of well-taken and produced photographs in colour and in habitat showing the beauty of the flowers. It contains many combinations of the proliferation of specific names that have appeared over the years, and is followed herein.

Species named are: *L. aurea* (& var. *dobeana*, var. *fallax*, var. *leucomalla*, var. *quinesensis*, var. *shaferi*), *L. backebergii* (& var. *oxyalabastra*, subsp. *hertrichiana*, subsp. *hertrichiana* var. *laui*, subsp. *hertrichiana* var. *simplex*, subsp. *schieliana*, subsp. *wrightiana*, subsp. *wrightiana* var. *chilensis*, subsp. *wrightiana* var. *winteriana*, subsp. *zecheri*), *L. buiningiana*, *L. caineana* (& var. *albiflora*), *L. campicola*, *L. chrysantha* (& var. *hypocyrta*, var. *klusacekii*, subsp. *jajoiana*, subsp. *jajoiana* var. *caspalensis*, subsp. *jajoiana* var. *paucicostata*, subsp. *jajoiana* var. *vatteri*, subsp. *marsoneri*, subsp. *marsoneri* var. *rubescens*), *L. chrysochete* (& var. *markusii*, var. *minutiflora*, var. *subtilis*, var. *tenuispina*), *L. cinnabarina* (& var. *gigantea*, var. *gracilis*, var. *walterspielii*, var. *zudanensis*, subsp. *acanthophlegma*, subsp. *acanthophlegma* var. *oligotricha*, subsp. *acanthophlegma* var. *pilosa*, subsp. *acanthophlegma* var. *roseiflora*, subsp. *prestoana*, subsp. *prestoana* var. *draxleriana*), *L. crassicaulis*, *L. divaricata*, *L. famatimensis* (& var. *jachalensis*, var. *sanjuanensis*), *L. ferox* (& var. *camargensis*, var. *longispina*, var. *potosina*), *L. formosa* (& subsp. *grandis*, subsp. *grandis* var. *pinchasensis*, subsp. *bruchii*, subsp. *bruchii* var. *nivalis*, subsp. *bruchii* var. *kieslingii*, subsp. *tarijensis*, subsp. *tarijensis* var. *bertramiana*, subsp. *tarijensis* var. *totorensis*), *L. glaucescens*, *L. haematantha* (& var. *elongata*, var. *fechseri*, var. *hualfinensis*, subsp. *kuehnrichii*, subsp. *kuehnrichii* var. *amblayensis*, subsp. *chorillensis*, subsp. *densispina*, subsp. *densispina* var. *pectinifera*, subsp. *densispina* var. *rebutioides*, subsp. *densispina* var. *sublimiflora*), *L. lateritia* (& var. *citriflora*, var. *cotagaitensis*, var. *kupperiana*, var. *sanguiniflora*), *L. maximiliana* (& var. *corbula*, subsp. *caespitosa*, subsp. *caespitosa* var. *altiplani*, subsp. *caespitosa* var. *charazanensis*, subsp. *caespitosa* var. *hermanniana* subsp.

88. *Lobivia aurea* var. *leucomalla*

89. *Lobivia backebergii* subsp. *hertrichiana*

90. *Lobivia cinnabarina* subsp. *acanthophlegma*

caespitosa var. *miniatiflora*, subsp. *caespitosa* var. *rinconadensis*, subsp. *caespitosa* var. *violacea*, subsp. *quiabayensis*, subsp. *quiabayensis* var. *leptacantha*, subsp. *westii*, subsp. *westii* var. *intermedia*), *L. miniatinigra*, *L. pampana*, *L. pentlandii* (& var. *hardeniana*, var. *larae*), *L. prolifera*, *L. pugionacantha* (& var. *bustilloensis*, var. *cornuta*, var. *culpinensis*, var. *haemantha*, var. *rossii*, var. *salitrensis* var. *sayariensis*, var. *versicolor*), *L. purpureominiata*, *L. rauschii*, *L. rosarioana* (& var. *rubriflora*), *L. saltensis* (& var. *multicostata*, var. *nealeana*, var. *schreiteri*, var. *stilowiana*), *L. sanguiniflora* (& var. *duursmaiana*), *L. silvestrii*, *L. tegeleriana* (& var. *akersii*, var. *incuiensis*, var. *puquiensis*), *L. tiegeliana* (& var. *dimorphipetala*, var. *flaviflora*, var. *fricii*, var. *pusilla*, var. *ruberrima*, var. *uriondoensis*), *L. toratensis*, *L. torreana*, *L. tuberculosa*, *L. vanurkeana*, *L. variispina*, *L. wegneriana*.

Rejected names and synonymies:

L. acanthophlegma = *L. cinnabarina* subsp. *acanthophlegma*
L. acanthophlegma var. *patula* = *L. cinnabarina* subsp. *acanthophlegma*
L. acanthophlegma var. *roseiflora* = *L. cinnabarina* subsp. *acanthophlegma* var. *roseiflora*
L. aculeata = *L. pentlandii* var. *hardeniana*
L. adpressispina = *L. pugionacantha* var. *cornuta*
L. aguilari = *Echinopsis obrepanda* var. *aguilari*
L. akersii = *L. tegeleriana* var. *akersii*
L. albicentra = *L. haematantha* ssp. *densispina*
L. albolanata = *L. haematantha* ssp. *densispina* var. *pectinifera*
L. allegraiana = *L. backebergii* ssp. *hertrichiana*
L. amblayensis = *L. haematantha* ssp. *kuehnrichii* var. *amblayensis*
L. amblayensis var. *albispina* = *do.*
L. amblayensis var. *costata* = *do.*
L. andalgensis = *Echinopsis huascha* var. *andalgensis*
L. apurimacana = *L. maximiliana* ssp. *westii* var. *intermedia*
L. arachnacantha = *Echinopsis ancistrophora* ssp. *arachnacantha*
L. arachnacantha var. *densiseta* = *do.* var. *densiseta*
L. arachnacantha var. *minor* = *do.*
L. arachnacantha var. *spinosior* = *do.*
L. arachnacantha var. *sulphurea* = *do.* var. *sulphurea*
L. arachnacantha var. *torrecillasensis* = *do.* var. *torrecillasensis*
L. arachnacantha var. *vallegrandensis* = *do.* var. *vallegrandensis*
L. arachnoidea = *L. haematantha* ssp. *densispina*
L. argentea = *L. pentlandii*
L. astranthema = *L. haematantha* ssp. *densispina* var. *pectinifera*
L. atacamensis = *Echinopsis atacamensis*
L. atrovirens = *Rebutia pygmaea* fa. *atrovirens*
L. auranitida & vars. = *Rebutia auranitida*
L. aurantiaca = *L. pentlandii* var. *hardeniana*
L. bertramiana = *L. formosa* var. *bertramiana*
L. binghamiana = *L. backebergii* ssp. *hertrichiana*
L. boedekeriana = *L. pugionacantha* var. *rossii*
L. boliviensis = *L. pentlandii*
L. boyuibensis = *Echinopsis obrepanda*?
L. brachyantha = *Rebutia steinmannii*
L. breviflora = *L. sanguiniflora* var. *breviflora*
L. bruchii = *L. formosa* ssp. *bruchii*
L. bruchii var. *nivalis* = *L. formosa* ssp. *bruchii* var. *nivalis*
L. bruneo-rosea = *L. pentlandii*
L. 'cabradai' = *L. haematantha* ssp. *densispina*
L. 'cabradai' var. *aureiflora* = *do.*
L. caespitosa & vars. = *L. maximiliana* ssp. *caespitosa*
L. calochrysea = *L. aurea* var. *fallax*
L. camataquiensis = *L. lateritia*
L. cardenasiana = *Echinopsis ancistrophora* ssp. *cardenasiana*
L. cardenasiana var. *rubriflora* = *do.* var. *rubriflora*
L. cariquinensis = *L. maximiliana*
L. carminantha = *L. pentlandii*
L. carnea = *L. haematantha* ssp. *densispina*

1   *Acanthocalycium violaceum*

2   *Aporocactus flagelliformis*

3   *Ariocarpus agavoides*

4   *Ariocarpus fissuratus*

5   *Ariocarpus fissuratus* var. *lloydii*

6 *Ariocarpus kotschoubeyanus*

7 *Ariocarpus kotschoubeyanus* var. *albiflo*

8 *Ariocarpus retusus*

9 *Ariocarpus retusus* var. *furfuraceus*

10 *Ariocarpus scapharostrus*

11   *Ariocarpus trigonus*

12   *Arthrocereus bylesianus*

13   *Astrophytum asterias*

14   *Astrophytum capricorne*

15   *Astrophytum myriostigma*

16

17

18

19

20

16 *Astrophytum ornatum*
(bedded out at Huntington
Botanic Garden, California,
USA)

17 *Austrocactus patagonicus*

18 *Aztekium ritteri*

19 *Blossfeldia liliputana*

20 *Borzicactus aureispinus*

21

22

23

24

25

21 *Borzicactus icosagonus*

22 *Borzicactus haynei*

23 *Borzicactus madisoniorum*

24 *Browningia hertlingiana*

25 *Cephalocereus estevesii*

26

27

28

29

30

26 *Cephalocereus militaris*

27 *Cephalocereus penicillatus*

28 *Cleistocactus santacruzensis*

29 *Cleistocactus vulpis-cauda*

30 *Copiapoa hypogaea*

31

32

33

34

35

31 *Corryocactus erectus*

32 *Coryphantha calipensis*

33 *Coryphantha elephantidens*

34 *Coryphantha macromeris*

35 *Coryphantha scheerii* (in habitat, in Texas, USA)

36

37

38

39

40

36 *Discocactus horstii*

37 *Disocactus nelsonii*

38 *Echinocactus grusonii* (bedded out in California, USA)

39 *Echinocactus horizonthalonius*

40 *Echinocereus delaetii*

41

42

43

44

45

41 *Echinocereus laui*

42 *Echinocereus palmeri*

43 *Echinocereus pectinatus* var. *dasyacanthus* (in habitat, Texas, USA)

44 *Echinocereus pulchellus* var. *amoenus*

45 *Echinocereus reichenbachii* var. *baileyi*

46

47

48

49

50

46   *Echinocereus sciurus*

47   *Echinocereus subinermis*

48   *Echinocereus viridiflorus* var. *davisii*

49   *Echinopsis ancistrophora* subsp. *cardenasiana*

50   *Echinopsis X Lobivia* hybrid

51

52

53

54

55

51   *Epiphyllum* hybrid

52   *Epithelantha micromeris*

53   *Escobaria macdougalii*

54   *Escobaria minima*

55   *Escobaria robbinsorum*

56

57

58

59

60

56 *Escobaria sneedii* var. *leei*

57 *Escobaria vivipara* var. *alversonii*

58 *Ferocactus cylindraceus* (in habitat in the Anza Borrego desert, California, USA)

59 *Ferocactus fordii* (in habitat in northern Baja California, Mexico)

60 *Ferocactus macrodiscus*

61

62

63

64

65

61   *Frailea asterioides*

62   *Frailea ybatense*

63   *Gymnocalycium buenekeri*

64   *Gymnocalycium friedrichii*

65   *Gymnocalycium horridispinum*

66   *Gymnocalycium leeanum* var. *netrelianum*

67   *Gymnocalycium megatae*

68   *Gymnocalycium pflanzii*

69   *Gymnocalycium ragonesii*

70   *Gymnocalycium weissianum* var. *atroroseum*

71

72

73

74

75

71   *Leuchtenbergia principis*

72   *Lobivia backebergii* subsp.
wrightiana var. *winteriana*

73   *Lobivia chrysantha* var.
jajoiana

74   *Lobivia maximiliana*

75   *Lophophora williamsii*

76

77

78

79

80

76   *Mammillaria baumii*

77   *Mammillaria beneckei*

78   *Mammillaria blossfeldiana*

79   *Mammillaria carmenae*

80   *Mammillaria guelzowiana*

91. *Lobivia famatimensis*

92. *Lobivia ferox* var. *longispina*

93. *Lobivia formosa* subsp. *bruchii*

L. *carneopurpurea* = do.

L. *caspalasensis* = L. *huascha* var. *caspalasensis* (& see L. *chrysantha* ssp. *jajoiana* var. *caspalasensis*)

L. *cerasiflora* = L. *haematantha* ssp. *densispina*

L. *charazanensis* = L. *maximiliana* ssp. *caespitosa* var. *charazanensis*

L. *charcasina* = L. *cinnabarina*

L. *chereannianus* = L. *cinnabarina*

L. 'chilensis' = L. *backebergii* ssp. *wrightiana* var. *chilensis*

L. *chionantha* = *Acanthocalycium chionanthum*

L. *chlorogona* & vars. = L. *haematantha* ssp. *densispina* var. *rebutioides*

L. *chorillosensis* = L. *haematantha* ssp. *chorillosensis*

L. *chrysochete* var. *chunchullensis* = L. *chrysochete*

L. *churinensis* = L. *tegeleriana* var. *akersii*

L. *cincero* = L. *haematantha* ssp. *kuehnrichii*

L. *cinnabarina* var. *grandiflora* = L. *cinnabarina* ssp. *prestoana*

L. *cintiensis* = L. *lateritia*

L. *cintiensis* var. *elongata* = L. *lateritia*

L. *citriflora* = L. *haematantha* ssp. *densispina*

L. *claeysiana* = L. *ferox* var. *longispina*

L. *columnaris* = *Rebutia einsteinii* var. *columnaris*

L. *conoidea* = *Rebutia einsteinii* var. *columnaris* fa. *conoidea*

L. *corbula* = L. *maximiliana* var. *corbula*

L. *cordipetala* = L. *haematantha* ssp. *densispina*

L. *cornuta* = L. *pugionacantha* var. *cornuta*

L. *costata* = *Rebutia costata*

L. *crispa* = L. *haematantha* ssp. *densispina*

L. *cruciaureispina* = L. *maximiliana* ssp. *westii*

L. *culpinensis* = L. *pugionacantha* var. *culpinensis*

L. *cumingii* = *Weingartia neocumingii*

L. *cylindrica* = L. *aurea*

L. 'deesziana' = L. *haematantha* ssp. *densispina* var. *pectinifera*

L. *densispina* & vars. = L. *haematantha* ssp. *densispina*

L. *digitiformis* = *Rebutia pygmaea*

L. *divaricata* = L. *backebergii* ssp. *hertrichiana*

L. *dobeana* = L. *aurea* var. *dobeana*

L. 'dragei' = L. *chrysacantha* (var. *klusacekii* or ssp. *marsoneri*)

L. *draxleriana* = L. *cinnabarina* ssp. *prestoana* var. *draxleriana*

94. *Lobivia lateritia*

95. *Lobivia pentlandii*

L. draxleriana var. *minor* = do.
L. drijveriana = *L. haemantha* ssp. *kuehnrichii*
L. drijveriana var. *astranthema* = *L. haemantha* ssp. *densispina* var. *pectinifera*
L. drijveriana var. *aurantiaca* = *L. haemantha* form
L. drijveriana var. *nobilis* = *L. haemantha* form
L. ducis-paulii = *L. ferox* var. *longispina*
L. ducis-paulii var. *rubriflora* = do.
L. durispina = do.
L. duursmaiana = *L. sanguiniflora* var. *duursmaiana*
L. echinata = *L. backebergii* ssp. *hertrichiana*
L. einsteinii & vars. = *Rebutia einsteinii*
L. elongata = *L. haemantha* var. *elongata*
L. emmae = *L. saltensis* var. *nealeana*
L. emmae var. *brevispina* = do.
L. euanthema = *Rebutia euanthema*
L. eucaliptana = *Rebutia eucaliptana*
L. fallax = *L. aurea* var. *fallax*
L. famatimensis Backeberg & vars. = *L. haemantha* ssp. *densispina* var. *pectinifera*
L. formosa var. *maxima* = *L. formosa*
L. formosa var. *polycephala* = *L. formosa*
L. fricii = *L. tiegeliana* var. *fricii*
L. gigantea = *L. haemantha* ssp. *densispina*
L. glauca = *L. chrysantha* ssp. *jajoiana*
L. glauca var. *paucicostata* = *L. chrysantha* ssp. *jajoiana* var. *paucicostata*
L. grandiflora = *Echinopsis rowleyi*
L. grandis = *L. formosa* ssp. *grandis*
L. grandis var. *flaviflora* = *L. formosa* ssp. *grandis* var. *pinchasensis*
L. grandis var. *pinchasensis* = *L. formosa* ssp. *grandis* var. *pinchasensis*
L. graulichii = *Echinopsis ancistrophora*
L. graulichii var. *cinnabarina* = *L. tiegeliana* var. *fricii*
L. gregeri = *L. chrysantha* ssp. *jajoiana* var. *vatteri*
L. haageana & vars. = *L. chrysantha* ssp. *marsoneri* var. *rubescens*
L. hardeniana = *L. pentlandii* var. *hardeniana*
L. hastifera = *L. ferox* var. *longispina*
L. hermanniana = *L. maximiliana* ssp. *caespitosa* var. *hermanniana*
L. hertrichiana = *L. backebergii* ssp. *hertrichiana*
L. higginsiana = *L. pentlandii*
L. hoffmanniana = *Sulcorebutia hoffmanniana*
L. horrida = *L. lateritia* var. *kupperiana*
L. horrida var. *sanguiniflora* = *L. lateritia* var. *sanguiniflora*
L. hualfinensis = *L. haemantha* var. *hualfinensis*
L. hualfinensis var. *fechseri* = *L. haemantha* var. *fechseri*
L. huarinensis = *L. pugionacantha* var. *rossii*
L. huascha var. *rubriflora* = *L. huascha* var. *andalgensis*
L. huilcanota = *L. backebergii* var. *hertrichiana*
L. hyalacantha = *L. huascha*
L. hystrix = *L. chrysochete*

L. imporana = *L. lateritia*

L. incaica = *L. backebergii* ssp. *hertrichiana*

L. incuiensis = *L. tegeleriana* var. *incuiensis*

L. intermedia = *L. maximiliana* ssp. *westii* var. *intermedia*

L. iridescens = *L. chrysantha* ssp. *marsoneri*

L. jajoiana = *L. chrysantha* ssp. *jajoiana*

L. jajoiana var. *carminata* = *L. chrysantha* ssp. *jajoiana*

L. jajoiana var. *caspalasensis* = *L. chrysantha* ssp. *jajoiana* var. *caspalasensis*

L. jajoiana var. *elegans* = *L. chrysantha* ssp. *jajoiana*

L. jajoiana var. *fleischeriana* = *L. chrysantha* ssp. *jajoiana*

L. jajoiana var. *splendens* = *L. chrysantha* ssp. *jajoiana*

L. janseniana = *L. chrysantha*

L. janseniana var. *leucacantha* = *L. chrysantha*

L. johnsoniana = *L. pentlandii*

L. 'jujuyana' = *L. chrysantha* ssp. *jajoiana* var. *vatteri*

L. 'kavinai' = *L. haemantantha* ssp. *densispina*

L. kieslingii = *L. formosa* ssp. *bruchii* var. *kieslingii*

L. klusacekii = *L. chrysantha* var. *klusacekii*

L. klusacekii var. *roseiflora* = *L. chrysantha* var. *klusacekii*

L. kreuzingeri = *L. haemantantha* ssp. *densispina*

L. kuehnrichii = *L. haemantantha* ssp. *kuehnrichii*

L. kuehnrichii var. *molinensis* = *L. haemantantha* ssp. *kuehnrichii*

L. kupperiana = *L. lateritia* var. *kupperiana*

L. kupperiana var. *rubriflora* = *L. lateritia* var. *kupperiana*

L. 'larabei' = *L. backebergii* ssp. *hertrichiana*

L. larae = *L. pentlandii* var. *larae*

L. larae var. *capinotensis* = *L. pentlandii* var. *larae*

L. lateritia var. *borealis* = *L. lateritia*

L. laui = *L. backebergii* ssp. *hertrichiana* var. *laui*

L. lauramarca = *L. maximiliana* var. *corbula*

L. leptacantha = *L. maximiliana* ssp. *quiabayensis* var. *leptacantha*

L. leucomalla = *L. aurea* var. *leucomalla*

L. leucomalla var. *rubrispina* = *L. aurea* var. *leucomalla*

L. leucorhodon = *L. pentlandii*

L. leucoviolacea = *L. pentlandii*

L. longispina = *L. ferox* var. *longispina*

L. 'longostigmatica' = *L. pentlandii* var. *hardeniana*

L. luteiflora = *L. aurea?*

L. 'maresii' = *L. haemantantha* ssp. *densispina*

L. markusii = *L. chrysochete* var. *markusii*

L. marsoneri = *L. chrysantha* ssp. *marsoneri*

L. maximiliana var. *breviflorior* = *L. maximiliana* ssp. *caespitosa* var. *hermanniana*

L. maximiliana var. *elegans* = *L. maximiliana*

L. megacarpa = *Echinopsis ayopayana*

L. 'melanea' = *L. haemantantha* ssp. *densispina*

L. 'microthele' = *L. cinnabarina* ssp. *acanthophlegma* var. *oligotricha*

L. miniatiflora = *L. maximiliana* ssp. *caespitosa* var. *miniatiflora*

L. 'minima grandiflora' = *L. haemantantha* ssp. *densispina*

L. minuta = *L. backebergii* ssp. *hertrichiana*

L. mizquensis = *Echinopsis obrepanda* var. *mizquensis*

L. 'moqueguana' = *L. pampana*

L. muhriae = *L. chrysantha* ssp. *marsoneri*

L. muhriae var. *flaviflora* = *L. chrysantha* ssp. *marsoneri*

L. multiflora = *L. haemantantha* ssp. *densispina*

L. napina = *L. haemantantha* ssp. *kuehnrichii?*

L. nealeana = *L. saltensis* var. *nealeana*

L. neocinnabarina = *L. cinnabarina* ssp. *acanthophlegma* var. *oligotricha*

L. neohaageana = *Rebutia pygmaea*

L. neohaageana var. *flavovirens* = *Rebutia pygmaea* var. *flavovirens*

L. nigricans = *Rebutia ritteri* var. *nigricans*

L. nigrispina = *L. haemantantha* ssp. *kuehnrichii*

L. nigrispina var. *rubriflora* = *L. haemantantha* ssp. *kuehnrichii*

L. nigrostoma = *L. chrysantha* ssp. *jajoiana* var. *vatteri*

L. 'nivosa' = *L. haemantantha* ssp. *densispina*

L. oculata = *Rebutia euanthema* fa. *oculata*

L. oligotricha = *L. cinnabarina* ssp. *acanthophlegma* var. *oligotricha*

L. oligotricha var. *pilosa* = *L. cinnabarina* ssp. *acanthophlegma* var. *oligotricha*

L. omasuyana = *L. pentlandii*

L. oreopepon = *L. formosa*

L. orurensis = *Rebutia orurensis*

L. oyonica = *L. tegeleriana* var. *akersii*

L. oxyalabastra = *L. backebergii* var. *oxyalabastra*

L. paucipetala = *L. haemantantha* ssp. *densispina*

L. peclardiana = *L. tiegeliana*

L. peclardiana var. *albiflora* = *L. tiegeliana*

L. peclardiana var. *winteriana* = *L. tiegeliana*

L. pectinata (Backeberg) = *Rebutia pygmaea*

L. 'pectinata' (Fric) = *L. haemantantha* ssp. *densispina*

L. pectinifera & vars. = *L. haemantantha* ssp. *densispina* var. *pectinifera*

L. penca-poma = *L. haemantantha* ssp. *kuehnrichii*

L. pentlandii var. *achatina* = *L. pentlandii*

L. pentlandii var. *albiflora* = *L. pentlandii*

L. pentlandii var. *atrocarnea* = *L. pentlandii*

L. pentlandii var. *cavendishii* = *L. pentlandii*

L. pentlandii var. *colmari* = *L. maximiliana*

L. pentlandii var. *ferox* = *L. pentlandii*

L. pentlandii var. *longispina* = *L. pentlandii*

L. pentlandii var. *ochroleuca* = *L. pentlandii*

L. pentlandii var. *pfersdorffii* = *L. pentlandii*

L. pentlandii var. *scheerii* = *L. pentlandii*

L. pentlandii var. *vittelina* = *L. pentlandii*

L. peterseimii = *Rebutia ritteri* fa. *peterseinii*

L. pictiflora = *L. ferox* var. *longispina*

L. pilifera = *Rebutia costata* fa. *pilifera*

L. planiceps = *L. backebergii* ssp. *hertrichiana*

L. pojoensis = *Echinopsis ancistrophora* ssp. *pojoensis*

Lobivia

L. pojoensis var. *grandiflora* = *Echinopsis ancistrophora* ssp. *pojoensis* var. *grandiflora*

L. polaskiana = *L. chrysantha* var. *klusacekii*

L. polyancistra = *Echinopsis ancistrophora* var. *polyancistra*

L. polycephala = *L. sanguiniflora* var. *duursmaiana*

L. potosina = *L. ferox* var. *potosina*

L. prestoana = *L. cinnabarina* ssp. *prestoana*

L. pseudocachensis & vars. = *L. saltensis* var. *nealeana*

L. pseudocariquinensis = *L. maximiliana*

L. pseudocinnabarina = *L. cinnabarina* ssp. *acanthophlegma*

L. pseudofamatimensis = *L. famatimensis* var. *oligotricha*

L. pseudoreichiana = *L. famatimensis*

L. pugionacantha var. *flaviflora* = *L. pugionacantha*

L. purpureominiata = *L. huascha* var. *purpureominiata*

L. pusilla = *L. tiegeliana* var. *pusilla*

L. pusilla var. *flaviflora* = *L. tiegeliana* var. *flaviflora*

L. pygmaea = *Rebutia pygmaea*

L. quiabayensis = *L. maximiliana* ssp. *quiabayensis*

L. raphidacantha = *L. pentlandii*

L. rebutioides & vars. = *L. haematantha* ssp. *densispina* var. *rebutioides*

L. ritteri = *Rebutia ritteri*

L. robusta sanguinea = *L. haematantha* ssp. *densispina*

L. rossii & vars. = *L. pugionacantha* var. *rossii*

L. 'ruberrima' = *L. haematantha* ssp. *densispina*

L. rubescens & var. = *L. chrysantha* ssp. *marsoneri* var. *rubescens*

L. salitrensis & var. = *L. pugionacantha* var. *salitrensis*

L. sanguiniflora var. *breviflora* = *L. sanguiniflora*

L. sanguiniflora var. *pseudolateritia* = *L. sanguiniflora*

L. 'sanguiniflora' (Fric) = *L. haematantha* ssp. *densispina*

L. schieliana & vars. = *L. backebergii* ssp. *schieliana*

L. schmiedcheniana = *Rebutia einstenii* fa. *schmiedcheniana*

L. schneideriana & vars. = *L. pentlandii*

L. schreiteri = *L. saltensis* var. *schreiteri*

L. 'schuldtii' = *L. chrysantha* ssp. *marsoneri*/var. *klusacekii*

L. scoparia = *L. haematantha* ssp. *densispina*

L. scopulina = *L. lateritia*

L. shaferi = *L. aurea* var. *shaferi*

L. sicuaniensis = *L. maximiliana* var. *corbula*

L. simplex = *L. backebergii* ssp. *hertirichiana* var. *simplex*

L. spinosissima (Backeberg) = *L. ferox* var. *longispina*

L. 'spinosissima' (Fric) = *L. haematantha* ssp. *densispina*

L. spiralisepala = *Rebutia spiralisepala*

L. staffenii & var. = *L. chrysantha*

L. steinmannii = *Rebutia steinmannii*

L. stilowiana = *L. saltensis* var. *stilowiana*

L. stollenwerkiana = *L. pugionacantha* var. *rossii*

L. sublimiflora = *L. haematantha* ssp. *densispina* var. *sublimiflora*

L. taratensis & var. = *L. cinnabarina* ssp. *acanthophlegma*

L. tarijensis = *L. formosa* ssp. *tarijensis*

L. tegeleriana var. *eckardiana* = *L. tegeleriana*

L. tegeleriana var. *medingiana* = *L. tegeleriana*

L. tegeleriana var. *plominiana* = *L. tegeleriana*

L. tenuispina = *L. chrysochete* var. *tenuispina*

L. thionantha = *Acanthocalycium thionanthum*

L. tiegeliana var. *albiflora* = *L. tiegeliana*

L. tiegeliana var. *distefanoiana* = *L. tiegeliana*

L. tiegeliana var. *winteriana* = *L. tiegeliana*

L. titicacensis = *L. pentlandii*

L. torrecillasensis = *Echinopsis ancistrophora* subsp. *arachnacantha* var. *torrecillasensis*

L. uitewaaliana = *L. chrysantha* ssp. *marsoneri*

L. varians & vars. = *L. pentlandii*

L. vatteri & var. = *L. chrysantha* ssp. *jajoiana* var. *vatteri*

L. versicolor = *L. pugionacantha* var. *versicolor*

L. vilcabambae = *L. backebergii* ssp. *hertrichiana* var. *simplex*

L. walterspielii & var. = *L. cinnabarina* var. *walterspielii*

L. wegheiana & var. = *L. pentlandii*

L. wessneriana = *L. haematantha* ssp. *densispina* var. *sublimiflora*

L. westii = *L. maximiliana* ssp. *westii*

L. winteriana = *L. backebergii* ssp. *wrightiana* var. *winteriana*

L. wrightiana & var. = *L. backebergii* ssp. *wrightiana*

L. zecheri & var. = *L. backebergii* ssp. *zecheri*

L. zudanensis = *L. cinnabarina* var. *zudanensis*.

Recommended species: *L. aurea* var. *leucomalla* has a dense, silvery white spined covering to the globular or slightly cone-shaped stems, and makes a large clump in time, to 8 in (20 cm) or more tall and wide, producing freely the hairy-tubed, butter yellow flowers.

L. backebergii is a variable species in form and colour of flowers. *L. backebergii* subsp. *hertrichiana* is a popular, clumping plant with bright red flowers. *L. backebergii* subsp. *wrightiana* var. *winteriana* has spectacular, large flowers; bright, deep pink with shading to a paler throat.

L. chrysantha var. *jajoiana* has most attractive flowers in yellow, orange or red, with a black ring in the throat contrasting wonderfully.

L. cinnabarina subsp. *acanthophlegma* is noted for its bright, flame coloured flowers.

L. famatimensis (long misapplied to the various forms of *L. haematantha*) is a uniquely short-spined species of *Lobivia*, with a yellowish-brown body colour, presenting some difficulty in cultivation and sometimes grown as a grafted plant to overcome this. The flowers, not so readily produced as in many *Lobivia* species, are short-tubed and yellow.

L. ferox var. *longispina*, formerly known as a *Pseudolobivia*, is a large growing, fiercely spined species with white flowers.

L. formosa subsp. *bruchii*, formerly of the genus *Soehrensia*, is a massive growing plant in the wild forming clumps a yard (1 m) or more across. In cultivation it will make a football sized stem in eight years or so, and will produce

96. *Lobivia saltensis* var. *stilowiana*

97. *Lophocereus schottii*, in habitat, southern Baja California, Mexico

its short-tubed, bright red flowers.

L. maximiliana has red, yellow or red and yellow flowers, the latter beautifully combining.

L. pentlandii is another with variously coloured flowers from red to pink and yellow, strongly spined and clustering.

L. saltensis var. *stilowiana* has deep red or orange-red flowers on spiny, strong growing plants.

Connoisseur's choice: L. *backebergii* subsp. *wrightiana* var. *winteriana*, L. *chrysantha* var. *jajoiana*, L. *maximiliana*.

Lophocereus (Bgr.) B. & R., *Contrib. U.S. Nat. Herb.* 12:426 (1909); Lindsay, *Cact. Amer.* 35:176 (1963)

The two species of this genus from New Mexico and Arizona, USA and Baja California, Mexico, are seldom grown to any significant size in cultivation, except in the monstrose form of *L. schottii*, which makes an odd, spineless, totem-pole like column. In the wild the normal form of this species makes a thick bristly growth when it reaches flowering size at about 4–5 ft (1.5 m) tall, and the small, cream or pink flowers are produced from among these bristles at the ribs in the upper part of the stem. Such maturity is rarely achieved in cultivation. This and the other species, *L. gatesii*, are of interest only to *Cereus* enthusiasts, like the one pictured beneath a giant of *L. schottii* in southern Baja California. Species named are: *L. gatesii*, *L. schottii* (& var. *litoralis*, & fa. *monstrosus*).

They are not recommended.

Lophophora Coulter, *Contrib. U.S. Nat. Herb.* 3:131 (1894); E. F. Anderson, *Peyote, The Divine Cactus* (1980)

This cactus genus is probably best known for the fact that it is a source of mescalin, a hallucinogenic drug used by Mexican Indians for ceremonial purposes, and by the 'civilised' in excess for degradation. For the cactus collector it is of interest for its slow growing, grey-blue, flat-globular stems, spineless, but producing tufts of cream-coloured wool, and a succession of pale pink flowers over a long period. A handful of names have appeared for what Anderson (see ref. above) regards as merely variations of the most common and widespread species, *L. williamsii*. His opinion is followed herein in view of the extensive study he has made of the genus, culminating in a fascinating book on the subject.

Species named are: L. *diffusa*, L. *williamsii*.

Rejected names and synonymies:
The varieties described of *L. williamsii* are regarded as variants not warranting separate recognition, so too are *L. fricii* and *L. jourdaniana*.

Recommended species: L. *williamsii*, the type. This makes a quite delightful plant, with stems about 2–3 in (5–8 cm) wide, and somewhat less tall, with sunken growing points, and cream-yellow tufts at each areole. A well-grown plant of this species with the wool teased out to show it at its best is a knockout. The small pink flowers appear over a period of months, sporadically, the pink berries emerging a few months or less later.

Connoisseur's choice: L. *williamsii*.

Loxanthocereus Backeb. (1937)

Referred to *Borzicactus*.

Lymanbensonia Kimnach, *Cact. Amer.* 56:100 (1984)

A genus erected for the former *Acanthorhipsalis micrantha*, an epiphyte from Peru, which grows disconcertingly upright or sprawling, not pendant from trees or rocks as with most epiphytic cacti. It has two or three angled stems, 'Epiphyllum'-like but with spines, and tubular, purplish red flowers. *Lymanbensonia micrantha* is recommended only for epiphyte enthusiasts.

Machaerocereus B. & R. (1920)

Referred to *Stenocereus.*

Maihuenia Philippi, *Gartenfl.* 32:260, t.1129 (1883)

This small genus, related to *Pereskia*, from Argentina and Chile, is little known in cultivation except for one, popular species, *M. poeppigii*. They are high altitude plants, and in the wild occur mostly below soil-level with just the shoot tips protruding. Maximum light and cool conditions seem to suit best, but flowering is unknown in cultivation in England to my knowledge, where the plant grows with its stems above the soil, white spines and persistent small, Sedum-like leaves intermingling. A picture of the species mentioned in the wild is shown on the front cover of the West German Society's journal for May 1984 (*Kakt. u.a. Sukk.* 35 (5).

Species named are: *M. albolanata* (& fa. *viridulispina*), *M. brachydelphys*, *M. cumulata*, *M. latispina*, *M patagonica*, *M. philippii*, *M. poeppigii*, *M. valentinii.*

Recommended species and ***connoisseur's choice:*** *M. poeppigii* is the only one seen in cultivation at present. It makes a panful of its slender, pencil-thick stems, which should be kept in maximum light to prevent them becoming etiolated. It will tolerate low temperatures.

Maihueniopsis Speg., *Nuev. Not. Cactol. (Anal. Soc. Cient. Arg.)* 6–9.1924 (1925)

Little is published of this genus from Argentina, which is here regarded as synonymous with *Opuntia*, subgenus *Cylindropuntia*. See under *Opuntia.*

Malacocarpus Salm-Dyck (1850)

As this name has already been used for a species in the Rutaceae, it was renamed by D.M. Porter in 1964 as *Wigginsia*, but this in turn has now been relegated to subgeneric status beneath *Notocactus.*

Mamillopsis Norren ex B. & R. (1923)

Because the flowers are differently shaped from most *Mammillaria* species, coloured bright red and with long tubes, there has been a reluctance to accept Hunt's placing

of this genus beneath a broad concept of *Mammillaria*. But there are more reasons for excluding other species of *Mammillaria* which are accepted, and the differences are more apparent than real. Referred to *Mammillaria.*

Mammillaria Haw., *Syn. Pl. Succ.* 177(1812); Craig, *The Mammillaria Handbook* (1945); Pilbeam, *Mammillaria – A Collector's Guide* (1981); D.R. Hunt, New Review of Mammillaria Names, *Bradleya* (Yearbook of British Cact. & Succ. Soc.) (1983 *et seq.*)

This popular genus, mainly from Mexico and the southwestern United States, but also with odd species occurring in the West Indies, central America and Colombia and Venezuela, has devotees who concentrate upon it almost to the exclusion of all other genera, since it satisfies most of cactus collectors' requirements within it. With something like 200 species recognized, there is a wide range of form, from acorn-sized stems to elongated, trailing stems up to 5 ft (1.5 m) long, from solitary stems no larger than 2–3 in (8 cm) tall fully grown, to massive clusters a yard (1 m) or more wide. And the spination varies from tiny, wispy clusters, 2 or 3 mm long, or hooked spines tenaciously attaching themselves to anything passing, to strongly spined monsters that will make a mockery of leather gloves when repotting. Flowers too vary from small ones, barely protruding through the spines, to large, widely opening blooms to about 2–3 in (5–8 cm) across. The genus is divided into 5 subgenera, embracing the more distinctive groupings, with the majority of species falling into the subgenus *Mammillaria*, which is further divided into 15 series. There has been some regrouping since the publication by the author in 1981 of *Mammillaria – A Collector's Guide*, and for the convenience of the reader the revised subgenera and series and species allocated to them are set out below. For a full list of species in alphabetical order see further below.

Subgenus *Mammilloydia*: *M. candida*
Subgenus *Oehmea*: *M. beneckei*
Subgenus *Cochemiea*: *M. pondii* (& var. *maritima*, var. *setispina*), *M. halei*, *M. poselgeri*
Subgenus *Mamillopsis*: *M. senilis*
Subgenus *Mammillaria*:
    Series *Longimammae* (ex subgenus *Dolichothele*): *M. baumii*, *M. carretii*, *M. longimamma* (& var. *uberiformis*), *M. melaleuca*, *M. sphaerica*, *M. surculosa*
    Series *Longiflorae*: *M. deherdtiana* (& var. *dodsonii*), *M. hernandezii*, *M. longiflora* (& fa. *stampferi*), *M. napina*, *M. saboae* (& fa. *goldii*, fa. *haudeana*)
    Series *Ancistracanthae*: *M. albicans*, *M. angelensis*, *M. armillata* (& var. *cerralboa*), *M. barbata*, *M. blossfeldiana*, *M. boolii*, *M. capensis*, *M. dioica* (& var. *estebanensis*), *M. fraileana*, *M. goodridgii*, *M. grahamii* (& var. *oliviae*),

98. *Maihuenia poeppigii*

99. *Mammillaria barbata* variants (back left M. 'santaclarensis', back right M. 'morricalii', front M. 'garessii')

100. *Mammillaria bombycina*

101. *Mammillaria barbata*

M. guelzowiana (& var. *robustior*), *M. heidiae*, *M. hutchisoniana* (& var. *louisiae*), *M. insularis*, *M. mainiae*, *M. mazatlanensis* (& var. *patonii*), *M. milleri*, *M. multidigitata*, *M. neopalmeri*, *M. occidentalis*, *M. phitauiana*, *M. schumannii*, *M. sheldonii*, *M. swinglei*, *M tetrancistra*, *M. thornberi*, *M. viridiflora*, *M. wrightii* (& fa. *wolfii*, & var. *wilcoxii*), *M. yaquensis*, *M. zephyranthoides*.

Series *Stylothelae*: *M aurihamata*, *M. berkiana*, *M. bocasana* (& var. *longicoma*), *M. bombycina*, *M. duwei*, *M. erythrosperma*, *M. fittkaui*, *M. glassii* (& var. *ascensionis*, var. *nominis -dulcis*, var. *siberiensis*), *M. glochidiata*, *M. guillauminiana*, *M. jaliscana*, *M. leucantha*, *M. limonensis*, *M. mathildae*, *M. mercadensis*, *M. moelleriana*, *M. nana*, *M. oteroi*, *M. painteri*, *M. pennispinosa* (& var. *nazasensis*), *M. perezdelarosae*, *M. pygmaea* (& var. *pubispina*), *M. rettigiana*, *M. sinistrohamata*, *M. stella-de-tacubaya*, *M. variflora*, *M. weingartiana*, *M. wildii* (& fa. *calleana*, fa. *crinita*), *M. zacatecasensis*, *M. zeilmanniana*

Series *Proliferae*: *M. albicoma*, *M. anniana*, *M. gracilis*, *M. picta* + var. *viereckii*, *M. pilispina*, *M. prolifera* (& var. *arachnoidea* var. *haitiensis*, var. *texana*), *M. schwarzii*, *M. vetula*

Series *Lasiacanthae*: *M. aureilanata*, *M. carmenae*, *M. egregia*, *M. herrerae* (& var. *albiflora*), *M. humboldtii*, *M. lasiacantha*, *M. laui* (& fa. *dasyacantha*, fa. *subducta*), *M. lenta*, *M. magallanii*, *M. pectinifera*, *M. plumosa*, *M. schiedeana* (& var. *dumetorum*), *M. solisioides*

Series *Sphacelatae*: *M. kraehenbuehlii*, *M. sphacelata* (& var. *viperina*), *M. tonalensis*

Series *Leptocladodae*: *M. densispina* (& var. *mieheana*), *M. elongata* (& var. *echinaria*), *M. microhelia*, *M. pottsii*

Series *Decipientes*: *M. decipiens* (& var. *camptotricha*)

Series *Heterochlorae*: *M. discolor*, *M. polythele*, *M. rhodantha* (& var. *aureiceps*, var. *calacantha*, var. *fera-rubra*, var. *mollendorffiana*, var. *pringlei*), *M. wiesingeri* (& var. *erectacantha*)

Series *Polyacanthae*: *M. backebergiana* (& var. *ernestii*),

102. *Mammillaria boolii*

103. *Mammillaria candida* var. *candida*

104. *Mammillaria capensis*

105. *Mammillaria compressa*

106. *Mammillaria crucigera*

107. *Mammillaria decipiens* var. *camptotricha*

M. duoformis, M. eriacantha, M. guerreronis, M. hubert-mulleri, M. magnifica (& var. *minor*), *M. matudae, M. meyranii, M. nunezii* (& var. *bella*), *M. rekoi, M. spinosissima* (& var. *centraliplumosa,* var. *pilcayensis,* var. *virginis*), *M. xaltianguensis*

Series *Supertextae: M. albilanata* (& var. *reppenhagenii,* var. *tegelbergiana*), *M. columbiana* (& var. *ruestii,* var. *yucatanensis*), *M. crucigera, M. dixanthocentron, M. fuauxiana, M. graessneriana, M. haageana* (& var. *conspicua,* var. *schmollii*), *M. huitzilopochtli, M. supertexta*

Series *Leucocephalae: M. brauneana, M. chionocephala, M. formosa, M. geminispina, M. hahniana* (& var. *woodsii*), *M. klissingiana, M. microthele, M. muehlenpfordtii, M. parkinsonii, M. perbella, M. sempervivi* (& var. *pseudocrucigera*)

Series *Mammillaria* (syn. *Macrothelae*): *M. arida, M. baxteriana* (& var. *marshalliana*), *M. bocensis, M. brandegei* (& var. *glareosa,* var. *lewisiana*), *M. canelensis, M. coahuilensis* (& var. *albiarmata*), *M. compressa, M. craigii, M. evermanniana, M. gigantea, M. grusonii, M. hertrichiana, M. heyderi* (& var. *gaumeri,* var. *gummifera,* var. *hemispherica,* var. *macdougalii,* var. *meiacantha*), *M. johnstonii, M. lindsayi, M. magnimamma, M. mammillaris, M. marksiana, M. melanocentra, M. miegiana, M. nivosa, M. orcuttii, M. peninsularis, M. petrophila* (& var. *gatesii*), *M. petterssonii, M. roseo-alba, M. rubrograndis, M. scrippsiana, M. sonorensis, M. standleyi, M. tayloriorum, M. uncinata* (& var. *lloydii*), *M. wagneriana, M. winterae, M. zeyeriana*

Series *Polyedrae: M. carnea, M. karwinskiana* (& var. *nejapensis*), *M. knippeliana, M. mystax* (& var. *casoi,* var. *huajuapensis*), *M. orcuttii, M. polyedra, M. sartorii, M. varieaculeata, M. voburnensis* (& var. *beiselii,* var. *collinsii,* var. *eichlamii*)

An alphabetical list of **species named** is as follows:

M. albicans, M. albicoma, M. albilanata (& var. *reppenhagenii,* var. *tegelbergiana*), *M. angelensis, M. anniana, M. arida, M. armillata* (& var. *cerralboa*), *M. aureilanata, M. aurihamata, M. backebergiana* (& var. *ernestii*), *M. barbata, M. baumii, M. baxteriana* (& var. *marshalliana*), *M. beneckei, M. berkiana, M. blossfeldiana, M. bocasana* (& var. *longicoma*), *M. bocensis, M. bombycina, M. boolii, M. brandegei* (& var. *glareosa,* var. *lewisiana*), *M. brauneana, M. candida* (& var. *caespitosa*), *M. canelensis, M. capensis, M. carmenae, M. carnea, M. carretii, M. chionocephala, M. coahuilensis* (& var. *albiarmata*), *M. columbiana* (& var. *ruestii,* var. *yucatanensis*), *M. compressa, M. craigii, M. crucigera, M. decipiens* (& var. *camptotricha*), *M. deherdtiana* (& var. *dodsonii*), *M. densispina* (& var. *mieheana*), *M. dioica* (& var. *estebanensis*), *M. discolor, M. dixanthocentron, M. duoformis, M. duwei* (= *M. nana?*), *M. egregia, M. elongata* (& var. *echinaria*), *M. eriacantha, M. erythrosperma, M. evermanniana, M. fittkaui, M. formosa, M. fraileana, M. fuauxiana, M. geminispina, M. gigantea, M. glassii* (& var. *ascensionis,* var. *nominis-dulcis,* var. *siberiensis*), *M. glochidiata,*

M. goodridgi, M. gracilis, M. graessneriana, M. grahamii (& var. *oliviae*), *M. grusonii, M. guelzowiana* & var. *robustior, M. guerreronis, M. guillauminiana, M. haageana* (& var. *conspicua,* var. *schmollii*), *M. hahniana* (& var. *woodsii*), *M. halei, M. heidiae, M. hernandezii, M. herrerae* (& var. *albiflora*), *M. hertrichiana, M. heyderi* (& var. *gaumeri,* var. *gummifera,* var. *hemisphaerica,* var. *macdougalii,* var. *meiacantha*), *M. hubertmulleri, M. huitzilopochtli, M. humboldtii, M. hutchisoniana* (& var. *louisiae*), *M. insularis, M. jaliscana, M. johnstonii, M. karwinskiana* (& var. *nejapensis*), *M. klissingiana, M. knippeliana, M. kraehenbuehlii, M. lasiacantha, M. laui* (& fa. *dasyacantha,* fa. *subducta*), *M. lenta, M. leucantha, M. limonensis, M. lindsayi, M. longiflora* (& fa. *stampferi*), *M. longimamma* (& var. *uberiformis*), *M. magallanii, M. magnifica* (& var. *minor*), *M. magnimamma, M. mainiae, M. mammillaris, M. marksiana, M. mathildae, M. matudae* (& var. *serpentiformis*), *M. mazatlanensis* (& var. *patonii*), *M. melaleuca, M. melanocentra, M. mercadensis, M. meyranii, M. microhelia, M. microthele, M. miegiana, M. milleri, M. moelleriana, M. muehlenpfordtii, M. multidigitata, M. mystax* (& var. *casoi,* var. *huajuapensis*), *M. nana, M. napina, M. neopalmeri, M. nivosa, M. nunezii* (& var. *bella*), *M. occidentalis, M. orcuttii, M. oteroi, M. painteri, M. parkinsonii, M. pectinifera, M. peninsularis, M. pennispinosa* (& var. *nazasensis*), *M. perbella, M. perezdelarosae, M. petrophila* (& var. *gatesii*), *M. petterssonii, M. phitauiana, M. picta* (& var. *viereckii*), *M. pilispina, M. plumosa, M. polyedra, M polythele, M. pondii* (& var. *maritima* var. *setispina*), *M. poselgeri, M. pottsii, M. prolifera* (& var. *arachnoidea,* var. *haitiensis,* var. *texana*), *M. pygmaea* (& var. *pubispina*), *M. rekoi* (& var. *aureispina,* var. *leptacantha*), *M. rettigiana, M. rhodantha* (& var. *aureiceps,* var. *calacantha,* var. *fera-rubra,* var. *mollendorffiana,* var. *pringlei*), *M. roseo-alba, M. rubrograndis, M. saboae* (& fa. *goldii,* fa. *haudeana*), *M. sartorii, M. schiedeana* (& var. *dumetorum*), *M. schumannii, M. schwarzii, M. scrippsiana, M. sempervivi* (& var. *pseudocrucigera*), *M. senilis, M. sheldonii, M. sinistrohamata, M. solisioides, M. sonorensis, M. sphacelata* (& var. *viperina*), *M. sphaerica, M. spinosissima* (& var. *centraliplumosa,* var. *pilcayensis,* var. *virginis*), *M. standleyi, M. stella-de-tacubaya, M. supertexta, M. surculosa, M. swinglei, M. tayloriorum, M. tetrancistra, M. theresae, M. thornberi, M. tonalensis, M. uncinata, M. varieaculeata, M. vetula, M. viridiflora, M. voburnensis* (& var. *beiselii,* var. *collinsii,* var. *eichlamii*), *M. wagneriana, M. weingartiana, M. wiesingeri* (& var. *erectacantha*), *M. wildii* (& fa. *calleana,* fa. *crinita*), *M. winterae, M. wrightii* (& fa. *wolfii* var. *wilcoxii*), *M. xaltianguensis, M. yaquensis, M. zacatecasensis, M. zeilmanniana, M. zephyranthoides, M. zeyeriana, M. zuccariniana.*

Rejected names and synonymies (this list takes as its starting point the species accepted in *Mammillaria – A Collector's Guide* by the author, published first in 1981, and reflects changes in taxonomy since that time):

M. albiarmata = *M. coahuilensis* var. *albiarmata*
M. aureiceps = *M. rhodantha* var. *aureiceps*
M. beiselii = *M. voburnensis* var. *beiselii*
M. bella = *M. nunezii* var. *bella*
M. cadereytensis = *M. parkinsonii*
M. calacantha = *M. rhodantha* var. *calacantha*
M. calleana = *M. wildii* fa. *calleana*
M. camptotricha = *M. decipiens* var. *camptotricha*
M. centraliplumosa = *M. spinosissima* var. *centraliplumosa*
M. cerralboa = *M. armillata* var. *cerralboa*
M. collinsii = *M. voburnensis* var. *collinsii*
M. crinita = *M. wildii* fa. *crinita*
M. durispina = *M. polythele*
M. eichlamii = *M. voburnensis* var. *eichlamii*
M. erectacantha = *M. wiesingeri* var. *erectacantha*
M. estebanensis = *M. dioica* var. *estebanensis*
M. fera-rubra = *M. rhodantha* var. *fera-rubra*
M. gasterantha = *M. spinosissima* var. *virginis*
M. gatesii = *M. petrophila* var. *gatesii*
M. gaumeri = *M. heyderi* var. *gaumeri*
M. glareosa = *M. brandegei* var. *glareosa*
M. goldii = *M. saboae* fa. *goldii*
M. gracilis var. *pulchella* = *M. gracilis*
M. kewensis = *M. polythele*
M. lewisiana = *M. brandegei* var. *lewisiana*
M. lloydii = *M. uncinata* var. *lloydii*
M. longicoma = *M. bocasana* var. *longicoma*
M. louisiae = *M. hutchisoniana* var. *louisiae*
M. maritima = *M. pondii* var. *maritima*
M. marshalliana = *M. baxteriana* var. *marshalliana*
M. microcarpa = *M. milleri*
M. microcarpa var. *grahamii* = *M. grahamii*
M. microcarpa var. *oliviae* = *M. grahamii* var. *oliviae*
M. mieheana = *M. densispina* var. *mieheana*
M. mollendorffiana = *M. rhodantha* var. *mollendorffiana*
M. morganiana = *M. parkinsonii*
M. nejapensis = *M. karwinskiana* var. *nejapensis*
M. obconella = *M. polythele*
M. pachycylindrica = *M. grusonii*
M. pilcayensis = *M. spinosissima* var. *pilcayensis*
M. pringeli = *M. rhodantha* var. *pringlei*
M. reppenhagenii = *M. albilanata* var. *reppenhagenii*
M. ruestii = *M. columbiana* var. *ruestii*
M. setispina = *M. pondii* var. *setispina*
M. slevinii = *M. albicans*
M. tegelbergiana = *M. albilanata* var. *tegelbergiana*
M. viereckii = *M. picta* var. *viereckii*
M. virginis = *M. spinosissima* var. *virginis*
M. yucatanensis = *M. columbiana* var. *yucatanensis*.

To select from this wonderful genus is an invidious task, and enthusiasts will not be deterred from seeking out for themselves the many more attractive species apart from those singled out below.

Recommended species: *M. candida* (subgenus *Mammilloydia*) with its dense covering of white spines, more or less tipped pink or red, comes in various forms, from solitary, thick stems to about 1 ft (30 cm) tall and 4–5 in (10–12 cm) wide, to more flat growing clusters of stems 3–4 in (8–10 cm) wide, but always with dense spines completely obscuring the plant body, with the flowers in pale cream-pink as a bonus.

M. beneckei (subgenus *Oehmea*) is a challenge, with a sunny position required and perhaps something more, to encourage production of its beautiful, large, deep yellow flowers. It needs a little more warmth than most Mammillaria species for safety (say a minimum of 50° F/10° c). It makes low clusters of stems each about 2 in (5 cm) tall and wide, with dark brown hooked spines.

The subgenus *Cochemiea* is still regarded by some as a good genus in its own right. With only five to choose from I am inclined to say 'get them all', but to evaluate more rigorously I would suggest that *M. halei* is the outstanding species, being unlike the others in having straight instead of hooked spines, with a yellowish-brown colouring. This is also probably the rarest and most difficult to obtain, since its occurrence on an island on the west side of the Baja California peninsula makes fresh collections of seed a rarity. If obtained it may be that it will flower more readily than other species, as its wild flowering season is in the spring, while others flower later in the year, but it has the same glorious, long-tubed bright scarlet flowers of this subgenus, well worth striving to produce in cultivation.

M. pondii var. *setispina* (syn. *M.* or *Cochemiea setispina*) would be my other choice were I restricted to only one other, which will make a low cluster of thick stems to about 6 in (15 cm) long and 2 in (5 cm) wide, with long hooked central spines, often nearly all white, but with varying degrees of tipping with brown. The flowers are equally as sumptuous as all in this subgenus.

Mamillopsis: M. senilis is the sole representative (except for a Yeti of a species, *M. diguetii*, with thicker, more yellow spines and shorter tubed flowers, whose separate standing is doubted) in the subgenus *Mamillopsis*, another favourite for separating from *Mammillaria* into its own genus, because of the large, long-tubed, bright red flowers, but everything else about it points to close relationship with this genus, and it is here so regarded. It makes a low clump of globular stems, densely covered in white, hooked spines I suspect for protection against the strength of the sun in its high mountainous Mexican habitat. It is sometimes difficult to flower in cultivation, and somewhat colder treatment in the winter in view of conditions in the wild may be the answer.

In the Series *Longimammae* (formerly subgenus *Dolichothele*) there are some large-flowered, scented, yellow-petalled species like *M. longimamma* and *M. sphaerica*,

108. *Mammillaria deherdtiana* var. *deherdtiana*

109. *Mammillaria densispina* var. *mieheana*

110. *Mammillaria fittkaui*

111. *Mammillaria fraileana*

112. *Mammillaria geminispina*

113. *Mammillaria gigantea*

114. *Mammillaria glassii* var. *nominis-dulcis* (Lau 1186)

115. *Mammillaria hahniana* var. *hahniana*

116. *Mammillaria halei*

but species with more attraction in their spination are *M. baumii*, with white glassy spines, hair-fine, and with medium sized yellow, scented flowers, and the densely clustering, hook-spined, small bodied *M. surculosa*, which will make a clump a foot (30 cm) across in very few years if room for its thick roots is granted.

Series *Longiflorae* has some of the most sought after species of the genus. *M. longiflora* itself makes a solitary, apple-sized globular stem, with long, red-brown (or yellowish-white) spines and even longer tubed rich pink flowers crowning the plant with glory in spring. A group of species thought of in one breath and now combined into only two species are real miniatures, slow growing and highly desirable for their free flowering out of all proportion in size and quantity with the diminutive plants. They are *M. saboae* (and fa. *haudeana* and fa. *goldii*) and *M. theresae*. The first two have tip of little finger sized stems, densely clustering to form a low mound, from which the long-tubed pink or lilac-pink flowers arise like

crocuses. *M. saboae* fa. *goldii* is for me the most desirable of the three forms of this species with larger stems, slower growth, and much more difficulty of cultivation. To get a cluster of the little, inch-wide (2.5 cm) conical stems the size of your hand will take ten years or so, and the long tubed, lilac-pink with white throat flowers are not so freely produced as in *M. saboae* and *M. saboae* fa. *haudeana*. All three have tiny, wispy, white spines on a prominent yellow areole. *M. theresae* stands apart, and is somewhat taller growing, purple bodied, and with feathery clusters of tiny spines; if anything the flowers are deeper lilac than the others in this group. Like *M. saboae* fa. *goldii* it is slower growing than the other two, and will take many years to make a clump of a dozen or so stems. All four come from northern Mexico.

M. deherdtiana and *M. deherdtiana* var. *dodsonii* are wonderful, large-flowered and with attractive spination, but fairly slow growing, with their close relative *M. napina* stealing pride of place with even slower growth, turnip

117. *Mammillaria heidiae*

118. *Mammillaria hutchisoniana* var. *hutchisoniana*

119. *Mammillaria hutchisoniana* var. *louisiae*

120. *Mammillaria huitzilopochtli*

121. *Mammillaria kraehenbuehlii*

122. *Mammillaria lasiacantha*

123. *Mammillaria laui* fa. *laui*

124. *Mammillaria longiflora* fa. *longiflora*

125. *Mammillaria magallanii*

rooted and producing breath-taking, large flowers, pink with white throat, well worth the effort of its difficult cultivation to achieve.

The Series *Ancistracanthae* is likewise blessed with some of the most attractively flowered and spined species, mostly coming from Baja California, Mexico, but extending into the Sonoran desert. They are generally shallow rooted, and seem to present some difficulty in cultivation; until it is realized that they need little root room and not too frequent watering, when they will do well. Potting on should be carried out into barely the next sized pot, keeping to shallow pots for preference, and an open, gritty soil. Again it is difficult to be selective, and all this Series is worth attention, but a grudging selection follows. *M. albicans* from southern Baja California and neighbouring islands is a mystery, and what is grown as this species is probably not correctly so named because of discrepancies in the flowers compared with the original descriptions of this and the probably synonymous *M. slevinii*. Nevertheless, the masquerader is covered with beautiful dense white spines, the projecting central spines with brown tips, straight or sometimes hooked. The flowers are large, pale pink with a darker midstripe and with vivid purple-pink stigmas setting them off.

M. barbata (syn. *M. garessii*, *M. morricalii* and *M. santaclarensis*) is a small growing plant, forming hand sized clusters of globular stems, each to about 2 in (5 cm) wide, densely covered with spines, varying from yellow to red and strongly hooked. The flowers are fringed in the manner of *Escobaria* species, and appear at or very near the growing centre.

M. blossfeldiana makes such an eye-catching sight with its large, pink and white striped flowers that it is worth the effort of trying to get it to form a good sized cluster, which it will do reluctantly it seems. Even in the wild only small single or 3–4 stemmed plants are found. It has shallow roots and is prone to lose them if overwatered or overpotted.

M. boolii is usually solitary, making a stem only about 2 in (5 cm) tall and wide, with magnificent, large pink flowers.

M. capensis is frequently misidentified, but distinctive enough with its strong, hooked spines and large-petalled cream-white flowers. It forms clusters of long, inch-wide (2–3 cm) stems and tends to sprawl, the individual stems getting to a foot (30 cm) long or so. It comes from the southernmost cape area of Baja California. *M. fraileana* is from the same area, but more widespread, growing in rocky, well drained slopes. It has strongly hooked, purple-brown spines, and large pale pink flowers with prominent purple-pink stigmas, forming clumps of thumb-thick stems to about 4–5 in (10–12 cm) long. *M. grahamii* and *M. milleri* (syn. *M. microcarpa*) have agreed to a separation, perhaps for a trial period. They are similar in appearance, with many white radial spines, hooked or straight brown or yellowish-brown central spines, and large pale pink flowers. They are found over a wide area in southern United States, but are not so easy to cultivate as their common appearance in the wild might lead you to believe, since they are susceptible to overwatering at any time. Their shallow roots should not be given too much pot to fill; keep them in shallow pots and a little underpotted for safety.

M. guelzowiana has sumptuous, large, shocking-pink flowers reflexing to cover the top of the plant in their abundance. It is somewhat sensitive to overwatering or overhead watering, which will in any case spoil the covering of fine hair-thin radial spines. The hooked central spines come in yellow or red-brown. *M. heidiae*, now removed to this Series from its original placing with species now in Series Longimammae (former subgenus Dolichothele) because of its flower structure, better reflecting its somewhat difficult character to grow successfully, is a low-growing, yellow green plant with greenish flowers, rarely opening fully, unlike almost any other species. *M. hutchisoniana* makes long stems, densely covered with white spines and hooked brown centrals and freely producing its large, white flowers with green stigmas.

M. hutchisoniana var. *louisiae* (syn. *M. louisiae*) is a squatter version, differing in having green or brown stigmas and less spines and a reputation for being touchy to excess watering. A more robust form from further east than the normal occurrence of this variety is larger and more strongly growing, but still with short stems, barely more than globular. Both type and variety are well worth growing. *M. mainiae* is another with prominent purple-pink stigmas on large, pale pink with darker stripe flowers. The stems are apple sized and make a large cluster, but are prone to be touchy if the conditions are not entirely to its liking; careful watering is called for.

M. schumannii, another jewel from southern Baja California makes small clumps of globular stems to a little elongated, with distinctive, greyish-green body colouring, blackish-brown hooked spines and large, deep pink flowers; it is still sometimes seen labelled as *Bartschella schumannii*. *M. sheldonii* makes a large clump of stems each about an inch (2.5 cm) wide and 6 in (15 cm) or so long, and puts on a glorious show of its large deep pink flowers. Spines are dark brown and hooked or straight. *M. swinglei* often turns out in cultivation to be a mislabelled *M. sheldonii*, the true plant having somewhat thicker stems, less clustering and with paler pink dark midstriped flowers. It is also much more susceptible to overwatering. To take this difficulty one step further it has been said that the only way to cultivate *M. tetrancistra* successfully is to graft it, and having lost many seedlings at various stages of growth I would support this view. It

126. *Mammillaria magnifica* var. *magnifica*

127. *Mammillaria mainiae*

128. *Mammillaria marksiana*

129. *Mammillaria matudae* var. *matudae*

comes from very dry areas in Arizona and northern neighbouring parts of Mexico, has long blackish-brown, hooked central spines, and stunning, shell-pink, large flowers.

M. thornberi and *M. yaquensis* are finger thick and pencil thick stemmed repectively, forming clumps of stems about 4–5 in (10–12 cm) high, with strongly hooked spines and easily detached stems, so that they fall apart every time they are repotted. Their flowers are a lovely pale pink with darker midstriped petals and with prominent, long-lobed, purple-pink stigmas. *M. wrightii* (and var. *wilcoxii* – the latter syn. *M. meridiorosei*) occurs in high mountainous areas in New Mexico where it suffers cold temperatures, remaining sunk at or below ground level in the dry cold weather. This habitat is difficult to mimic in cultivation, and as a result these plants are easily lost through overwatering, or perhaps through over-warm conditions when they are resting. Plants are more or less globular, sometimes clustering, but too often not living long enough to even start trying to do so. They have long, fine, hooked spines and large purple flowers (white in *M. wrightii* fa. *wolfii*), followed by large, purple, small-grape sized fruits unlike any other species.

The Series *Stylothelae* is the other large group of hooked spine Mammillarias, but with generally finer spines and smaller and less colourful flowers. Some of the more attractive to grow are: *M. bocasana*, a common plant in cultivation, but with some less common variations, viz. pink flowered compared with cream coloured, or very densely woolly; although the species is noted for this character the form sold often as *M. bocasana* var. *multilanata* (not a valid name) is worth growing. The species forms clumps of stems to 1 ft (30 cm) wide or more and flowers freely. *M. bombycina* is still a show stopper and will often carry off the prize for best *Mammillaria*, if not best cactus, in shows. Eventually it makes a colossal clump to 2 ft (60 cm) or more wide, with its somewhat elongated but thick stems swathed with silky, fine, white spines and red-brown or yellow hooked spines standing out, among which the reddish-lilac flowers push out in the spring to complete the picture. *M. erythrosperma* makes quick clusters of globular stems with deep pink flowers, and *M. fittkaui* is similar, with paler pink to almost white flowers. *M. glassii* (& var. *ascensionis*) make clusters of densely white spined, small globular stems about an inch (2.5 cm) in diameter, with smallish pink flowers, larger in *M. glassii* var. *ascensionis*, and larger still and more deeply coloured pink; the recently named *M. glassii* var. *nominis-dulcis* (Lau 1186 & 1186A) and *M. glassii* var. *siberiensis* (Lau 1322).

M. moelleriana has thicker, hooked spines than most in this Series, coloured brown or golden yellow and with flowers freely produced in either cream yellow or pale pink. Unusually for this Series it generally remains

130. *Mammillaria milleri* (syn. *M. microcarpa*)

131. *Mammillaria moelleriana*

132. *Mammillaria parkinsonii*

133. *Mammillaria pectinifera*

solitary, for some years at least. *M. nana* is variable in its size and spination, and probably embraces the recently described species *M. duwei*, with more or less feathery white radial spines and brown or yellow central spines, sometimes not present or appearing sporadically. *M. pennispinosa* is a slow growing delight, covered with pinkish-brown, hooked, feathery spines, with pale pinkish-cream flowers to match. It rarely gets larger than a clump of 4–5 in (10–12 cm) tall and wide, and is susceptible to overwatering and overhead watering. Similarly *M. pennispinosa* var. *nazasensis* will scarcely outgrow its welcome, being somewhat flatter in growth than the type and with yellow or brown spines and creamy yellow flowers. Described very recently the stunning new species, *M. perezdelarosae* will be extremely popular, with its dense white radial spines setting off blackish-brown, hooked centrals very attractively. *M. stella-de-tacubaya* (syn. *M. gasseriana*) is slow and difficult, densely covered

in white appressed, radial spines with pinkish-brown central spines, hooked and appearing randomly. Flowers are pinkish-brown or greenish brown. *M. weingartiana* (syn. *M. unihamata*) is generally solitary, low and slow growing, pushing up from its 2–3 in (5–8 cm) wide stem a lethal forest of hooked, dark brown, solitary central spines. Flowers are greenish-yellow with brownish stripe.

The small Series *Proliferae*, apart from the very widespread, variable *M. prolifera*, consists of species showing little variation, and most do not excite collectors wildly, although a well grown, large plant of the common *M. prolifera* or *M. gracilis* is a beautiful sight. *M. pilispina* has a subtlety of colouring in the spines if grown in good light conditions that bears close appreciation, as does *M. picta*. But the outstanding member of this Series is *M. schwarzii*, covered in spun-glasslike, white, fine splinters of spines, and forming hand-sized clumps slowly over about five years or so. The spine colour varies from

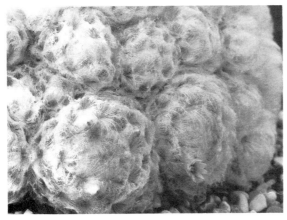

134. *Mammillaria pennispinosa* var. *nazasensis*

135. *Mammillaria plumosa*

136. *Mammillaria plumosa* ('golfball' form)

pure white, through white tinged pink to white with intermingling deep red spines, the latter form being much sought after. Flowers are cream coloured.

The Series *Lasiacanthae* is a rag-bag of highly prized species, with some of the most wonderfully spined in the genus. None can be omitted from a recommended *M. aureilanata* (& fa. *alba* n.n. — with white spines) is one of the earliest Mammillarias to flower, buds just starting at the turn of the year in England, the pale pink flowers emerging in early spring through the soft covering of fine, golden-yellow spines, like teased wool. As with several species in this Series the solitary plants sit on a thick tap-root. *M. carmenae*, only recently rediscovered by Alfred Lau in the more remote areas in the north-east of Mexico, is now common in cultivation, with soft, yellow to white, sunray clusters of fine spines densely clothing the globular, clustering stems, which become elongated with age. Flowers are white, or less commonly pale pink. *M. egregia* is still regarded as a dubious species, but plants in cultivation are stunning, and sufficiently distinct to ensure the name survives — on labels at least. Stems are usually solitary, covered with dense clusters of spines, brightly white, radiating and intermingling to completely cover the plant body, which is globular and no more than an inch or two (3–5 cm) across. *M. herrerae* and *M. humboldtii* are similarly densely white-spined, the latter clustering after several years to form small clusters, but *M. herrerae* has large, wide opening pale pink flowers (white in *M. herrerae* var. *albiflora*) and *M. humboldtii* has smaller more readily produced deep purple-pink flowers. *M. lasiacantha* is usually solitary, densely white-spined, sometimes with very feathery spines, low growing to an inch or two wide and with small brownish or pinkish striped white flowers. *M. laui*, discovered by Alfred Lau at the same time as he found *M. carmenae*, is a beautifully spined species, varying from dense, white, soft spines (*M. laui* fa. *dasyacantha*) to stiffer white spines (*M. laui* fa. *laui*) and yellow or brown-tipped yellow spines (*M. laui* fa. *subducta*). All cluster to form clumps in time quite large (to 6 in/15 cm or more) and have deep pink flowers. *M. lenta* is a low growing, flat-globular stemmed species, stems about 2–3 in (5–8 cm) wide, finely white-spined, with wide opening, white flowers with a narrow red stripe down each petal. *M. magallanii* is another early flowerer in England, with pinkish-brown spines and flowers. *M. pectinifera* (syn. *Solisia pectinata*) has somewhat elongated areoles on which the spines are arranged neatly in two rows, one each side; the plants in circulation these days tend to be seedlings, rather than the battered imported specimens seen ten or more years ago, and form neat golf ball sized single stems, sometimes clustering. Flowers are produced on the sides, and are pale pink or white with pink midstripes on the petals. *M. plumosa* occurs in several forms, all with the feathery white spines this species is so

137. *Mammillaria poselgeri*

138. *Mammillaria pondii* var. *setispina*

139. *Mammillaria pottsii*

140. *Mammillaria rhodantha* var. *pringlei*

141. *Mammillaria saboae* fa. *goldii*

142. *Mammillaria saboae* fa. *goldii* (cristate form with normal stems as well)

143. *Mammillaria schiedeana* var. *schiedeana*

144. *Mammillaria schumannii*

well known for, the variation being mainly in the size and shape of the stems, from small evenly flat-rounded tops merging together to form even mounds, to larger headed, separately standing stems, like piles of cumulus clouds burgeoning up. It is a shallow rooted species, and is susceptible to overhead watering, or overwatering at any time. It has the slightly annoying habit of flowering in the depths of winter, but I am of the opinion that to take this as an indication that it needs watering then is asking for trouble. The flowers are small and whitish cream, although if they are produced at a more sunny time of year they have more of a pinkish cream colouring. *M. schiedeana* is another variable species, with golden clusters of radiating spines set closely together on narrow tubercles closely placed together on the globular plant body; in some forms the spines are whiter and more feathery, to which the undescribed name *M. schiedeana* var. *plumosa* is sometimes attached. Flowers are white, appearing sporadically throughout the year, but par-

ticularly in the autumn in England. *M. schiedeana* var. *dumetorum* has almost white, lesser in number spines, and more tendency to form large clusters of stems than the type. *M. solisioides* is another in this Series which flowers in late autumn or holds the buds over for flowering in the spring, infuriatingly sometimes not managing to hold them over when they dry up. It is a small, globular stemmed plant, often solitary, taking many years to form a cluster, with chalk white, sometimes pinkish-tipped radiating spines, and yellow with red midstripe flowers.

The series *Sphacelatae* contains only three species, all presenting some difficulty in cultivation. *M. sphacelata* (& var. *viperina*) are reluctant in this country at least to produce their flowers unless the sunniest spot is found, and *M. tonalensis* is more reluctant still to do so. But perhaps the best looking plant of the three is in any case less difficult in this respect, though no push-over, and *M. kraehenbuehlii*, forming mounds of globular stems, rather than the straggling stems of the other species, is a neater

92

145. *Mammillaria sempervivi* var. *pseudocrucigera*

146. *Mammillaria sheldonii*

147. *Mammillaria sphacelata* var. *viperina*

148. *Mammillaria spinosissima* var. *spinosissima*

looking plant covered with fine, white spines and having deep pinkish-red flowers with a delightful paler margin to the petals, unlike almost any other in the genus.

The series *Leptocladodae* have *M. pottsii* with them as an uncomfortable visitor, with elongated stems covered with the white radial spines and blue-black central spines incurving and making it difficult for the red flowers to

emerge. It grows on limestone ridges in the wild, in Texas, and presents some difficulty in cultivation until this is realized and a limey compost offered, with good drainage and a light hand on the watering, since it grows with very good drainage in the wild too.

M. elongata is easy to dismiss as a common, nondescript plant, but its form and spination is so variable that it is worth looking out for some of the more attractive coloured or heavily spined variants. Sometimes the spines are really quite red, or deep chocolate brown, and these plants make an attractive pan of the finger like stems. *M. elongata* var. *echinaria* has thicker stems, with prominent central spines, and the same amount of variation in coloration, from bright yellow to brown or red. Flowers are fairly insignificant on both, smallish and cream to lemon yellow. *M. densispina* var. *mieheana* is about intermediate between *M. densispina*, a globular, golden yellow and red-brown spined species, and *M. elongata*. It is like a thicker stemmed, slower growing version of *M. elongata*, with pale golden yellow spines and greenish yellow flowers.

The series *Decipientes* has now resolved as only one species, and for me the outstanding variety is *M. decipiens* var. *camptotricha* (formerly *M. camptotricha*), with curling, yellow-brown spines, forming a dense, interwoven covering for the flat-globular cluster of stems, which will fill a 10 in (25 cm) pan in four or five years. The flowers are small, white, and barely noticeable among the swirling spines.

The series *Heterochlorae* contains spiny, globular to columnar species with generally small crimson-purple flowers, making up for their lack of size by the successive rings over a period of several weeks. The widespread and variable *M. rhodantha* has its best representative in *M. rhodantha* var. *pringlei* (syn. *M. pringlei*) with long, curling, golden yellow spines incurving and forming a basketwork of spines over the top of the plant, making life for the small emerging flowers difficult in the extreme. *M. wiesingeri* is a squat similar species, and *M. wiesingeri* var. *erectacantha* is a more attractively spined version.

The series *Polyacanthae* has even spinier plants than the former series, the individual count on each areole often approaching a hundred or so. *M. matudae* is a narrowly columnar species with closely fitting fine spines, the fine white radial spines contrasted by short centrals varying from yellowish-brown to dark chestnut brown. I have seen up to 10 successive rings of the dark reddish purple flowers on a mature stem of this species, which in the wild can get to 5 ft (1.5 m) long, and in cultivation will get to half this size within six or seven years. *M. magnifica* is well named, forming truly magnificent clumps of elongated stems, densely covered with golden-yellow spines, the centrals long and strongly hooked. Flowers are pink.

M. nunezii (& var. *bella* – syn. *M. bella*) is a more globular member of this series, clustering slowly, with many ginger-red spines, either hooked or straight; *M. nunezii* var. *bella* has finer, white spines, tipped reddish-brown. The smallish flowers of both are deep reddish-pink. *M. spinosissima* is the largest growing in the Series, with thick stems, to about 3 in (8 cm) wide, and getting

to 1 ft (30 cm) or more tall, clustering occasionally to form massive clumps, but often solitary. The spines are fine and numerous, coloured variously from yellowish white to red-brown. Flowers are reddish-pink, produced in several rings. *M. spinosissima* var. *pilcayensis* (syn. *M. pilcayensis* and *M. pitcayensis*) is an even finer and shorter spined variety, with either yellow or white tipped red-brown spines, neat and of such uniform length as to appear carefully and closely cropped. Flowers are similar to the type.

The series *Supertextae* is noted for the pleasing, geometric spirals of spine clusters, which are generally numerous and quite short, nonetheless completely covering the plant bodies. *M. albilanata* makes thick snow poles, with close white spines and thick wool in the growing area, in which the blood red flowers stand out like rubies. *M. crucigera* is a highly adapted species, living in harsh conditions in the wild, on steep slopes of crumbling gypsum. It makes stems no more than 2 in (5 cm) tall and wide, dichotomously dividing and offsetting to form low clumps. The spines are tiny, no more than 2 mm long, with white radials and four thicker, but no longer, brown, cruciform centrals. Flowers too are small, reddish-pink. *M. huitzilopochtli* is similar, but larger growing and tending to remain solitary in cultivation for some years at least, and developing long, unusual black central spines in maturity. *M. supertexta*, an old name resurrected on rediscovery of plants in the wild, is a globular to short columnar species with wonderfully symmetric spirals of clusters of short white spines. Flowers are pinkish-red with white throats.

The series *Leucocephalae* has, as the name would imply, some beautiful white-spined species. *M. geminispina* is probably the most well known, making wide mounds of white spined stems, each about 2–3 in (5–8 cm) wide and becoming somewhat taller in time. One of the more attractive forms is that sometimes known as *M. geminispina* var. *nobilis*, which has very long central spines, to an inch (2.5 cm) or more. Spines are chalk white with brown or black at the very tip. Flowers are sometimes reluctantly produced, usually late in the summer or early autumn in England, and are bright reddish-pink. *M. hahniana* varies considerably in the amount of long hairlike bristles it produces, the longest naturally the most sought after, and the bristles on some I have seen have been 2–3 in (5–8 cm) long or more, giving the whole plant an ethereal aspect. Flowers are small, reddish pink, contrasting well with the white spines and bristles. There are two distinct forms in cultivation apart from the differing length of spines, some remaining solitary, others clustering to form low mounds of hairy stems. *M. hahniana* var. *woodsii* has much less hair than the type, with prominent strong blackish brown central spines. *M. klissingiana* makes large mounds, very slowly, of globular stems about 3 in (8 cm) in diameter, densely covered with

149. *Mammillaria spinosissima* var. *pilcayensis*

150. *Mammillaria surculosa*

151. *Mammillaria thornberi*

152. *Mammillaria tonalensis*

white spines and thick wool in the axils. Flowers are pink, prominently striped reddish-pink. *M. parkinsonii* is taller growing, to about 6–8 in (15–20 cm) forming clusters of stems, dividing dichotomously. It has many stark white radial spines and long, white, brown-tipped centrals. Flowers are creamy-yellow with prominent red midstripes down the petals. *M. sempervivi* makes a solitary, flat-globular stem, with angled, dark green tubercles surmounted by short, stiff blackish-brown spines, two or four in number, the latter with usually more wool in the growing area from the axils and pink with deep reddish-pink midstripe (*M. sempervivi* var. *pseudocrucigera*), the former with less wool and cream-coloured flowers.

The series *Mammillaria* (syn. *Macrothelae*) includes a few 'big fellows' in a mostly quite modest-sized species. These can make clusters to 2–3 ft (60–90 cm) wide, although most get to no more than about half this size in cultivation. *M. magnimamma* probably makes the largest sized clumps, and is quite variable in its spination and flower colour, as well as its propensity to form clumps, but a more handsome species generally is *M. compressa*, with its downwards pointing, stark white, brown tipped spines and smaller stems, making a most handsome specimen 18 in (45 cm) across in about 10 years or so. The flowers are not large, but make a colourful show of deep purple-pink when produced in rings around each stem in the spring. For a really large, solitary species *M. gigantea*

153. *Mammillaria varieaculeata*

154. *Mammillaria weingartiana*

155. *Mammillaria wiesingeri* var. *erectacantha*

156. *Mammillaria winterae*

157. *Mammillaria wrightii* var. *wilcoxii*

158. *Mammillaria yaquensis*

81

82

83

84

85

81 *Mammillaria herrerae*

82 *Mammillaria humboldtii*

83 *Mammillaria klissingiana*

84 *Mammillaria lenta*

85 *Mammillaria longiflora* (white spined form)

86

87

88

89

90

86 *Mammillaria napina*

87 *Mammillaria pennispinosa*

88 *Mammillaria saboae* fa.
haudeana

89 *Mammillaria schwarzii*

90 *Mammillaria senilis*

91

92

93

94

95

91 *Mammillaria setispina*

92 *Mammillaria solisioides*

93 *Mammillaria tetrancistra*

94 *Mammillaria theresae*

95 *Mammillaria voburnensis* var. *eichlamii*

96

97

98

99

100

96   *Melocactus matanzanus*

97   *Mila nealeana*

98   *Neolloydia conoidea* var. *grandiflora*

99   *Neolloydia smithii* var. *beguinii*

100   *Neolloydia viereckii*

101

102

103

104

105

101 *Neoporteria chilensis* var. *albidiflora*

102 *Neoporteria islayensis*

103 *Neoporteria napina* var. *spinosior*

104 *Neoporteria nidus*

105 *Neowerdermannia peruviana*

106 *Nopalxochia phyllanthoides*

107 *Notocactus leninghausii*
(bedded out in 'Lotusland', a
private garden in California, USA)

108 *Notocactus magnificus*

109 *Notocactus minimus*

110 *Notocactus scopa* var.
ramosus

111

112

113

114

115

111 *Notocactus uebelmannianus* (in a nursery in California, USA)

112 *Opuntia basilaris*

113 *Opuntia invicta* (in habitat, northern Baja California, Mexico)

114 *Opuntia subterranea*

115 *Oroya peruviana*

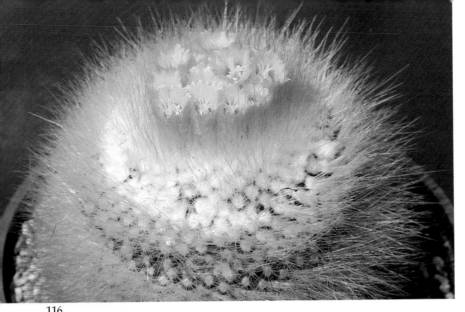

116

117

118

119

120

116 *Parodia chrysacanthion*

117 *Parodia nivosa*

118 *Parodia subterranea*

119 *Pediocactus knowltonii*

120 *Pediocactus peeblesianus*

121 *Pediocactus simpsonii*

122 *Pelecyphora asselliformis*

123 *Pelecyphora strobiliformis*

124 *Pterocactus kuntzei*

125 *Rebutia flavistyla*

126

127

128

129

130

126   *Rebutia heliosa*

127   *Rebutia narvaecensis*

128   *Rebutia perplexa*

129   *Rebutia wessneriana* var. *krainziana*

130   *Rhipsalis houlletiana*

131

132

133

134

135

131   *Schlumbergera orssichiana*

132   *Schlumbergera opuntioides*

133   *Selenicereus pteranthus*

134   *Stenocactus crispatus*

135   *Stenocereus eruca* (in habitat in southern Baja California, Mexico)

136

137

138

139

140

136   *Strombocactus denegrii*

137   *Strombocactus disciformis*

138   *Strombocactus lophophoroides*

139   *Strombocactus pseudomacrochele*

140   *Strombocactus pseudopectinatus*

141

142

143

144

145

141 *Strombocactus schmiedickeanus*

142 *Strombocactus valdezianus*

143 *Sulcorebutia arenacea*

144 *Sulcorebutia canigueralii*

145 *Sulcorebutia flavissima*

146

147

148

149

150

146	*Sulcorebutia langeri*
147	*Sulcorebutia mizquensis*
148	*Sulcorebutia rauschii*
149	*Sulcorebutia tiraquensis* var. *bicolorispina*
150	*Thelocactus bicolor* var. *bolansis*

151

152

153

154

155

151 *Thelocactus erectocentrus* (in habitat in Arizona, USA)

152 *Thelocactus johnsonii* (in habitat in Arizona, USA)

153 *Thelocactus polyancistrus* (in habitat in California, USA)

154 *Thelocactus uncinatus*

155 *Thelocactus unguispinus* var. *laui*

156

157

158

159

160

156 *Thelocactus whipplei*

157 *Toumeya papyracantha* (in habitat, New Mexico, USA)

158 *Uebelmannia flavispina*

159 *Uebelmannia pectinifera*

160 *Weingartia neumanniana.*

takes some beating, with usually dark blackish-brown central spines, plenty of wool in the growing area at the apex, through which the yellow flowers emerge. *M. petterssonii* is a similar large plant, with generally brown spines and deep pink flowers. Both these species will get to about 9–10 in (to 20 cm) or more tall and wide after seven years or so.

M. marksiana is a challenge to grow well, but in time, with careful treatment, not overwatering and giving a well drained compost, it will form a cluster of large globular stems, each about 4 in (10 cm) wide, bright, glossy green, with short, weakish yellow spines and lovely yellow flowers. *M. peninsularis*, from the southern cape area of the Baja California peninsula, is one of the smallest of this series, getting to no more than about 4 in (10 cm) wide, and is usually solitary, very slow growing, making less height than width. It has short, stiff spines and yellow flowers.

M. winterae makes as large a plant in width as *M. gigantea*, but is much flatter growing, barely more than about 2–3 in (5–8 cm) high compared with nearly a foot (30 cm) wide at maturity. Flowers are large, cup-shaped and pale yellow.

The series *Polyedrae* has angular tubercled species, two of which are outstanding, viz. *M. varieaculeata* and *M. voburnensis*, in particular *M. voburnensis* fa. *eichlamii*. *M. varieaculeata* has very individual, wayward central spines, which appear in maturity, not from every areole, and pointing this way and that in a tousled manner, one or two from each areole that is so blessed. The flowers are lilac-pink with white throats. *M. voburnensis* fa. *eichlamii* is a little tender, coming from Guatemala, and makes mounds of stems each about 2 in (5 cm) tall and wide, with short brown and white spines, and with colourful yellow wool in the axils, its main feature. Flowers are pale yellow.

Connoisseur's choice: *M. baumii, M. beneckei, M. blossfeldiana, M. carmenae, M. guelzowiana, M. herrerae, M. humboldtii, M. klissingiana, M. lenta, M. longiflora, M. napina, M. pennispinosa, M. saboae, M. schwarzii, M. senilis, M. setispina, M. solisioides, M. tetrancistra, M. theresae, M. voburnensis* var. *eichlamii, M. wrightii.*

Mammilloydia F. Buxb. (1951)

Referred to *Mammillaria*.

Marenopuntia Backeb. (1950)

Referred to *Opuntia*.

159. *Mammillaria zeilmanniana*

160. *Melocactus onchyacanthus* (young plant without cephalium development)

161. *Melocactus violaceus* (stem no larger than about 4 in/10 cm)

Marginatocereus Backeb., (1942)

Referred to *Pachycereus*.

Maritimocereus Akers (1950)

Referred to *Borzicactus.*

Marniera Backeb. (1950)

Referred to *Epiphyllum.*

Marshallocereus Backeb. (1950)

Referred to *Stenocereus.*

Matucana B. & R. (1922); Kimnach, *Cact. Amer.* 32:8 (1960)

Since the reduction to synonymy with the broad concepts of the genus *Borzicactus,* *Matucana* has hung on both in nursery listings and in collections. While applauding Myron Kimnach's bold, broad generic concept it must be said that it highlights the difficulties collectors have in accepting such changes while the custom remains of binomial labelling. It would have been much more readily assimilated I believe if it were customary to include subgeneric placings, e.g. *Borzicactus (Matucane) haynei,* on labels, but perhaps labels would have to be made larger – a small price to pay for a more informative and instructive habit. See under *Borzicactus.*

Mediocactus B. & R. (1920)

Referred to *Selenicereus.*

Mediolobivia Backeb. (1934)

Similar arguments as outlined above apply to this attractive group of plants, now generally accepted as falling beneath the wide concept of *Rebutia* – see under *Rebutia.*

Melocactus Link & Otto, *Verh. Beförd, Gartenb. Preuss. Staat.* 3:417, tt.12,25 (1827); N. P. Taylor, *Cact. GB* 42(3):63–70 (1980); l.c.44(1):7–8 (1982); l.c.(4):89–90 (1982)

This wonderfully individual genus of globular cacti (sometimes becoming short-columnar in age), with a central woolly cephalium in which the tiny red or deep pink flowers appear, comes from a wide area of tropical South America, Central America and the West Indies. Like the similar, but large, white, nocturnal flowered genus, *Discocactus,* most *Melocactus* species require a minimum temperature of 50° F (10° c) for safety, and are more comfortable at 55° F (13° c) plus. A few produce their cephalium at a modest size 3–4 in (8–10 cm) across, but most do not do so before they get to about 6 in (15 cm) wide or more. Once they do produce this tufted growth in the centre the plant body puts on little more in size. There seem to be many more species named than is justified, and N. P.

Taylor of Kew has been tackling the problem in recent years (see refs above).

Species named are: *M. acunai, M. albicephalus, M. amoenus, M. amstutziae, M. amethystinus, M. ammotrophus, M. arcatispinus, M. azureus, M. bellavistensis, M. brederooianus, M. broadwayi, M. caesius, M. communis, M. concinnus, M. conoideus, M. coronatus, M. curvicornis, M. curvispinus, M. dawsonii, M. deinacanthus, M. delessertianus, M. depressus, M. douradaensis, M. fortalezensis, M. giganteus, M. glaucescens, M. glauxinus, M. guaricensis, M. guitartii, M. harlowii, M. huallancaensis, M. intortus* (& var. *antonii*), *M. jansenianus, M. lanssensionus, M. lemairei, M. lensselinkianus, M. levitestatus, M. lobellii, M. loboguerreroi, M. macrocanthus, M. matanzanus, M. maxonii, M. mazelianus, M. neryi, M. oaxacensis, M. obtusipetalus, M. onchyacanthus* (& var. *albescens,* var. *conicus*), *M. oreas* (& subsp. *bahiensis*), *M. paucispinus, M. peruvianus* (& var. *canetensis,* var. *lurinensis*), *M. ruestii, M. salvadorensis, M. saxicola, M. schatzlii, M. trujilloensis* (& var. *schoenii*), *M. unguispinus, M. violaceus, M. zehntneri* (& var. *viridis*).

Rejected names and synonymies

M. acispinosus = *M. oreas* subsp. *bahiensis*?

M. amethystinus = *M. brederooianus* var *amethystinus*?

M. arachnites = *M. diersianus* = *M. levitestatus* var. *diersianus*?

M. axiniphorus = *M. concinnus*

M. azulensis = *M. florschuetzianus* = *M. oreas* var. *florschuetzianus*?

M. bahiensis = *M. oreas* subsp. *bahiensis*

M. canescens (& var. *montealtoi*) = *M. zehntneri* var. *canescens*?

M. cremnophilus = *M. oreas* var. *cremnophilus*?

M. diersianus = *M. levitestatus* var. *diersianus*?

M. disciformis n.n = M. salvadorensis

M. ernestii = M. oreas

M. erythracanthus = *M. oreas* var. *erythracanthus*?

M. ferreophilus = *M. azureus* var. *ferreophilus*?

M. florschuetzianus = *M. oreas* var. *florschuetzianus*?

M. gonioaacanthus = nom. dub.

M. griseoloviridis = *M. lensselinkianus*

M. helvolilanatus = *M. zehntneri*

M. horridus = *M. oreas*?

M. inconcinnus = *M. brederooianus* var. *inconcinnus*?

M. interpositus = *M. oreas*

M. krainzianus = *M. azureus* var. *krainzianus*

M. longicarpus = *M. deinacanthus*

M. longispinus = *M. oreas*

M. macrodiscus (& var. *minor*) = *M. zehntneri* var. *macrodiscus*?

M. margaritaceus nom. inval.

M. melocactoides nom. dub.

M. montanus = *M. florschuetzianus*? = *M. oreas* var. *florschuetzianus*?

M. mulequensis = M. deinacanthus
M. nitidus = M. florschuetzianus = M. oreas var.
  florschuetzianus?
M. pachyacanthus = M. azureus var. *pachyacanthus*
M. pentacentrus = M. violaceus
M. permutabilis = M. inconcinnus
M. pruinosus = M. zehntneri
M. robustispinus = M. macrodiscus = M. zehntneri var.
  macrodiscus?
M. rubrisaetosus = M. oreas var. *rubrisaetosus?*
M. rubrispinus = M. levitestatus var. *rubrispinus?*
M. securituberculatus = M. levitestatus var.
  securituberculatus?
M. warasii = M. levistestatus var. *warasii?*

It must be said that in England many species will take 10 years or so to produce the cephalium, until which most species are fairly ordinary round, spiny cacti. For this reason, and for that of space too, the recommended species are mainly those which will oblige by producing a cephalium at a relatively small size, but some of the larger species are also recommended since they are such beautiful plants that it is worth the waiting time for the cephalium's development. And some of the larger species are also attractive in the juvenile stage, e.g. *M. azureus* or *M. glaucescens*, with blue colouring.

Recommended species: M. azureus or *M. glaucescens* sport an attractive blue colour even in the early stages and the blue gets more intense as they get older. Both form a cephalium at about pineapple size, but will grow quite quickly and produce it in about six or eight years if grown on well, more quickly of course if grafted.

M. matazanus is probably the best known of the species which form a cephalium at a comparatively small size, indeed after a few years the cephalium overtopping the body tends to look disproportionately large. It may be expected to appear when the plant reaches about 3 in (8 cm) in diameter, and is suffused with gingery spines, giving a reddish cast to the creamy white wool of the cephalium; the short curving spines are neatly arranged on the vertical ribs, making for a most attractive species to grow. It does need a minimum of 50° F (12° C) for safety.

M. onchyacanthus is most attractively spined, with thick, curling spines enveloping the body. It will take some time to get to the 5–6 ins (15 cm) diameter needed before it forms a cephalium, but until it does so is a most attractive plant.

M. violaceus is another of the small growing species, forming a cephalium at about 3–4 in (8–10 cm) wide, with tiny deep pink to purple flowers, and dark brown spines setting off the white cephalium.

Connoisseur's choice: M. matanzanus.

Micranthocereus Backeb. (1938)

Referred to *Cephalocereus.*

Micropuntia Daston (1947)

Referred to *Opuntia,* under subgenus *Cylindropuntia.*

Mila B. & R., *The Cact.* 3:211, t.22 (1922)

This small genus from Peru (the name is an anagram of the capital Lima) is not often seen in cultivation and even more seldom seen well grown or flowering. Plants form small clusters of short-columnar stems, varying in the density of the spination in the dubiously distinct species, which are reminiscent in their growth habit of the better-known genus, *Echinocereus.* Flowers are small, about 1 in (2–3 cm) wide and yellow.

Species named are: *M. albisaetaceus, M. albo-areolata,* (*M. breviseta = M. nealeana* fa. *senilis*), *M. caespitosa, M. cereoides, M. colorea,* (*M. densiseta = M. nealeana* fa. *senilis*), *M. fortalezensis, M. kubeana, M. lurinensis, M. nealeana* (& fa. *senilis,* var. *tenuior*), *M. pugionifera, M. sublanata* (var. *pallidior = M. nealeana* fa. *senilis*).

Recommended species: according to the lumpers there is only one species, the first named, *M. caespitosa,* and it could be that the names are little more than just names, indicating a variable species. That said, there is such a dearth of offered plants of this genus, almost any offering is worth obtaining and growing, in full sun to stand a chance of seeing the flowers, reluctant in England to appear. The plants grow slowly but steadily, and one or two of the best plants I have seen have been on grafts, which may also encourage easier flowering through the stronger growth.

Connoisseur's choice: any species.

Miqueliopuntia Fric ex Ritt., *Kakt. Sudamer.* 3:869 (1980)

A monotypic genus erected for *Opuntia miquelii,* here regarded as referable to *Opuntia.*

Mirabella Ritt. *Kakt. Sudamer.* 1:108 (1979)

This genus was set up by Ritter for two Brazilian species of columnar cacti, one formerly described as *Acanthocereus albicaulis,* the other newly described as *M. minensis.* The standing of this new genus is yet to be assessed, and for the moment the formerly described species is still listed under *Acanthocereus.*

Mitrocereus Backeb. (1942)

Referred to *Cephalocereus.*

Monvillea B. & R. *The Cact.* 2:21, t.3 (figs 20–23) (1920)

The 15 or so species of this genus are slender stemmed, usually clambering to about 6 ft (2 m) or more tall, needing support in cultivation, and producing their large, white or yellowish flowers at night, which may be expected to appear after they are about 2 feet (60 cm) tall. The spines are not very strong, black or brown, and the stem in some species is attractively marbled. They come from the West Indies and South America.

Species named are: *M. alticostata, M. amazonica, M. apoloensis, M. ballivianii, M. breviflora, M. calliantha, M. campinensis, M. cavendishii, M. chacoana, M. diffusa, M. ebenacantha, M. euchlora, M. haageana, M. jaenensis, M. lauterbachii, M. leucantha, M. lindenzweigiana, M. maritima, M. markgrafii, M. parapetiensis, M. paxtoniana* (& var. *borealis*), *M. phaeacantha, M. phatuosperma, M. piedadensis, M. pugionifera, M. rhodoleucantha, M. saxicola, M. smithiana, M. spegazzinii.*

Recommended species: few are seen in cultivation, the most common being *M. spegazzinii*, also seen as a monstrose or cristate plant. It has a most attractively marked stem, mottled in shades of glaucous green and blue. Flowers are long tubed, white with brownish outer petals.

Connoisseur's choice: M. spegazzinii.

Morangaya Rowley, *Ashingtonia* 1:44 (1974); N. P. Taylor, *Echinocereus* (1985)

Long known as an *Echinocereus*, and now recombined by Nigel Taylor, a Kew Gardens taxonomist, Rowley's *Morangaya pensilis* (the only species) from mountainous areas in the south of Baja California, Mexico, reputedly two days' trek from the road, is named for those Baja endemics Ed Gay and Reid Moran. It is not a tidy grower, making sprawling, whangy, rope-thick stems (1 in/2.5 cm), several feet or metres long, and not floriferous in England, although the odd reddish-orange flower is produced at the expense of half a yard of stem. It is not recommended, except for those who covet rarities or are buddies of Reid Moran or Ed & Betty Gay. And it is only my affection for the plant as seen growing like a bramble at the Gays' nursery in California, where I was invited to take a yard or two (not just a small piece as I requested) which makes me include a longer reference to it than perhaps it deserves. See under *Echinocereus*.

Myrtillocactus Console, *Boll. R. Ort. Bot. Palermo* 1:8 (1897)

This is a small genus of attractively coloured columnar cacti from Mexico and Guatemala, making low, candelabra-like trees of branching, blue-grey or grey-green stems, with short spines well-spaced on the ribs, and small, white flowers. They make attractively coloured stems in cultivation and take some time to outgrow their welcome, but are inclined to be a little tender, and require a minimum of 50° F (10° C) for safety from marking.

Species named are: *M. cochal, M. eichlamii, M. geometrizans* (& var. *grandiareolatus*), *M. schenckii.*

Recommended species: M. geometrizans has blue-green stems in youth and later develops strong, short, thick black-brown clusters of spines at the areoles; it needs to be at least 2 ft (60 cm) tall before flowering may be expected.

M. cochal is more grey-green in colour, but similar in habit; it is not so often seen offered by nurseries.

Connoisseur's choice: M. cochal.

Navajoa Croizat (1943)

Referred to *Pediocactus.*

Neoabbottia B. & R., Smith's *Misc. Coll.* 72:2, tt.1–4 (1921)

This is a monotypic genus (*N. paniculata* and *N. paniculata* var. *humbertii*) from Haiti and the Dominican Republic, little known in cultivation and if grown requiring more heat than most cacti (50° F/10° C) for safety. It forms branching columnar plants, eventually with a thick main trunk.

It is not recommended.

Neobesseya B. & R. (1923)

Referred to *Escobaria.*

Neobinghamia Backeb. (1950); Ritter, *Kakt. Sudamer.* 4:1451 (1981)

Ritter's opinion that the handful of species in this genus are natural hybrids is upheld. They are considered to be naturally occurring hybrids between *Espostoa* and *Borzicactus* or *Haageocereus.*

Neobuxbaumia Backeb. (1938)

Referred to *Cephalocereus.*

Neocardenasia Backeb. (1949)

Referred to *Neoraimondia.*

Neochilenia Backeb. (1942)

The problem of the genus *Neochilenia* is on the one hand the illegitimacy of the name (*Nichelia* is the preferred name if regarded as a separate genus) and on the other hand the strong school of thought taxonomically for its sinking, whatever you call it, beneath the broader concept of *Neoporteria*. Against this is the persistence of the name for collectors and nurserymen for clearly identifiable plants from *Neoporteria* in the narrow sense. As expounded elsewhere in this book, if the general use of subgeneric names were customary, e.g. *Neoporteria* (*Neochilenia*) *napina*, instead of the binomial labelling we now use, such combinations might be more readily accepted. See under *Neoporteria*.

Neodawsonia Backeb. (1949)

Referred to *Cephalocereus*.

Neoevansia W. T. Marshall (1941)

Referred to *Peniocereus*.

Neogomesia Castaneda (1941)

Referred to *Ariocarpus*.

Neolloydia B. & R., *Bull. Torrey Bot. Club* 49:251 (1922)

This is a genus which has been taken to include some controversial small genera in the past few years, including most significantly *Gymnocactus*, as well as the lesser used *Cumarinia* and *Rapicactus*. It comes from Mexico and Texas, USA, and consists mainly of small, globose to short-cylindric, clustering plants, freely flowering and presenting few difficulties in cultivation.

Species named are: *N. aguirriana*, *N. conoidea* (& var. *ceratites*, var. *grandiflora*, var. *matehualensis*, var. *texensis*), *N. gielsdorfiana*, *N. horripila*, *N. knuthiana*, *N. mandragora*, *N. odorata*, *N. pilispina*, *N. pulleiniana*, *N. roseana*, *N. saueri*, *N. smithii* (& var. *beguinii*, cv. *senilis*), *N. subterranea* (& var. *zaragosae*), *N. viereckii* (& var. *major*), *N. warnockii*, *N. ysabelae* (& var. *brevispina*).

Synonymies of rejected species:

N. beguinii = *N. smithii* var. *beguinii*
N. beguinii var. *senilis* = *N. smithii* cv. *senilis*

162. *Myrtillocactus cochal*, in habitat, northern Baja California, Mexico

163. *Neolloydia aguirriana*

Neolloydia

N. ceratites = N. conoidea var. ceratites
N. grandiflora = N. conoidea var. grandiflora
N. matehualensis = N. conoidea var. matehualensis.

Recommended species: *N. conoidea.* In any of its varieties this is a delightful plant to grow, with stems barely more than a few inches (8–10 cm) tall and no more than an inch (2·5 cm) wide, with a dense covering of white radial spines and long, black centrals, sometimes not present. The flowers are large and a rich pink, coming in succession over a period of weeks in the summer.

N. gielsdorfiana has a blue-green body colouring and easily knocked off clusters of long, curving black tipped spines, with pale yellow flowers in succession from the growing point.

N. horripila has become more readily available in recent years, and makes a low clump of globular stems, covered with dense white radial and dark-tipped central spines; flowers are purple.

N. knuthiana is one of the earliest to flower in the spring, and will often stay solitary for several years before clumping gently to form a hand-sized clump of globular to very short-columnar stems, covered with white, flexible, bristle-like spines and producing its soft pink flowers from the centre.

N. roseana, ascribed for many years to *Escobaria*, is a lovely golden-yellow spined plant making a clump to 8–10 inches (20–25 cm) in a few years, with short, columnar stems to about 3 in (12 cm) tall and about an inch or more (3 cm) wide; flowers are pale yellow.

N. smithii, more readily coming to mind as *N. beguinii*, but now reduced to varietal status beneath this older name, makes short columns, densely clothed with upwards pointing white tipped brown, stiff spines, longer and more flexible in the cultivar, *N. smithii* cv. *senilis.* Flowers are deep pink.

N. subterranea, as the name implies has more growth beneath the soil than on the top, where it makes a small tufted top-shaped stem, absolutely covered with long, white, dark brown tipped spines, through which the pink flowers push with difficulty.

N. viereckii makes a stunning mound of short-columnar stems, each about 2 in (5 cm) wide and a little taller, with startling white wool and spines covering the body, set off by dark, long central spines almost black in colour; flowers come in white or deep pinkish-purple.

Connoisseur's choice: *N. smithii* var. *beguinii*, *N. conoidea* var. *grandiflora*, *N. viereckii.*

164. *Neolloydia conoidea*, in habitat atop limestone hills, Big Bend area, Texas, USA

165. *Neolloydia gielsdorfiana*

166. *Neolloydia horripila*

167. *Neolloydia knuthiana*

168. *Neolloydia roseana*

169. *Neolloydia subterranea* var. *zaragosae*

Neolobivia Y. Ito, *Expl. Diagr.* 284 (1957)

A genus recently resurrected by Ritter for a small group of *Lobivia* species, here regarded as equating to *Lobivia*.

Neomammillaria B & R. (1923)

Referred to *Mammillaria*

Neoporteria B. & R., *The Cact.* 3:94, t.8, figs 103–108 (1922); Donald & Rowley, *Cact. GB* 28:54 (1966)

The broadened concept of *Neoporteria*, taking in *Neochilenia, Islaya, Horridocactus, Pyrrhocactus* and the less commonly seen nowadays generic names *Chileorebutia, Reicheocactus* and *Thelocephala* has gained in acceptance, although there is some reluctance on the part of commercial purveyors of seed and plants to lose the names completely. The answer for the discerning collector is perhaps to use the former generic, now subgeneric, name in brackets, to distinguish the different categories, which are clearly identifiable, e.g. *Neoporteria (Islaya) islayensis*,

or *Neoporteria (Neochilenia) dimorpha*.

Neoporteria in the narrow sense comprises very densely spined plants found in central and northern Chile, the spines obscuring the body and usually incurving to form an interlaced basketwork at the apex of the globular to short-columnar plants, through which the bicoloured flowers at the top push with difficulty. The petals are arranged so that an inner layer remain fairly close to the stigma and stamens, straight or slightly incurving, with the outer petals standing away from them and recurving; mostly the colours are varying shades of pink, often paler or yellow towards the base of the petals.

Neochilenias, from the western side of the Andes in Chile, have generally less dense spination, showing the dark pigmented plant bodies, and have pastel coloured, wide, funnel-shaped flowers, opening broadly, also coming from the centre growing point. Islayas, from southern Peru and northern Chile, are strongly spined in well defined, vertical ribs. Slow-growing, they form globular to short-columnar, small plants, with spiky petalled, yellow flowers from the centre.

170. *Neoporteria crispa*

171. *Neoporteria dubia*

172. *Neoporteria hankeana*

173. *Neoporteria maritima*

Horridocactus, from central and northern Chile on the west of the Andes mountains is less well defined, and Backeberg differentiates them from *Pyrrhocactus*, mainly by their flowers and fruit – sparsely woolly compared to quite densely woolly and/or bristly *Pyrrhocactus*.

Pyrrhocactus, as indicated, is not easily differentiated from *Horridocactus*, coming from east of the Andes in western Argentina. Species formerly allocated here are generally globular, later shortly columnar, slow growing, strongly spined, with usually yellow flowers. The combination of these genera makes even more sense when the synonymies, as shown in brackets for each species below, are looked at, with different views as to their placing being taken by different authorities.

Species named (with the first few letters of the former allegiances in brackets, except for *Neoporteria* in the narrow sense) are: *N. (Neoch)andreaeana*, *N. (Neoch/Pyrr)aricensis*, *N. (Neoch)aspillagai*, *N. (Neoch)atra*, *N. (Pyrr)backebergii*, *N. (Isl)bicolor*, *N. (Pyrr)bulbocalyx*, *N. (Neoch/Pyrr)calderana* (& fa. *gracilis*), *N. (Neoch)carneoflora*, *N. (Pyrr)catamarcensis*, *N. (Pyrr)chanariensis*, *N. (Neoch) chilensis* (& var. *albidiflora*, var. *chilensis* fa. *confinis*), *N. (Horr/Pyrr)choapensis*, *N. (Neoch/Pyrr)chorensis*, *N. clavata* (& var. *parviflora*, var. *procera*), *N. coimasensis* (& var. *robusta*), *N. (Pyrr)coliguayensis*, *N. (Neoch/Pyrr)confinis*, *N. (Pyrr)crispa*, *N. (Horr/Pyrr)curvispina* (& var. *aconcaguensis*, var. *aconcaguensis* fa. *orientalis*, var. *andicola*, var. *andicola* fa. *descendens*, var. *andicola* fa. *mollensis*, var. *carrizalensis*, var. *echinus*, var. *garaventai*, var. *geissei*, var. *geissei* fa. *albicans*, var. *heinrichiana*, var. *kesselringiana*, var. *kessel-*

174. *Neoporteria monte-amargensis*

175. *Neoporteria napina* var. *mitis*

176. *Neoporteria odieri*

ringiana fa. *subaequalis*, var. *lissocarpa*, var. *lissocarpa* fa. *gracilis*, var. *transitensis*, var. *vallenarensis*), N. (*Neoch*) *deherdtiana*, N. (*Neoch/Pyrr*)*dimorpha*, N. (*Pyrr*)*dubia*, N. (*Horr/Pyrr*)*engleri* (& var. *krausii*), N. (*Neoch*)*eriocephala* (& var. *glaucescens*), N. (*Horr/Neoch/Pyrr*)*eriosyzoides* (& var. *domeykoensis*), N. (*Neoch*)*esmeraldana*, N. (*Neoch/Thel*) *fankhauseri*, N. (*Isl*)*flavida*, N. (*Neoch/Pyrr*)*floccosa* (& var. *minor*), N. (*Neoch/Thel*)*fulva*, N. (*Neoch/Pyrr*)*fusca*, N. (*Neoch*)*hankeana* (& var. *minor*, var. *taltalensis*), N. (*Horr/Pyrr*)*horrida* (& var. *aconcaguensis*, var. *mutabilis*, var. *orientalis*, var. *robusta*), N. (*Neoch/Pyrr*)*huascensis*, N. (*Neoch/Pyrr*)*intermedia*, N. (*Neoch/Pyrr*)*iquiquensis*, N. (*Isl*)*islayensis* (& var. *copiapoides*, var. *copiapoides* fa. *chalaensis*, var. *copiapoides* fa. *pseudomollendensis*, var. *divaricatiflora*, var. *grandis*, var. *grandis* fa. *brevispina*, var. *islayensis* fa.

brevicylindrica, var. *islayensis* fa. *mollendensis*), N. (*Neoch*) *jussieui* (& var. *australis*, var. *forbeana*, var. *spinosior*), N. (*Pyr*)*krausei*, N. (*Neoch/Pyrr*)*kunzei*, N. *laniceps*, N. (*Pyrr*) *limariensis*, N. (*Isl*)*lindleyi* (& var. *curvispina*), N. (*Neoch/ Thel*)*longirapa*, N. (*Isl*)*maritima*, N. (*Horr/Pyrr*)*marksiana* (& var. *tunensis*), N. (*Neoch*)*mebbesii* (& var. *centrispina*), N. (*Pyrr*)*melanacantha*, N. (*Isl*)*minuscula*, N. (*Neoch*)*monte-amargensis*, N. (*Neoch/Thel*)*napina* (& var. *mitis*, var. *mitis* fa. *glabrescens*, var. *spinosior*, var. *spinosior* fa. *mebbesii*), N. (*Neoch*)*neofusca*, N. *nidus* (& var. *mitis*, var. *mitis* fa. *densi-spina*, var. *gerocephala*, var. *matancillana*), N. (*Thel*)*nuda*, N. (*Neoch/Pyrr*)*occulta*, N. (*Neoch*)*odieri*, N. (*Neoch*) *odoriflora*, N. (*Pyrr*)*pamaensis*, N. (*Neoch/Horr*) *paucicostata* (& var. *viridis*), N. (*Neoch/Pyrr*)*pilispina* (& fa. *pygmaea*), N. *planiceps*, N. (*Pyrr*)*platyacantha*,

177. *Neoporteria pilispina* fa. *pygmaea*

178. *Neoporteria reichii* var. *reichii* fa. *imitans*

179. *Neoporteria ritteri*

180. *Neoporteria rupicola*

N. polyrhaphis, N. (Horr/Pyrr)pulchella, N. (Neoch/Pyrr)re-condita, N. (Neoch)reichei (& var. reichei fa. aerocarpa, var. reichei fa. carneoflora, var. reichei fa. duripulpa, var. reichei fa. floribunda, var. reichei fa. imitans, var. reichei fa. lembckei, var. reichei fa. neoreichei, var. reichei fa. pseudoreichei, var. malleolata, var. malleolata fa. krausii, var. malleolata fa. solitaria), N. (Neoch/Pyrr)residua, N. (Neoch/Pyrr)ritteri, N. (Neoch/Pyrr/Horr)rupicola, N. (Neoch/Pyrr)sanjuanensis,

N. (Neoch/Pyrr)saxifraga, N. (Neoch/Pyrr/Horr)scoparia, N. (Neoch/Pyrr)setiflora, N. (Neoch/Pyrr)setosiflora (& var. intermedia), N. (Horr/Neoch/Pyrr)simulans, N. sociabilis, N. (Pyrr)strausiana, N. (Pyrr)subaiana, N. subgibbosa (& var. mammillarioides, var. microsperma, var. microsperma fa. serenana, var. nigrihorrida, var. nigrihorrida fa. major, var. nigrihorrida fa. minor, var. orientalis, var. subgibbosa fa. castanea, var. subgibbosa fa. castaneoides, var. *subgibbosa* fa. *heteracantha*, var. *subgibbosa* fa. *litoralis*, var. *subgibbosa* fa. *subcylindrica*, var. *subgibbosa* fa. *tunensis*), *N. (Neoch/Pyrr)taltalensis*, *N. (Neoch/Thel)tenebrica*, *N. (Pyrr)tenuis*, *N. (Neoch/Pyrr)totoralensis*, *N. (Pyrr)transiens*, *N. (Pyrr)trapichensis*, *N. (Pyrr)truncatipetala*, *N. (Horr/Pyrr)tuberisulcata*, (& var. *armata*, var. *atroviridis*, var. *cupreata*, var. *froehlichiana*, var. *nigricans*, var. *robusta*, var. *vegasana*), *N. (Pyrr)umadeave* (& var. *marayensis*, *N. (Isl)unguispina*, *N. (Horr)vallenarensis*, *N. (Pyrr)vexata*, *N. villosa* (& var. *atrispinosa*, var. *cephalophora*), *N. (Pyrr)volliana* (& var. *breviaristata*), *N. wagenknechtii*.

Rejected names and synonymies:

N. aconcaguensis = N. curvispina var. *aconcaguensis*
N. aerocarpa = N. reichei var. *reichei* fa. *aerocarpa*
N. andicola = N. curvispina var. *andicola*
N. armata = N. tuberisulcata var. *armata*
N. atrospinosa = N. backebergii
N. atroviridis = N. tuberisulcata var. *atroviridis*
N. carrizalensis = N. curvispina var. *carrizalensis*
N. castanea = N. subgibbosa var. *subgibbosa* fa. *castanea*
N. castaneoides = N. subgibbosa var. *subgibbosa* fa. *castaneoides*
N. cephalophora = N. villosa var. *cephalophora*
N. copiapoides = N. islayensis var. *copiapoides*
N. copiapoides var. *chalaensis = N. islayensis* var. *copiapoides* fa. *chalaensis*
N. copiapoides var. *pseudomollendensis = N. islayensis* var. *copiapoides* fa. *pseudomollendensis*
N. cupreata = N. tuberisulcata var. *cupreata*
N. curvispina var. *echinus* fa. *minor = N. floccosa* var. *minor*
N. curvispina var. *grandiflora = N. maritima*
N. divaricatiflora = N. islayensis var. *divaricatiflora*
N. duripulpa = N. reichei var. *reichei* fa. *duripulpa*
N. echinus = N. curvispina var. *echinus*
N. forbeana = N. jussieui var. *forbeana*
N. froehlichiana = N. tuberisulcata var. *froehlichiana*
N. garaventai = N. curvispina var. *garaventai*
N. geissei = N. curvispina var. *geissei*
N. gerocephala = N. nidus var. *gerocephala*
N. glaucescens = N. eriocephala var. *glaucescens*
N. gracilis = N. calderana fa. *gracilis*
N. grandiflora = N. maritima
N. grandis = N. islayensis var. *grandis*
N. heinrichiana = N. curvispina var. *heinrichiana*
N. heteracantha = N. subgibbosa var. *subgibbosa* fa. *heteracantha*
N. imitans = N. reichei var. *reichei* fa. *imitans*
N. islayensis fa. *spinosior = N. maritima*
N. kesselringiana = N. curvispina var. *kesselringiana*
N. kesselringiana var. *subaequalis = N. curvispina* var. *kesselringiana* fa. *subaequalis*
N. krausii = N. reichei var. *malleolata* fa. *krausei*

181. *Neoporteria tuberisulcata* var. *atroviridis*

182. *Neoporteria umadeave*

N. lembckei = N. reichei var. *reichei* fa. *lembckei*
N. lissocarpa = N. curvispina var. *lissocarpa*
N. litoralis = N. subgibbosa var. *subgibbosa* fa. *litoralis*
N. malleolata = N. reichei var. *malleolata*
N. malleolata var. *solitaria = N. reichei* var. *malleolata*
N. mammillarioides = N. subgibbosa var. *mammillarioides*
N. microsperma = N. subgibbosa var. *microsperma*
N. mitis = N. napina var. *mitis*
N. multicolor = N. nidus
N. nidus fa. *senilis = N. nidus* var. *gerocephala*
N. nigricans = N. tuberisulcata var. *nigricans*
N. nigrihorrida = N. subgibbosa var. *nigrihorrida*
N. nigriscoparia = N. crispa
N. paucispinosa = N. lindleyi
N. pseudoreichei = N. reichei var. *reichei* fa. *pseudoreichei*
N. pygmaea = N. pilispina fa. *pygmaea*
N. robusta = N. coimasensis var. *robusta*

N. *subcylindrica* = N. *subgibbosa* var. *subgibbosa* fa. *subcylindrica*
N. (*Horr*) *taltalensis* Ritter = N. *rupicola*
N. *transitensis* = N. *curvispina* var. *transitensis*
N. (*Neoch*)*wagenknechtii* = N. *ritteri*
N. *woutersiana* = N. *ritteri*.

Recommended species: N. *chilensis* has dense, yellow spines, quite unlike its fellow species in the former genus *Neochilenia*,but with the typical wide funnel-shaped flowers, white flushed pink.

N. *crispa* is noted for its dark, curling spines on purplish stems, with pale shell-pink, funnel-shaped flowers.

N. *dubia* is strongly-spined, with yellow flowers produced on the shoulders of the stems.

N. *hankeana* tends to be green stemmed, with strong, incurving brown to grey spines. Flowers are creamy white.

N. *islayensis* has short, strong spines and like all the former *Islaya* species is slow growing. Flowers are lemon yellow.

N. *maritima* is similar to the preceding species, but with more prominently tufted areoles and larger flowers.

N. *monte-amargensis*, although considered by Ritter to be probably a natural hybrid, is a charming tiny-bodied plant clustering from the base. The spines are short on brown stems, and it will flower at barely an inch (2·5 cm) wide, creamy yellow.

N. *napina* is well known as a slow growing, tuberous rooted species, with dark grey-brown stems, usually solitary, short black spines and off-white to cream-coloured flowers. An exception is N. *napina* var. *spinosior*, which has quite a lot longer spines, recurving on to the stem, and more colourful, pastel pink flowers.

N. *nidus* is one of the very densely-spined species, formerly *Neoporteria* in the narrow sense, the spines interlacing over the top of the plant to form a basketwork through which the bicoloured, pink and yellow flowers improbably push.

N. *odieri* will eventually make a low cluster of short-spined, brown stems, with white, funnel shaped, wide opening flowers.

N. *pilispina* is well-spined and flowers freely, with white, scented flowers.

N. *reichei* has closely set prominent areoles and short brown spines. The flowers on N. *reichei* var. *reichei* fa. *imitans* are a lovely combination of yellow inner and sooty-brown outer petals.

N. *ritteri* (syn. *Neochilenia wagenknechtii*) is another charm-

183. *Neoporteria villosa*

184. *Neowerdermannia vorwerkii*

ing, small growing plant of dark body colour with slender spines and pale yellow flowers.

N. rupicola has dark bodies, almost purple, with stiff, upcurving, grey and dark brown spines, and white to lilac-pink flowers.

N. tuberisulcata has strong, recurving, dark brown spines set in areoles slightly sunken in the tubercles, with pale yellowish white flowers.

N. umadeave has proved difficult in cultivation, and many imported plants have suffered a lingering death in collectors' glasshouses, defying attempts to get them rooted. Seedlings are available occasionally, and give a better chance of growing this symphony of dense, silvery-white and brown spines. Flowers are pale yellow.

N. villosa is well known for its long, almost hair-like khaki-brown spines, which intertwine, curling and twisting to form a dense covering to the plant body. Flowers are bicoloured, pink and white.

Connoisseur's choice: *N. chilensis, N. islayensis , N. napina* var. *spinosior, N. nidus.*

Neoraimondia B. & R., *The Cact.* 2:181, figs 257–260 (1920)

This is a genus of about four species, best seen growing in the wild, where it forms large branching shrubs or short-trunked tree-like candelabras of thick stems. The genus *Neocardenasia* is referred here.

Species named are:

N. arequipensis (& var. *gigantea*, var. *rhodantha*, var. *roseiflora*). *N. aticensis, N. herzogiana, N. peruviana.*

Synonymies of rejected species:

N. gigantea = *N. arequipensis* var. *gigantea*
N. macrostibus = *N. peruviana*
N. roseiflora = *N. arequipensis* var. *roseiflora.*

They are not recommended.

185. *Notocactus buenekeri*

Neowerdermannia Fric, *Kaktusar* 1:11, 85 (1930)

In spite of its relegation to *Gymnocalycium* by Backeberg, and recently also by Rowley, the individuality of this small genus from Peru and Chile has persisted, and it has retained its separate identity for the present. The handful of species, dubiously distinct from one another, are instantly separable from *Gymnocalycium* with their spine clusters seemingly sunk, perversely, in the axil, rather than as with most cacti at the tip of the tubercle. This is a *trompe l'oeil*, as close examination reveals that the 'tubercle' is in fact a humped formation on the rib, more exaggerated but similar to that found in some *Gymnocalycium* species. But the flower is very different in appearance, with shorter tubes, emanating invariably from the growing point and often coloured purple or white flushed purple, a colour seen only faint-heartedly in *Gymnocalycium*. They occur from northern Argentina to northern Bolivia, straying into Chile and southern Peru.

Species named are: *N. chilensis, N. peruviana, N. vorwerkii* (& var. *erectispina*, var. *gielsdorfiana*).

Recommended species: dubiously distinct, it is difficult to single out any, and any which become available are worth a try.

Connoisseur's choice: *N. peruviana.*

Nichelia Bullock, *Bull. Misc. Inf.*, 7:297 (1938)

This is the more correct name for the genus popularly known as *Neochilenia*, but both have been submerged beneath the broad concept of the genus *Neoporteria*.

Nopalea Salm-Dyck (1850)

Rarely used nowadays, and regarded as *Opuntia* species. See under *Opuntia*.

Nopalxochia B. &. R., *The Cact.* 4:204 (1923); Rowley, *Ashingtonia* 1(1):11 (1973)

The few species of this genus are often confused in collectors' minds with the many and varied hybrid 'Epiphyllums', which they superficially resemble. They have arching, leaf-like stems, usually less vigorous than their hybrid cousins, and produce freely the large, showy flowers. They come from Mexico.

Species named are: *N. ackermannii* (& var. *conzattianum*), (*N. conzattianum* = *N. ackermannii* var. *conzattianum*), *N. macdougalii, N. phyllanthoides.*

Recommended species: *N. phyllanthoides* is the most popular, and justifiably so, since its pale pink cup-and-saucer flowers are a joy to behold, the centre petals tending to stand more upright (the cup), the outer petals flattening out to lie at right angles to the inner ones (the saucer).

Connoisseur's choice: *N. phyllanthoides.*

Normanbokea Kladiwa & F. Buxbaum (1969)

Referred to *Strombocactus.*

Notocactus (Schum.) Backeb. & Knuth, *Kaktus ABC*:253 (1935); A.W. Mace, *Notocactus* (1975)

This is a deservedly popular genus of mostly modest-sized, globular or short columnar plants from Brazil, Paraguay, Uruguay and Argentina. There is considerable variation in form and spination, a few being densely spined but most less so. The prevalent colour of flowers is yellow, but species with red, purple, pink and orange flowers have become more available over the last several years. A broad view of the genus is taken herein, to include former genera *Brasilicactus, Eriocactus* and *Wigginsia*, but not, as has recently been suggested, *Parodia.*

Species named are: *N. acuatus, N. acutus, N. agnetae* (& var. *aureispinus*, var. *minor*), *N. alacriportanus, N. allosiphon, N. ampliocostatus, N. apricus, N. arachnites* (& var. *minor*), *N. arechavaletai* (& var. *alacriportanus*, var. *aureus*, var.

186. *Notocactus buiningii*

187. *Notocactus crassigibbus*

buenekeri, var. *horstii*, var. *limiticola*, var. *nanus*, var. *rubescens*), *N. beltranii*, *N. bezrucii* (& var. *centrispinus*, var. *corniger*), *N. bommeljei*, *N. brevihamatus* (& fa. *conjungens*, var. *mollispinus*), *N. buenekeri* (& fa. *conjungens*, var. *intermedius*), *N. buiningii*, *N. caespitosus*, *N. campestrensis*, *N. carambeiensis*, *N. catarinensis*, *N. claviceps*, *N. concinnus*, *N. corynodes*, *N. courantii*, *N. crassigibbus*, *N. cristatoides*, *N. curvispinus*, *N. elachisanthus*, *N. eremiticus*, *N. erubescens*, *N. erythracanthus*, *N. euvelenovskyi*, *N. ferrugineus*, *N. floricomus* (& var. *flavispinus*, var. *rubrispinus*, var. *spinosissimus*, var. *velenovskyi*), *N. fricii*, *N. fuscus* (& var. *longispinus*), *N. gibberulus*, *N. glaucinus* (& var. *depressus*, var. *gracilis*), *N. globularis*, *N. graessneri* (& var. *albisetis*, var. *flaviflorus*), *N. grossei* (& var. *aureispinus*), *N. harmonianus*, *N. haselbergii* (& var. *stellatus*), *N. herteri*, *N. horstii* (& var. *purpureiflorus*), *N. kovaricii*, *N. laetivirens*, *N. leninghausii* (& var. *longispinus*, var. *major*, var. *minor*, fa. *apelii*), *N. leprosorum*, *N. leucocarpus*, *N. linkii* (& fa. *multiflorus*, var. *buenekeri*, var. *guaibensis*), *N. longispinus*, *N. macrogonus*, *N. magnificus*, *N. mammulosus* (& var. *brasiliensis*), *N. megalanthus*, *N. megapotamicus* (& var. *alacriportanus*, var. *crucicentrus*, var. *horstii*, var. *vulgatus*), *N. minimus*, *N. muellermelchersii* (& var. *gracilispinus*), *N. mueller-moelleri*, *N. multicostatus*, *N. muricatus*, *N. neobuenekeri*, *N. neohorstii* (& var. *juvenaliformis*), *N. nigrispinus*, *N. orthacanthus*, *N. ottonis* (& var. *acutangularis*, var. *albispinus*, var. *arechavaletai*, var. *elegans*, var. *paraguayensis*, var. *schuldtii*, var. *stenogonus*, var. *tenuispinus*, var. *tortuosus*, var. *uruguayensis*, var. *vencluisianus*, var. *vila-velhensis*), *N. oxycostatus*, *N. pauciareolatus*, *N. paulus*, *N. permutatus*, *N. polyacanthus*, *N. prolifera*, *N. pseudoherteri*, *N. pulvinatus*, *N. purpureus*, *N. rauschii*, *N. rechensis*, *N. roseoluteus*, *N. rubricostatus*, *N. rubropedatus*, *N. rutilans* (& fa. *storianus*), *N. schlosseri*, *N. schumannianus*, *N. scopa* (& var. *albilanata*, var. *daenikerianus*, var. *glauserianus*, var. *ramosus*), *N. securituberculatus* (& var. *miniatispinus*), *N. sellowi* (& var. *macracanthus*, var. *turbinatus*, var. *vorwerkianus*), *N. sessiliflorus* (& var. *martinii*, var. *stegmannii*), *N. soldtianus*, *N. spinibarbis*, *N. stockingeri*, *N. submammulosus* (& var. *pampeanus*), *N. sucineus*, *N. tabularis*, *N. tarijensis*, *N. tenuicylindricus*, *N. uebelmannianus* (& var. *flaviflorus*), *N. vanvlietii* (& var. *gracilis*), *N. veenianus*, *N. vorwerkianus*, *N. warasii*, *N. werdermannianus*.

Rejected names and synonymies:

N. brasiliensis = *N. mammulosus* var. *brasiliensis*
N. erinaceus = *N. acuatus*
N. erinaceus sv. *courantii* = *N. courantii*
(*Wigginsia*) *horstii* = *N. neohorstii*
(*Wigginsia*) *horstii* var. *juvenaliformis* = *N. neohorstii* var. *juvenaliformis*

188. *Notocactus floricomus*

189. *Notocactus graessneri*

N. *langsdorfii* = N. *polyacanthus*
N. *macracanthus* = N. *sellowi* var. *macracanthus*
N. *ottonis* var. *brasiliensis* = N. *linkii.*
N. *ottonis* var. *multiflorus* = N. *linkii* fa. *multiflorus*
N. *pampeanus* = N. *submammulosus* var. *pampeanus*
N. *sellowi* var. *courantii* = N. *courantii*
N. *stegmannii* = N. *sessiliflorus* var. *stegmannii*
N. *tephracanthus* = N. *acuatus*
N. *turbinatus* = N. *sellowi* var. *turbinatus.*

Recommended species: N. *buiningii.* This is immediately distinguishable by its blue-grey body-colour, deep furrowed ribs, strong, outstanding yellow to yellow-brown spines and habit of being difficult to grow to any real size without going off its roots. It produces small yellow flowers with red stigma lobes prominent in the centre, as in many *Notocactus* species.

N. *crassigibbus* has one of the largest blooms in the genus, to 5 in (13 cm) wide or more when fully open, with the usual yellow, silky petals.

N. *herteri* is a challenge to grow well, but if its potential of a large, single-stemmed, 6–8 in (15–20 cm) wide, flat-globular plant can be achieved, it will produce its spiral of sumptuous, purple-red flowers and delight you. It has a tendency to brown up from the base of the stem in an unsightly manner, but encouraging rapid growth by frequent repotting and feeding in the early years seems to keep this at bay.

N. *horstii* has even more the bad habit of the last mentioned species in browning up from the base if grown too slowly, but is still worth growing for its unusually coloured orange flowers produced late in the season – in late summer or early-autumn.

N. *leninghausii* is well-known, with its thick-columnar habit, clustering later in life from the base, making for large, handsome show specimens if grown well for the ten or more years it takes to produce a 1 ft high (30 cm) plant in England. It is densely covered with fine, flexible, yellow spines and will usually oblige with its large, saucer-shaped, all-yellow flowers after it reaches about 6 in (15 cm) in height.

N. *magnificus* is appropriately named. With its blue-green body colour and neat ribs of straw-yellow, flexible, thin spines, freely produced large yellow flowers, and, above all, its facility for making magnificent, 1 ft wide (30 cm) clumps of globular stems, each about 6 in (15 cm) in diameter, it has everything going for it. The snag (isn't it always the way?) is that it has a tendency to form brown, unsightly marks on the body in the winter if the air is kept too cold and still.

190. *Notocactus haselbergii*

191. *Notocactus herteri*

192. *Notocactus horstii*

193. *Notocactus leprosorum*

194. *Notocactus ottonis* var. *tortuosus*

195. *Notocactus sucineus*

N. minimus has the smallest stems in diameter of the whole genus, no more than 2–3 cm wide, and getting to no more than about 4–5 in (10–12 cm) tall in time. The flowers are yellow, about an inch or so (3 cm) wide. It is difficult on its own roots, but not impossible with an open compost and careful watering, i.e. not too much so that it sits for any length of time with its roots damp and soggy. Grafting is recommended if you experience repeated failure to grow this species on its own roots.

N. scopa is an old favourite, with a mixture of white and red-brown spines, varying from plant to plant, but densely covering the elongated stem. The recently introduced variety, *N. scopa* var. *ramosus* makes a very handsome low growing cluster, with often more prevalent white spines.
N. uebelmannianus comes with either yellow or purple flowers, the latter much sought after and well worth obtaining. It will make a large, flat-globular stem about

113

5–6 in (15 cm) or more tall and wide in time, and the flowers are produced in abundance.

Connoisseur's choice: *N. magnificus, N. minimus, N. uebelmannianus.*

Nyctocereus (Bgr.) B. & R., *Contrib. U.S. Nat. Herb.* 12:423 (1909)

A small genus of slender, cylindrical, clambering cacti with nocturnal, white flowers, from Mexico, Guatemala and Nicaragua. The handful of species is of interest only to *Cereus* enthusiasts.

Species named are: *N. chontalensis, N. guatemalensis, N. hirschtianus, N. neumannii, N. oaxacensis, N. serpentinus* (& var. *ambiguus*, var. *pietatis*, var. *splendens*, var. *strictior*).

Recommended species: *N. serpentinus* is the most commonly seen in cultivation, and will flower at a reasonable size, about 2 ft (60 cm).

Obregonia Fric (1925)

Referred to *Strombocactus.*

Oehmea F. Buxb. (1951)

Referred to *Mammillaria*

Opuntia Mill., *Gard. Dict.,* abr. ed. 4 (1754); Benson, *Cacti of U.S. & Canada* 269–533 (1982)

This large genus of cacti contains, among others, the well-known, flat-padded, branching cacti which the layman most readily identifies as 'a cactus'. With its barbed spines it is also the cactus genus with which most collectors have been most intimately and painfully acquainted at one time or another. Popular with beginners and with a few die-hard masochistic collectors, this genus tends to lose favour with most because of its spiteful habits, its propensity to grow too large in most of its species for all but the very roomy glasshouses, and, in England, its reluctance to flower in all but a few species, and even in them with nowhere near the effort it puts into it in the wild.

Apart from the flat-padded species mentioned above, Opuntias come in a variety of shapes and sizes, which has given rise to the creation of several separate genera: *Cylindopuntia,* for the cylindrical-jointed, 'jumping chollas' of the southern United States and northern and central Mexico: *Austrocylindropuntia,* for similar species occurring further south in a wide area, including Ecuador, Peru,

196. *Nyctocereus serpentinus*

197. *Opuntia* cv. 'albata'

Chile, Bolivia and Argentina; *Corynopuntia,* for low-growing, globular or ovoid-jointed species, from southern United States and northern Mexico; *Micropuntia,* dubiously distinct from *Corynopuntia,* characterized by their thick roots; *Tephrocactus,* for the low-growing equivalent of *Corynopuntia* found in southern parts of South America, in Peru, Chile, Bolivia and Argentina. Other seldom seen genera include *Miqueliopuntia Quiabentia, Grusonia, Marenopuntia* and *Maihueniopsis.* The tendency in the taxonomy of the Cactaceae at present leans towards broader concepts of genera, and consequently all the aforementioned genera are treated here under the broad genus *Opuntia.* Gordon Rowley divides the genus into three subgenera along the lines indicated above, as follows:

subgenus *Opuntia* (syn. *Brasilopuntia, Grusonia, Consolea, Nopalea, Tacinga*) with more or less flat, disc-like, jointed, leaf-like stems;

subgenus *Cylindropuntia* '(syn. *Austrocylindropuntia, Corynopuntia, Micropuntia, Miqueliopuntia Maihueniopsis*) with cylindrical stems, varying from a few inches (3–5 cm) to foot long or more (30 cm plus). Although Rowley puts *Marenopuntia* with *Pterocactus,* Kiesling's view that it properly belongs here is followed herein.

subgenus *Tephrocactus,* low-growing, with globular, ovoid or short-cylindroid jointed stems.

Species named (divided into the three subgenera, for ease of reference) are as follows (for detailed account of North America species see Benson – ref. above):

subgenus *Opuntia* (including *Consolea, Nopalea, Tacinga, Platyopuntia, Brasilopuntia*) *O. abjecta, O. acaulis, O. aequatorialis, O. albisaetacens* (& var. *robustior*) *O. alko-tuna, O. allairei, O. anyclaea, O. anacantha, O. anahuacensis, O. angustata, O. antillana, O. apurimacensis, O. arechavaletai, O. arenaria, O. argentina, O. armata, O. arrastradillo, O. assumptionis, O. atrispina, O. atrocapensis, O. atropes, O. atro-virens, O. auberi, O. aulacothele, O. aurantiaca, O. azurea, O. bahamana, O. bahiensis, O. basilaris* (& var. *aurea,* var. *brachyclada,* var. *longiareolata,* var. *treleasei*), *O. beckeriana, O. bella, O. bensonii, O. bergeriana, O. bernichiana, O. bisetosa, O. bispinosa, O. boldinghii, O. bonaerensis, O. bonplandii, O. borinquensis, O. brachyacantha, O. brasilensis, O. bravoana, O. brittonii, O. brunneogemmia, O. brunnescens, O. calcicola, O. candelabriformis, O. cantabrigiensis, O. canterai, O. caracasana, O. cardiosperma, O. catingicola, O. chaffeyi, O. chakensis, O. chilensis, O. chlorotica, O. cochabambensis, O. cochenillifera, O. cognata, O. comonduensis, O. compressa* (& var. *ammophila,* var. *austrina*), *O. conjungens, O. coralicola, O. cordobensis, O. corrugata, O. covillei, O. crassa, O. cretochaeta, O. crystallina, O. cubensis, O. cumulicola, O. curassavica* (& var. *columbiana*), *O. curvospina, O. darrahiana, O. deamii, O. decumbens, O. dejecta, O. delaetiana, O. depauperata, O. depressa,*

198. *Opuntia articulata* var. *oligacantha*

O. discolor, O. distans, O. dobbieana, O. drummondii, O. dumetorum, O. durangensis, O. eburnispina, O. echios (& var. *barringtonensis,* var. *gigantea,* var. *inermis,* var. *zacana*), *O. eichlamii, O. ekmanii, O. elata, O. elatior, O. ellisiana, O. engelmannii* (& var. *discata*), *O. erinacea* (& var. *columbiana,* var. *hystricina,* var. *ursina,* var. *utahensis*), *O. escuintiensis, O. excelsa, O. falcata, O. feroacantha, O. ficus-indica, O. flavescens, O. fragilis* (& var. *brachyarthra,* var. *denudata,* var. *parviconspicua*), *O. fulginosa, O. fuscoatra, O. fusicaulis, O. galapageia* (& var. *brossetii,* var. *echios,* var. *gigantea,* var. *hamiltonii,* var. *helleri,* var. *insularis,* var. *macrocarpa,* var. *myriacantha,* var. *profusa,* var. *saxicola,* var. *zacana*), *O. gaumeri, O. glaucescens, O. grandiflora, O. grandis, O. grosseiana, O. guatemalensis, O. guilandii, O. hanburyana, O. heliae, O. helleri, O. hernandezii, O. hitchcockii, O. hoffmannii, O. hondurensis, O. horstii, O. howeyi, O. huajuapensis, O. humifusa* (& var. *ammophila,* var. *austrina*), *O. hyptiacantha, O. hystricina* (& var. *bensonii,* var. *nicholii,* var. *ursina*), *O. ianthinantha, O. imbricata* (& var. *argentea,* var. *cardenche,* var. *lloydii*), *O. impedata, O. inaequilateralis* (& var. *angustior*), *O. inamoena* (& var. *flaviflora,* fa. *spinigera*), *O. inaperta, O. infesta, O. insularis, O. interjecta, O. jaliscana, O. jamaicensis, O. karwinskiana, O. keyensis, O. kiska-loro, O. laetevirens, O. lagunae, O. lanceolata, O. lasiacantha, O. lata, O. leucotricha, O. lindheimeri* (& var. *chisosensis,* var. *cuija,* var. *lehmannii,* var. *linguiformis,* var. *tricolor*), *O. littoralis,* (& var. *austrocalifornica,* var. *martiniana,* var. *piercei,* var. *vaseyi*), *O. longispina* (& var. *agglomerata,* var. *brevispina,* var. *corrugata,* var. *flavidispina,* var. *intermedia*), *O. lubrica* (& var. *aurea*), *O. lutea, O. macateei, O. mac-*

115

dougaliana, O. mackensenii, O. macrantha, O. macrarthra, O. macrocalyx, O. macrorhiza (& var. *pottsii*)*, O. magnifica, O. maldonadensis, O. marnierana, O. matudae, O. maxima, O. maxonii, O. megacantha, O. megalantha, O. megapotamica, O. megarhiza, O. megasperma* (& var. *mesophytica,* var. *orientalis*)*, O. melanosperma, O. microdasys* (& var. *albispina,* var. *laevior,* var. *pallida,* var. *rufida,* var. *rufida* fa. *minima*)*, O. microdisca, O. mieckleyi, O. militaris, O. millspaughii, O. moniliformis, O. montevidensis, O. multiareolata, O. nana, O. nashii, O. nejapensis, O. nemoralis, O. neoargentina, O. nicholii, O. nigrispina, O. nitens, O. nuda, O. obliqua, O. ochrocentra, O. orbiculata, O. oricola, O. orurensis, O. pailana, O. palmadora, O. palmeri, O. panellana, O. paraguayensis, O. pascoensis, O. peckii, O. penicilligera, O. pennellii, O. pes-corvi, O. pestifer, O. phaeacantha* (& var. *camanchica,* var. *charlestonensis,* var. *discata,* var. *flavispina,* var. *laevis,* var. *major,* var. *mojavensis,* var. *spinosibacca,* var. *superbospina,* var. *wootonii*)*, O. picardoi, O. pilifera* (& var. *aurantisaeta*)*, O. pisciformis, O. pittieri, O. pituitosa, O. plumbea, O. poecilacantha, O. pollardii, O. polyacantha* (& var. *juniperina,* var. *rufispina,* var. *schweriniana,* var. *trichophora*)*, O. polyacarpa, O. prasina, O. procumbens, O. pubescens, O. pumila, O. pusilla, O. pycnantha* (& var. *margaritana*)*, O. pyriformis, O. pyrrhantha, O. quimilo, O. quipa, O. quitensis, O. rastrera, O. repens, O. retrorsa, O. retrospina, O. ritteri, O. riviereana, O. robinsonii, O. rohorensis, O. robusta* (& var. *guerrana,* var. *larreyi,* var. *longiglochidiata,* var. *maxima,* var. *viridior*)*, O. rubescens, O. rubiflora, O. rubrogemmia, O. rufida, O. salagria, O. salmiana, O. salvadorensis, O. sanguinea, O. santamaria, O. sarca, O. saxatilis, O. saxicola, O. scheerii, O. schickendantzii, O. schulzii, O. schumannii, O. securigera, O. soederstrominiana, O. soehrensii* (& var. *grandiflora,* var. *tilcarensis,* var. *transiens*)*, O. spinibarbis* (& var. *grandiflora*)*, O. spinosissima, O. spinulifera, O. stenarthra, O. stenochila, O. stenopetala, O. streptacantha, O. stricta* (& var. *dillenii*)*, O. strigil* (& var. *flexospina*)*, O. subsphaerocarpa, O. subulata* (& var. *exaltata*)*, O. sulphurea* (& var. *hildmannii,* var. *pampana*)*, O. tampona, O. tardospina, O. tayapayensis, O. taylorii, O. tehuantepecana, O. tenuiflora, O. thurberi* (& var. *alamosensis*)*, O. tilcarensis, O. tomentella, O. tomentosa* (& var. *herrerae,* var. *rileyi,* var. *spranguei*)*, O. tortispina* (& var. *cymochila*)*, O. tracyi, O. treleasii, O. triacantha, O. tuna, O. tuna-blanca, O. turbinata, O. turgida, O. undulata, O. urbaniana, O. utkilio, O. vaseyi, O. velutina* (& var. *affinis,* var. *macdougaliana*)*, O. violacea* (& var. *castetteri,* var. *gosseliana,* var. *macrocentra,* var. *santa-rita*)*, O. viridirubra, O. vitelliniflora, O. vulgaris, O. vulpina, O. wentiana, O. whipplei,* (& var. *multigeniculata*)*, O. whitneyana* (& var. *albiflora*)*, O. wilcoxii, O. woodsii, O. zebrina.*

Subgenus *Cylindropuntia* (including *Austrocylindropuntia, Corynopuntia, Grusonia, Maihueniopsis, Micropuntia, Miqueliopuntia,* and *Tephrocactus,* all to a greater or lesser extent, following in particular revisions recently brought about by Ritter in *Kakteen in Sudamerika*):

O. acanthocarpa (& var. *coloradensis,* var. *ganderi,* var. *major,* var. *thornberi*)*, agglomerata, O. alamosensis, O. albomarginata, O. alcahes, O. arbuscula. O. archiconoidea, O. atacamensis, O. barkleyana, O. bigelovii* (& var. *hoffmannii*)*, O. brachyrhopalica, O. bradleyi, O. bradtiana, O. brevispina, O. brittonii, O. bulbispina, O. burrageana, O. californica, O. calmalliana, O. camachoi, O. caribea, O. cholla, O. chuquisacana, O. cineracea, O. ciribe, O. clavarioides, O. clavata, O. clavellina, O. colorea, O. colubrina, O. conoidea, O. crassispina, O. cylindrica, O. darwinii, O. densiaculeata, O. domeykoensis, O. echinocarpa* (& var. *nuda,* var. *wolfii*)*, O. exaltata, O. floccosa, O. fulgida* (& var. *mamillata*)*, O. gracicylindrica, O. grandiflora, O. hualpanensis, O. hypogaea, O. hypsophila, O. imbricata* (& var. *argentea*)*, O. inarmata, O. intermedia, O. invicta, O. kelvinensis, O. kleiniae* (& var. *tetracantha*)*, O. lagopus* (& fa. *rauhii*)*, O. lauliacoana, O. leoncito, O. leptocaulis* (& var. *badia,* var. *brevispina,* var. *glauca,* var. *longispina,* var. *pluriseta,* var. *robustior,* var. *tenuispina,* var. *vaginata*)*, O. leptoclada, O. lloydii, O. machacana, O. malyana, O. mandragora, O. marenae, O. metuenda, O. miquelii, O. moelleri, O. molesta, O. molfinoi, O. molinensis, O. mortolensis, O. munzii, O. neuquensis, O. ovallei, O. pachypus, O. parryi* (& var. *serpentina*)*, O. planibulbispina, O. prolifera, O. pulchella, O. pygmaea, O. rahmeri, O. ramosissima, O. recondita* (& var. *perrita*)*, O. reflexispina, O. rosarica, O. rosea* (& var. *atrorosea*)*, O. santamaria, O. schottii* (& var. *grahamii*)*, O. shaferi* (& var. *humahuacana*)*, O. spinosior, O. stanlyi* (& var. *kunzei,* var. *parishii,* var. *peeblesiana*)*, O. steiniana, O. stellata, O. subulata, O. tarapacana, O. tephrocactoides, O. teres, O. tesajo, O. tetracantha, O. thurberi, O. tuberculosirhopalica, O. tunicata* (& var. *aricensis,* var. *chilensis,* var. *davisii*)*, O. verschaffeltii* (& var. *hyposhila,* var. *longispina*)*, O. versicolor, O. vestita, O. vilis, O. vivipara, O. wagenknechtii, O. whipplei* (& var. *multigeniculata,* var. *viridiflora*)*, O. wiegandii, O. wigginsii.*

Subgenus *Tephrocactus* (some species have been transferred by Ritter to subgenus *Opuntia* – the genus *Platyopuntia* according to Ritter –, others to *Cylindropuntia* – the genera *Austrocylindropuntia* and *Maihueniopsis* according to Ritter – see *Kakteen in Sudamerika* for details): *O. albiscoparia, O. alboareolata, O. alexanderi* (& var. *subsphaerica*)*, O. articulata* (& var. *oligacantha,* var. *ovata,* fa. *syringacantha*)*, O. asplundii, O. atroglobosa, O. australis, O. berteri, O. blancii, O. boliviana, O. bruchii, O. catacantha, O. chaffeyi, O. chichensis* (& var. *colchana*)*, O. crassicylindrica, O. curvispina, O. cylindrarticulata, O. dactylifera, O. echinacea, O. famatinensis, O. ferocior, O. flexispina, O. flexuosa, O. frigida, O. galerasensis, O. geometrica, O. glomerata, O. hegenbartiana, O. hickenii, O. hirschii, O. hypogaea* (& var. *rossiana*)*, O. hystrix, O. ignescens,*

O. ignota, O. kuehnrichiana, O. leonina, O. longiarticulata, O. melanacantha, O. microclada, O. microsphaerica, O. minor, O. minuscula (& var. silvestris), O. minuta, O. mistiensis, O. muelleriana, O. multiareolata, O. noodtiae, O. ovata (& fa. calva, fa. sterilis), O. paediophila, O. pampana, O. parviseta, O. pentlandii (& var. adpressa, var. colchana, var. dactylifera, var. fauxiana), O. platyacantha (& var. angustispina, var. deflexispina, var. monvillei, var. neoplatyacantha), O. pintacaillan, O. pyrrhacanthus (& var. leucoluteus), O. rarissima, O. rauppiana, O. rossiana, O. skottsbergii, O. strobiliformis, O. subinermis, O. subterranea, O. ticnamarensis, O. tortispina, O. tubercularis, O. tumida, O. unguispina (& var. major), O. virgulta, O. weberi (& var. dispar, var. setiger), O. wetmorei, O. wilkeanus, O. yanganucensis, O. zehnderi.

Rejected names and synonymies (a full list is not included here, but changes brought about in the last few years are included: South American *Opuntia* enthusiasts are recommended to study Ritter's *Kakteen in Sudamerika*; for North American Opuntias Benson's *Cacti in United States and Canada* is recommended):

O. aoracantha = O. ovata
O. articulata var. inermis = O. strobiliformis
O. atroviridis = O. floccosa
O. bicolor = O. kuehnrichiana
O. boliviensis = O. soehrensii
O. campestris = O. berteri
O. canina = O. retrorsa
O. cedergreniana = O. soehrensii
O. corotilla = O. berteri
O. crispicrinitus = O. floccosa
O. cylindrolanatus = O. floccosa
O. diademata = O. articulata fa. syringacantha
O. dimorpha & var. pseudorauppiana = O. berteri
O. erectocladoda = O. microdisca
O. floccosa var. cardenasii = O. malyana
O. fulvicoma var. bicolor = O. kuehnrichiana
O. haematacantha = O. verschaffeltii
O. heteromorpha = O. weberi
O. humahuacana = O. vestita
O. ipatiana = O. salmiana
O. leucophaea = O. berteri
O. macbridei & var. orbicularis = O. quitensis
O. mira = O. kuehnrichiana
O. papyracantha = O. articulata fa. syringacantha
O. pseudoudonis = O. floccosa
O. rauhii = O. lagopus fa. rauhii
O. reichiana = O. leoncito
O. russelii = O. ovata
O. shaferi = O. vestita

199. *Opuntia clavarioides*

200. *Opuntia clavata*

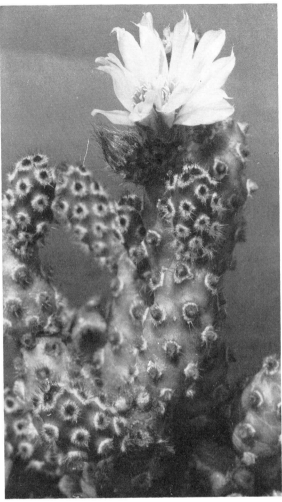

201. *Opuntia molinensis*

O. sphaerica = *O. berteri*
O. tilcarensis var. *rubellispina* = *O. soehrensii*
O. udonis = *O. floccosa*
O. variflora = *O. subterranea*
O. verticosa = *O. floccosa*.

Recommended species: subgenus *Opuntia*. Those chosen are selected for attractive colouring or spination coupled with a reasonably modest size, since this is a prime consideration for collectors in giving room to this subgenus of mostly large growing plants; flowering capabilities in England are modest, and a mature plant with a sunny position in the glasshouse is necessary to achieve this at all:

O. basilaris: the 'beaver-tail' Opuntia from south-western United States is a glorious plant in the wild, producing purple-grey flat pads, with virtually no spines, apart from the short glochids on the areoles. Each pad has an edge of bright, rose-pink flowers in the spring. In cultivation it maintains its low growth habit, rarely making more than two pads tall, before branching out at the sides, and the colouring of the bodies is also comparable to that in the wild. An occasional flower or two may be produced in a sunny glass house.

O. microdasys is a popular plant in any of its spine colour forms, from white to yellow to red-brown, but rarely flowers in cultivation, except for the form which has appeared in cultivation in the last few years, usually labelled Opuntia 'albata' or, painfully, Opuntia 'Angels Wings', distinguished by not only a lack of barbs on the glochids, which are attractively pure white and closer set than in the normal white spined form, but also by a more compact growth habit and a facility for flowering quite freely; the flowers are pale yellow.

O. picardoi is a low-growing, creeping species, with pads no more than an inch or so (2–3 cm) broad, obliquely shaped. It comes from northern Argentina, and is recommended, apart from its modest size, for occasionally obliging with yellow or red flowers, given good exposure to maximum sunlight available.

O. pycnantha is a very handsomely spined species, densely covered with pinkish-brown, 1 in long (2·5 cm) spines, later longer, on thick, disc-shaped pads about 6 in (15 cm) or so in diameter. It is slow growing, making a plant two feet or so (60 cm) tall in four or five years.

O. violacea, particularly *O. violacea* var. *santa-rita*, although eventually making a plant 2 ft (60 cm) tall and wide, is worth the space for its wonderfully coloured pads, greyish-violet, with contrasting blackish-brown spines in mature growth, one to each areole, an inch or more (2·5 cm) long. The yellow flowers with red throats are occasionally produced in cultivation as a bonus.

Subgenus *Cylindropuntia*. Many of this subgenus are unsuitable for glass house cultivation because of their propensity to grow long and leggy and attach themselves to anything or any part of your body which passes anywhere near them, becoming instantly detached and problematical to remove, so lovingly do the barbed spines attach themselves to your skin. Few match up to the spine growth in the wild, and fewer still will oblige with flowers – but there are a few worth space:

O. clavarioides is a spineless, most peculiarly shaped species, with two or three differently-shaped sorts of stems, some club-shaped, some with a thickened stem at the top where it is flattened to form a mushroom-like growth, branching normally and semi-dichotomously to form wide, low mats of stems no more than about 3–4 in (8–10 cm) tall. The stems are grey-brown with almost vestigial areoles and little sign of the most tiny spines. Flowers are frequently produced in cultivation, and are yellow.

O. clavata, principally from New Mexico, USA, is a low-growing, matforming species, barely more than one or two joints tall, running sideways and rooting as it goes, although running is hardly the word in cultivation, as it is extremely slow growing, making only one or two new joints on each stem each year. Its attraction is in its white, broad, dagger like spines, pointing downwards and thickly occurring on each close-spaced areole. Its yellow flowers are rarely seen in cultivation.

O. invicta is a similarly fiercely spined species from Baja California, Mexico, where it forms large, ever widening circles of low-growing (to a foot high – 30 cm) jointed stems, each joint about 3–4 in (8–10 cm) long and $1\frac{1}{2}$ in (4 cm) wide, with grey spines, red in the new growth. The wild plants are like circles of barbed wire, serving as such for the small animals which build their nests (carefully I suspect) in the midst of their dead stems. They are fairly slow growing in cultivation, making one or two of the wonderfully colourful new joints on each stem every year, but rarely producing their yellow flowers.

O. molinensis is a touchy species to grow, a few years' success often dashed by a sudden, apparently whimsical, dropping of the painfully slowly produced joints. It will not be hurried in producing its almost globular, $\frac{1}{2}$–$\frac{3}{4}$ in (1–2 cm) long stems with bright ginger-brown tufts of tiny harpoon-like glochids, which, in spite of their potential penetration of your person, are its main attraction, since the flower, when rarely produced, is a disappointing, nondescript, washed out pale pink. Less difficulties are found with grafted plants.

O. pachypus is one of the most sought for species, making a thick, slow column, about $1\frac{1}{4}$ in (3 cm) thick, and a foot (30 cm) or more tall, with short, creamy yellow-brown spines quite densely covering the stem. It is rarely seen branching, or flowering, although it will sometimes produce the odd bloom at the apex of the stem in a good sunny position. The cristate form is very attractive too, although for preference it should be grown on a graft, since it is inclined to push itself out of the soil if grown on its own roots. Grafting Opuntias is a dangerous, painful pastime undertaken only for very good friends or by devoted-to-the-hobby nurserymen.

O. tesajo is a late recommendation, from seeing this species growing in Baja California, Mexico, where it makes a low, spreading shrub about 1 ft (30 cm) or two wide by a little less tall, consisting of narrow, pencil-thick stems, nicely marked, grey-green, and with long barbed spines to about $1\frac{1}{2}$ in (4 cm), yellow brown in the young growth, later blackish-brown. The flowers are a lovely pale, primrose

202. *Opuntia picardoi*

203. *Opuntia strobiliformis*

204. *Opuntia tesajo*, in habitat, northern Baja California, Mexico

205. *Opuntia violacea* var. *santa-rita*, in habitat, Texas, USA

yellow. It is worth a try in cultivation.

Subgenus *Tephrocactus:* some species formerly placed in *Tephrocactus* have been transferred by Ritter via *Platyopuntia* to the subgenus *Opuntia* and via *Maihueniopsis* and *Cumulopuntia* to the subgenus *Cylindropuntia*; this is not entirely unexpected, as for too long any Opuntia-like plant from the south which formed small mounds was regarded as *Tephrocactus*, without consideration for its more pertinent flower characteristics, and doubts as to their placing had already been voiced, cf. Iliff and Leighton-Boyce, *Tephrocactus* (1973), page 44. The remainder have many devotees, as they are accommodating, small growing species, making attractive low mounds of many globular to ovoid stems, with sometimes wonderfully protective well developed spines.

Tephrocactus has more than its fair share of unnamed plants in cultivation too, defying naming, and often without any information as to their origins: *O. articulata*, particularly *O. articulata* var. *oligacantha*, is one of the well known group of papery spined Opuntias with very lightly attached joints. It makes a branching shrub of ovoid joints, each about an inch (2·5 cm) or so long, and half as wide, with brown to almost black papery spines, and, fairly regularly produced shining white flowers with prominent yellow stamens. *O. mistiensis* is typical of this subgenus,

in its slow growth, and low growing habit, making a small hand sized clump of ovoid stems in several years, a light grey-green in colour, with yellow glochids and short spines, becoming much more dense on the areoles in older growth. *O. ovata* (syn. *O. russellii*) is a popular, small, low-growing species clumping heavily with egg-shaped joints, the narrow end uppermost, bearing long, thin, white spines, and occasionally yellow flowers.

O. strobiliformis makes a short shrub, with several branches and loosely attached joints, almost globular to short rounded oblong in shape, grey and with wrinkles, hence the name, meaning 'like a pine cone'. It has no spines, and I have not heard of it flowering in cultivation. *O. subterranea*, as its name implies, has much of its growth underground, with a large rootstock, from which the green, gherkin-shaped stems arise, curiously almost spineless at their apex, with more spines in tufts in the lower parts. An occasional flower may be won in cultivation, which is a large, saucer shape, opening widely, pale pink with cream lower parts to the petals.

Oreocereus (Bgr.) Riccobono (1909)

There has been a fair amount of resistance to the sinking

120

206. Pachycereus pringlei, in habitat, Northern Baja California, Mexico, top of flowering stem

O. borchersii var. *fuscata* = O. borchersii
O. laxiareolata = O. peruviana
O. laxiareolata var. *pluricentralis* = O. peruviana var. *pluricentralis*
O. neoperuviana & vars. = O. peruviana
O. subocculta & vars. = O. peruviana.

Recommended species and connoisseur's choice:
There is little to choose between them, but *O. peruviana* seems more ready to oblige with flowers and grows strongly.

Ortegocactus Alexander (1971)

Referred to *Escobaria.*

Pachycereus (Bgr.) B. & R., *Contrib. US. Nat. Herb.* 12:420 (1909)

This is a genus of generally large, tree-like plants, including some of the largest growing of all cacti, coming from Mexico, in Baja California and widespread in mainland Mexico.

They are of interest primarily to *Cereus* enthusiasts, since their appeal is largely as magnificent plants in the wild, but young plants of *P. pringlei* in particular make thick, spiny, handsome columns, although they are painfully slow to get to more than a few feet tall (1 m or so).

Species named are: *P. calvus, P. gigas, P. grandis, P. marginatus* (& var. *gemmatus,* var. *oaxacensis*) *P. orcuttii, P. pecten-aboriginum, P. pringlei, P. weberi.*

Recommended species: *P. marginatus, P. pringlei.*

Parodia Speg., *Ann. Soc. Cient. Argent.* 96:70 (1923)

This is a popular genus of small, mainly globular cacti, solitary or clustering, with usually dense spines, straight or often hooked, flowering profusely at the apex with red, orange or yellow flowers and all shades between. They are in the main shallow rooted, and should not at any time be potted in a pot deeper than is needed to accommodate the roots comfortably – half pots or pans are to be preferred. They come from a wide area including Brazil, Paraguay, Bolivia and Argentina.

There has been a proliferation of names in the last few years, not by any means all soundly based it seems, and the task of rationalizing them for anyone planning a handbook or monograph on the genus is now monumental. Ritter's views on some of these recent names as expressed in volume 2 of his *Kakteen in Sudamerika* (1980) are followed herein.

Species named are: *P. albofuscata, P. argerichiana, P. atroviridis, P. aureicentra* (& var. *albifusca,* var. *omniaurea*), *P.*

of this genus beneath *Borzicactus,* but there is no more reason to retain it separately than for any other of those genera making up the broad concept of this latter genus, except its woolly covering, which has tended to make it a favourite among collectors. Referred to *Borzicactus.*

Oroya B. & R., *The Cact.* 3:102 (1922)

This comparatively small genus of globular cacti from Peru is not as widely grown as might be, maybe because they are somewhat sparing in flower production in all but the sunniest spots in England. Seed and seedlings have been readily available in recent years and plants grow lustily to about 3–4 in (8–10 cm) wide usually before flowers may be expected, increasing in size to about 8–9 in (20 cm) over the years and in the right situation, forming large clusters to about 15 in (50 cm) or more across. Ritter recently rationalized the many names which have appeared over the last several years, and reduced them to three species.

Species named are: *O. borchersii, O. gibbosa, O. peruviana* (& var. *pluricentralis*).

Rejected names and synonymies:
O. baumannii & vars. = O. peruviana var. *pluricentralis*

aureispina (& var. *australis*, var. *elegans*, var. *rubriflora*, var. *scopaoides*, var. *vulgaris*), P. *ayopayana* (& var. *elata*), P. *backebergiana*, P. *bellavistana*, P. *belliata*, P. *bermejoensis*, P. *betaniana*, P. *bilbaoensis*, P. *borealis*, P. *brasiliensis*, P. *camargensis* (& var. *camblayana*, var. *prolifera*), P. *capillitaensis*, P. *carapariana*, P. *cardenasii*, P. *carminata*, P. *carrerana*, P. *castanea*, P. *catamarcensis* (& var. *rubriflorens*), P. *chaetocarpa*, P. *challamarcana*, P. *chirimoyarana*, P. *chlororocarpa*, P. *chrysacanthion*, P. *cintiensis*, P. *columnaris* (& var. *ochraceiflora*), P. *comarapana* (& var. *paucicostata*), P. *commutans*, P. *comosa*, P. *compressa*, P. *cotacajensis*, P. *culpinensis*, P. *dextrohamata* (& var. *stenopetala*), P. *dichroacantha*, P. *echinus*, P. *elachiseta*, P. *elegans*, P. *escayachensis*, P. *exquisita*, P. *faustiana* (& var. *tenuispina*), P. *fechseri*, P. *firmissima*, P. *formosa*, P. *friciana*, P. *fulvispina* (& var. *brevihamata*), P. *fuscato-viridis*, P. *gibbulosa*, P. *glischrocarpa*, P. *gokrauseana*, P. *gracilis*, P. *gutekunstiana*, P. *haageana*, P. *hausteiniana*, P. *herzogii*, P. *horrida*, P. *hummeliana*, P. *idiosa*, P. *juyjuyana*, P. *kilianana*, P. *koehresiana*, P. *krasuckiana*, P. *laui*, P. *lohaniana*, P. *maassii* (& var. *albescens*, var. *carminatiflora*, var. *intermedia*, var. *rectispina*, var. *shaferi*), P. *maceduosa*, P. *mairanana* (& var. *atra*), P. *malyana* (& var. *igneuiflora*, var. *rubriflora*, & fa. *citriflora*), P. *matthesiana*, P. *maxima*, P. *mercedesiana*, P. *mesembrina*, P. *microsperma* (& var. *aurantiaca*, var. *cafayatensis*, var. *erythrantha*, var. *macrancistra*, var. *microthele*, var. *rubriflora*), P. *miguellensis*, P. *minima*, P. *minuta*, P. *miranda*, P. *muhrii*, P. *multicostata*, P. *mutabilis* (& var. *carneospina*, var. *elegans*, var. *ferruginosa*), P. *neglecta*, P. *nivosa* (& var. *cruci-albicentra*), P. *obtusa* (& var. *atochana*), P. *ocampoi*, P. *occulta*, P. *otaviana*, P. *otuyensis*, P. *pachysa*, P. *paraguayensis*, P. *penicillata* (& var. *fulviceps*, var. *nivosa*), P. *perplexa*, P. *piltziorum*, P. *pluricentralis*, P. *procera*, P. *pseudoayopayana*, P. *pseudostuemeri*, P. *pseudosubterranea*, P. *punae*, P. *purpureo-aurea*, P. *pusilla*, P. *quechua*, P. *rigida*, P. *rigidispina*, P. *ritteri*, P. *roseoalba* (& var. *australis*), P. *rostrumsperma*, P. *rubida*, P. *rubristaminea*, P. *salmonea* (& var. *carminata*), P. *saintpieana*, P. *sanagasta* (& var. *viridior*), P. *sanguiniflora* (& var. *comata*, var. *violacea*), P. *schuetziana*, P. *schwebsiana* (& var. *applanata*, var. *salmonea*), P. *scoparia*, P. *setifera* (& var. *longihamata*), P. *setispina*, P. *setosa*, P. *sotomayorensis*, P. *spanisa*, P. *spegazziniana*, P. *splendens*, P. *stereospina*, P. *stuemeri* (& var. *robustior*), P. *subterranea*, P. *subtilihamata*, P. *superba*, P. *suprema*, P. *tafiensis*, P. *tarabucina*, P. *taratensis*, P. *thionantha*, P. *tilcarensis*, P. *tredecimcostata* (& var. *aurea*, var. *minor*), P. *tuberculata*, P. *tuberculosicostata*, P. *uebelmanniana*, P. *variicolor* (& var. *robustispina*), P. *weberiana*, P. *weskampiana*, P. *yamparaezi*, P. *zaletaewana*, P. *zecheri*.

Rejected names and synonymies:

P. *aglaisma* = P. *subtilihamata*
P. *alacriportana* = *Notocactus alacriportanus*
P. *andreae* = P. *subtilihamata*
P. *andreaeoides* = P. *subtilihamata*
P. *aureicentra* var. *lateritia* = P. *aureicentra* var. *aureicentra*

207. *Parodia camargensis* var. *camblayana*

P. *aureispina* var. *rubriflora* = P. *microsperma* var. *rubriflora*
P. *brevihamata* = *Notocactus brevihamatus*
P. *camblayana* & fa. *rubra* = P. *camargensis* var. *camblayana*
P. *erythrantha* = P. *microsperma* var. *erythrantha*
P. *gibbulosoides* = P. *gibbulosa*
P. *gummifera* = *Uebelmannia gummifera*
P. *ignorata* = P. *sotomayorensis*
P. *lamprospina* = P. *maassii* var. *albescens*
P. *maasii* var. *camargensis* = P. *camargensis*
P. *maassii* var. *commutans* = P. *commutans*
P. *maassii* var. *commutans* fa. *maxima* = P. *maxima*
P. *maassii* var. *rubida* = P. *rubida*
P. *maassii* var. *subterranea* = P. *subterranea*
P. *maassii* var. *suprema* = P. *suprema*
P. *microthele* = P. *microsperma* var. *microthele*
P. *mutabilis* var. *sanguiniflora* = P. *sanguiniflora*
P. *neglectoides* = P. *comarapana* var. *paucicostata*
P. *pseudoprocera* = P. *procera*
P. *rauschii* = P. *aureicentra* var. *omniaurea*
P. *ritteri* var. *cintiensis* = P. *cintiensis*
P. *rubellihamata* = P. *uebelmanniana*
P. *rubellihamata* var. *chlorocarpa* = P. *chlorocarpa*
P. *rubricentra* = P. *stuemeri*
P. *rubriflora* = P. *aureispina* var. *rubriflora*
P. *rubrispina* = P. *stuemeri*

208. *Parodia maassii*

209. *Parodia malyana*

P. scopaoides = P. aureispina var. *scopaoides*
P. uhligiana = P. aureicentra var. *albifusca*.

For *Parodia* enthusiasts seed of many of the more newly described species has been available from commercial sources in recent years, and is worth the extra effort needed to raise successfully. In particular many of the seedlings of *Parodia* species are tiny compared with other cactus genera, and need to be left under cover for longer, perhaps a year or so, before being pricked out.

Recommended species: P. aureispina is usually solitary, globular becoming short columnar. It has prominent rows of white woolled areoles accentuated by short white radial spines and densely covered with short hooked central spines varying from honey-yellow to reddish-brown. The bright yellow to orange flowers are readily and abundantly produced in a jostling bunch at the top of the plant in spring or early summer. It comes from Salta, Argentina.

P. camargensis, from South Cinti, Bolivia, is a strong spined, tall growing species. P. camargensis var. *camblayana* is perhaps better known, and has orange-brown spines and orange flowers.

P. chrysacanthion, from Jujuy in northern Argentina, is well known for its very closely set, pale yellow spines,

like glass splinters. Its yellow flowers are somewhat lost in effect because of their similar colour, yellow.

P. hausteiniana, from Mizque, Bolivia, is a quite small stemmed species (to 5 cm/2 in) wide, with hooked, yellow spines and yellowish-orange flowers.

P. maassii is a large, robust, strongly growing species from southern Bolivia and northern Argentina, with long, hooked, central spines and orange to red flowers. Several similar species have been reduced beneath it at one time or another, but Ritter, with his extensive field knowledge which commands respect, disputes the amalgamation of some of them.

P. mairanana from Bolivia, Florida province, is a popular, clustering species making magnificent, low clusters. It has dark brown hooked spines and burnt orange flowers.

P. malyana from Catamarca, Argentina, is another small species to about 2 in (5 cm) wide, densely covered with white radial spines and wool, with brownish-red centrals, and orange to red flowers.

P. nivosa, from Salta, Argentina is the whitest spined species of Parodia, the glassy, straight, dense spines set amongst thick white wool. The intensely bright red flowers make a striking contrast.

P. penicillata has either yellow or white spines in thick tufts like paintbrushes (the meaning of the specific name)

210. *Parodia penicillata*

211. *Parodia ritteri*

212. *Parodia sanguiniflora*

213. *Parodia schwebsiana*

sprouting from each areole. It makes large, globular stems to 5–6 in (15 cm) wide and to a foot (30 cm) tall or more, often clustering. Flowers are red.

P. ritteri from Tarija, Bolivia, is solitary, to a foot (30 cm) tall or more, and about 4 in (10 cm) wide, with delicate pink and white colouring, most distinctive. Flowers are red.

P. schwebsiana from Bolivia, near Cochabamba, is popular for its dense wool formed in the growing area at the apex, through which the yellowish-brown, hooked spines project, accompanied in the spring by deep red flowers.

P. subterranea, from South Cinti, Bolivia, is a delightful combination of colours, with thick white wool in the growing area at the apex, black hooked central spines,

and deep red flowers.

P. yamparaezi, from Bolivia, in Chuquisaca, near Yampa-raez, is a solitary stemmed species, growing to about 4 in (10 cm) or more tall, and half as broad again, with spiralling ribs of white to brownish spines. Flowers are blood red.

Connoisseur's choice: *P. chrysacanthion, P. nivosa.*

Pediocactus B. & R. in Britton & Brown, *Ill. Fl.* ed. 2, 2:569 (1913) Benson, *Cact. Amer.* 33:49 (1961); l.c.34:17, 57, 163 (1962); Arp, l.c.44:218 (1972); Heil, Armstrong & Schleser, l.c.53:17 (1981)

The concept of *Pediocactus* has been broadened in the last few years to include other, equally difficult to cultivate species from southern United States, formerly placed in monotypic genera, viz. *Utahia sileri, Navajoa peeblesiana* and *Toumeya papyracantha*, although the inclusion of the last named is still somewhat disputed. *Sclerocactus* was also included by Gerald Arp in 1972, but opinion has swung away from its inclusion, and it is here included with *Thelocactus. Toumeya* is regarded separately.

The species of *Pediocactus* are among the most difficult to cultivate successfully in England, or almost anywhere I gather, unless you live in New Mexico and surrounds. They come from well drained alkaline soils, at generally a high altitude, varying from species to species and ranging from about 3000 feet (900 m) to over 11,000 feet (3300 m)

214. *Pediocactus bradyi*

in Utah, Nevada, Colorado, northern Arizona, northern New Mexico and Wyoming. The authors of the 1981 study of this genus (see last ref. above) advocate grafting these plants, which 'are prone to rotting from the roots up ... come from areas of low rainfall, extreme summer heat and low humidity ... are subjected to severe winter cold – to $-34°$ c ($-30°$ F).' In England cultivation of some species in gritty soils, with a nervous hand on the watering can has given good results, but they are all (especially *P. sileri*) exceptionally prone to rot at the least excuse. This is not surprising in view of the disparity between their natural habitat and an English climate, which differs in almost every respect. Fortunately they can be grown successfully on grafts, provided that the stock is treated 'hard' in terms of an open, gritty soil and sparing watering, to encourage slow growth and flowering; if treated too well the grafted scion will elongate, cluster unduly prolifically and rarely flower.

Species named are: *P. bradyi, P. despainii, P. knowltonii, P. paradinei, P. peeblesianus* (& var. *fickeiseniae*), *P. sileri, P. simpsonii* (& var. *minor,* var. *robustior*), *P. winkleri.*

Recommended species (all of them): *P. bradyi* grows in limestone ridges in flaky limestone near the Marble Canyon overlooking the Colorado river. It is generally solitary in habitat and in cultivation unless grafted, with

Pediocactus

215. *Pediocactus paradinei*

216. *Pediocactus peeblesianus* var. *fickeisenii*

217. *Pediocactus winkleri*

stems no more than about 1½ in (4 cm) wide and the same or a little taller, with yellow or white, woolly areoles, and with only radial, pectinate spines, usually from 13 to 16 in number. Flowers are whitish-yellow, about ¾ in (1·5 cm) wide.

P. despainii, only recently described (in 1980) comes from grassy hills where it grows in rocky slopes on the edges of a juniper forest in high parts of the Navajoan desert in south-eastern Utah, at about 6000 feet altitude. The stems are usually solitary, more or less globular, up to 2 in or so (6 cm) tall and to about 4 in (9·5 cm) wide in the wild. Spines are all radial, nine to 13 or occasionally up to 15, radiating evenly, white and slender. Flowers are up to 2·5 cm long and wide, 'yellow bronze to peach bronze'.

P. knowltonii has been available in cultivation for some time, and is often seen as a grafted, prolifically clustering plant. Like the other species in this genus it can with care be grown on its own roots, when it will stay solitary for some time, clustering sparingly later. It is notable for its creamy yellow, woolly areoles, with from 18 to 26 tiny radial spines coloured white, pink or red-brown, the clusters not overlapping and so not obscuring the body from view. Flowers, not readily forthcoming, but not unknown in England, are up to nearly 1½ in (3·5 cm) long and to an inch (2·5 cm) wide, pink to yellowish pink. It comes from the Colorado and New Mexico border in a very restricted area on the banks of the Los Pinos river near La Boca, at nearly 7000 feet altitude, among Pinyon-Juniper woodland and sagebrush, flat areas.

P. paradinei is not a common plant yet in cultivation, although it was first described nearly 30 years ago. Like its fellow species it is not easy to grow on its own roots, and grafting is a better proposition, perhaps trying to root and grow on its own roots an occasional offset, to see if you can succeed where most fail. It comes from the extreme north of Arizona, USA, in Houserock Valley, Coconino County, where it grows in gravelly limestone soil on south facing slopes, at 1500 to 2100 m (5,000 to 7000 feet) altitude. It is reported to grow up to about 3 in (8 cm) wide, and about the same tall, shrinking beneath the ground, as many species of this genus do, in the winter, forming small clumps of stems. It is characterized by hair-like whitish spines, to over 2 in (3 cm) long, increasing in density with age. Flowers are light yellow to pink.

P. peeblesianus, still often known affectionately as *Navajoa peeblesiana*, is another extremely difficult species to grow on its own roots, and it is seldom seen in cultivation except as a grafted plant. As such, with not too much good living, it will stay a reasonable size and produce its curving, spongy, creamy white, flexible spines, four to eight in number, one centrally placed, from a few millimetres long to about 2 cm (¾ in). Flowers are cream, yellow or yellowish-green.

P. peeblesianus var. *fickeiseniae* grows a little larger, and has usually a central spine, and more than the usual four radial spines of the type, more raggedly arranged. It comes from ledges above the Colorado River in the Grand Canyon area.

P. sileri is very rarely seen grown successfully in cultivation except as a grafted plant, and even then not commonly. This emphasizes the difficulty of growing what is a highly adapted plant to harsh conditions in the wild, where it is successful to the point of being abundant. It occurs in Arizona, near Fredonia, on hard packed, white gypsum soils, and nearby on surrounding red sandstone based soils, with pH of 7·8. It gets quite large in the wild, 2–6 in (5–15 cm) or more tall, and to 4 in (11 cm) or so wide, usually slightly taller than wide, not shrinking into the soil in the dry periods. It is densely covered with white radial spines and dark brown to black central spines, becoming grey with age and fraying at the base of the stem in the manner of some *Coryphantha* and *Thelocactus* species. Flowers are yellow to greenish yellow. It is becoming increasingly rare in cultivation since raising it from seed is very difficult, and its wild occurrence is both within an Indian reservation and is in any case now protected by US legislation for the protection of endangered species.

P. simpsonii and varieties present the difficulty in cultivation that accompanies high mountain plants, since it comes from high mountain areas in central Colorado and New Mexico, and south-eastern Wyoming, where temperatures often fall below freezing. A plant of this species has been growing (or rather, surviving) in the Alpine House at Kew for some years now, along with other high mountain plants enduring such temperatures well. It does not seem so difficult on its own roots as some species, and will make quite a large plant in a few years, to 3–4 in (to 10 cm) or more wide and tall, occasionally forming large clusters in the wild. It is finely spined, the radials white, centrals usually red-brown, densely covering the stem, with thick wool in the growing area at the apex, from which the variably coloured flowers, white, pink, magenta, yellow or yellowish-green, emerge. The varieties differ mainly in being more elongate and branched (var. *robustior*), or consistently smaller (var. *minor*).

P. winkleri was described only in 1979, and has not become commonly available as yet, although propagation by way of grafting is under way. It is known only from a restricted locality in Wayne County, south-eastern Utah, on south facing hills in the Navajoan desert, at about 1500 m (5000 ft) altitude. It is a neatly spined globular species, to nearly 3 in (7 cm) tall and 2 in (5 cm) wide, usually solitary, occasionally found in small clusters. The spines are short, all radial, mostly 9–11 in number, $\frac{1}{16}$–$\frac{3}{16}$ in (1·5–4 mm) long, white with a prominent white areole. Flowers are peach to pink. In the wild, temperatures range from 40° c (105° F) in the summer down to as low as −34° c (−30° F) in the winter, when of course, like other species, this one has shrunk below the soil for protection. Difficult terrain to match up to in cultivation, but the plant seems to be tolerant of our conditions.

Connoisseur's choice: P. bradyi, P. knowltonii, P. paradinei, P. winkleri.

Pelecyphora Ehrenb., *Bot. Zeit.* 1:737 (1843)

Although in the past a few other species have been referred to this genus, it is now generally accepted to consist of just two, slow-growing species from San Luis Potosi, Mexico. They are both in the top drawer of cacti, being slow growing, difficult to cultivate successfully unless they are given time to grow at their own very slow rate, and are almost impossible to raise from seed, although they are occasionally seen offered as seedlings from very clever growers.

Species named are: P. asselliformis, P. strobiliformis.

Rejected names and synonymies:

P. pseudopectinata = Strombocactus pseudopectinatus
P. valdeziana = Strombocactus valdezianus.

Recommended species:

P. asselliformis has unique tubercles for cacti, highly adapted, and looking just like inverted wood-lice (pill bugs). The body-colour is grey-green, and there are no spines, the peculiar tubercles with a hard surface effectively screening the body of the plant from the sun in the way that spines do in most cacti. Individual stems get to about $1\frac{1}{2}$ in (4 cm) tall and wide, and it is some years before the single stem of a seedling will cluster to form a small, hand-sized clump. Flowers are purple-pink, produced in succession over a period of several weeks, from the centre growing point. P. strobiliformis (syn. *Encephalocarpus strobiliformis*) is named for its resemblance to a pine-cone, with overlapping, triangular tubercles clothing the outside of the globular to short columnar stem, each with tiny, wispy spines at its tip. It is very slow growing, producing its purple-pink flowers when very young, at only an inch or so (2·5 cm) wide.

Connoisseur's choice: P. asselliformis, P. strobiliformis.

Peniocereus (Bgr.) B. & R., *Contrib. US. Nat. Herb.* 12:428 (1909); Sanchez-Mejorada, *Cact.y Suc. Mex.* 18:13 (1973); & 19(2):37 (1974); Bravo-Hollis, *Las Cactaceas de Mexico* (ed.2):366 (1978)

This genus has been expanded recently to include *Neoevansia* and some *Wilcoxia* species, W. striata and W. viperina; other Wilcoxias have been referred by Taylor to *Echinocereus*.

These are tuberous rooted plants. In the wild they wind their slender shoots among shrubs for support. They come from south-western United States and northern Mexico, often in dry conditions on rocky slopes, but sometimes in sandy soil on the desert floor. The almost spineless stems are usually brown or greyish matching the shrubs they favour, and their presence in the wild is often difficult to determine until the large showy flowers appear, mostly white and nocturnal. Sufficient room for the root to develop fully should be allowed in a gritty, well-drained compost, and some support for the stems will be needed. Flowering is sometimes difficult in cultivation, and the best treatment to achieve this seems to be to keep the base of the plant shaded, allowing the top of the stems to have maximum exposure to sunlight.

Species named are: P. castellae, P. cuixmalensis, P. fosterianus (& var. multipetala, var. nizandensis), P. greggii (& var. transmontanus), P. johnstonii, P. lazaro-cardenasii, P. macdougalii (& var. centrispinus), P. marianus, P. marnieranus, P. occidentalis, P. rosei, P. striatus, P. tepalcatepecanus, P. viperinus, P. zopilotensis.

Rejected names and synonymies:

P. diguetii = P. striatus
P. haackeanus nom. dub.
P. maculatus = Acanthocereus maculatus.

Recommended species: P. greggii is not too difficult to persuade to grow in cultivation, given room to develop. The brown, harmlessly short spined stems needing

218. *Peniocereus greggii*

219. *Pereskia aculeata*

support, especially when they produce their large, heavily-scented, nocturnal, white flowers. The lower part of the stem tends to become woody, brown and unsightly. It is widespread in the southern United States and in northern Mexico.

P. striatus is similar, more slender, and relucant to produce its smaller, white to pale pink flowers, about $2-2\frac{1}{2}$ in (5–6 cm) wide, also nocturnal. It comes from Baja California, Mexico.

Connoisseur's choice: P. greggii.

Pereskia Mill., *Gard. Dict.* abr. ed. 4 (1754); Benson, *Cacti of US & Canada*, 264 (1982)

This primitive genus of shrubby or tree-like cacti is the only one which bears persistent, true leaves. If you have the room and the desire to grow something very like a rambler rose in your glasshouse then this genus is just the ticket. They can be grown in pots and restricted in their growth by not repotting too frequently, but watch out that they do not root through into the ground and defeat your object. They will flower after they are about a foot or so tall (30 cm), but eventually they will demand a lot more space than most have room for – but they can easily be restarted from cuttings. Flowers too are reminiscent of English hedgerow dog-roses. Few species are seen in cultivation.

Species named are: *P. aculeata* (& var. *godseffiana*, var. *rubescens*), *P. aureiflora*, *P. autumnalis*, *P. bahiensis*, *P. bleo*, *P. colombiana*, *P. cubensis*, *P. diaz-roemeriana*, *P. grandifolia*, *P. guamacho*, *P. horrida*, *P. lychnidiflora*, *P. moorei*, *P. nicoyana*, *P. pititache*, *P. portulacifolia*, *P. sacharosa*, *P. sparsiflora*, *P. stenantha*, *P. tampicana*, *P. vargasii* (& var. *longispina*, var. *rauhii*), *P. weberiana*, *P. zinniaeflora*.

Recommended species: none are recommended, but if you must, then look out for *P. aculeata* var. *rubescens*, which has beautiful, olive-green leaves with purple undersides.

Pereskiopsis B. & R., *Smith's Misc. Coll.* 50:331 (1907)

This genus of cacti from Mexico and Guatemala is grown in cultivation rarely except as a grafting stock, especially for young seedling grafting, because of its sappy, narrow stem and extreme vigour. It is a leafy relative of Pereskia, and similarly will make a large, sprawling plant in a very short time.

Species named are: *P. aquosa*, *P. blakeana*, *P. chapistle*, *P. diguetii*, *P. gatesii*, *P. kellermannii*, *P. opuntiaeflora*, *P. porteri*, *P. rotundifolia*, *P. scandens*, *P. spathulata*, *P. velutina.*

They are not recommended.

Peruvocereus Akers (1947)

Referred to *Haageocereus*.

Pfeiffera Salm-Dyck (1845)

This is a well-known genus of epiphytic cacti, noted for its production of mistletoe-like berries. It has been referred to *Rhipsalis*.

Phellosperma B. & R. (1923)

This monotypic genus (*P. tetrancistra*) has been long since referred to *Mammillaria*.

Phyllocactus Link (1831)

Referred to *Epiphyllum*.

Philippicereus Backeb. (1942)

Referred to *Eulychnia*.

Pilocanthus B. W. Benson & Backeb. (1952)

Referred to *Pediocactus*.

Pilocereus Lem. (1839)

Referred to *Cephalocereus*.

Pilocopiapoa Ritt. (1961)

Referred to *Copiapoa*.

Pilosocereus Byles & Rowley (1957)

Referred to *Cephalocereus*.

Piptanthocereus (Bgr.) Riccobono (1909)

Referred to *Cereus*.

Polaskia Backeb. (1949)

Referred to *Stenocereus*.

Porfiria Boed. (1926)

The single species, *P. schwartzii*, has been referred to *Mammillaria* and the name changed to *M. coahuilensis* to avoid confusion with the prior homonym *M. schwarzii*.

Praecereus Buxb. (1968)

Referred to *Monvillea*.

Pseudoacanthocereus Ritt., *Kakt. Sudamer.* 1:47 (1979)

Referred to *Acanthocereus*.

Pseudoespostoa Backeb. (1934)

Referred to *Espostoa*.

Pseudolobivia Backeb. (1934)

Referred variously to *Echinopsis* and *Lobivia*.

Pseudomammillaria F. Buxb. (1951)

Referred to *Mammillaria*.

Pseudomitrocereus Bravo & Buxb. (1961)

Referred to *Pachycereus*.

Pseudonopalxochia Backeb. (1958)

Referred to *Nopalxochia*.

Pseudorhipsalis B. & R. (1923)

Referred to *Disocactus*.

Pseudozygocactus Backeb., (1938)

Referred to *Rhipsalis*.

Pterocactus Schum., *Monatsschr. Kakteenk.* 7:6 (1897); Kiesling, *Cact. GB* 44(3):51 (1982)

Rowley maintains this genus separately from *Opuntia* and couples with it the monotypic genus *Marenopuntia* (*M. marenae*), but Roberto Kiesling has refuted the amalgamation of this Mexican genus (*Pterocactus*) with *Marenopuntia* otherwise entirely from south and western Argentina, and maintains its separate standing. Kiesling is followed here.

The species of this genus have a large, underground tuber, from which annual stems arise in the wild. And in cultivation they also have a tendency to die back in the winter resting period, which Bill Weightman advocates helping complete by cutting them back to the tuber at this time, which (for him) results in strong, flowering shoots being produced, the brownish-yellow flowers coming terminally at the end of the shoots.

Species named are: *P. araucanus, P. australis, P. fischeri, P. gonjianii, P. hickenii, P. kuntzei* (& fa. *lelongii*), *P. meghollii, P. reticulatus, P. valentinii.*

Rejected names and synonymies:
P. pumilus = *P. valentinii*
P. tuberosus = *nom. dub.*

Recommended species: apart from *P. kuntzei* (often labelled *P. tuberosus*, rejected by Kiesling as unidentifiable) few are seen in cultivation, although one or two others have appeared in the last few years. As indicated above, this species can be induced to flower, and if cut back as suggested keeps a less unkempt appearance than when allowed to retain the previous year's growth. Allow room for the large root which will develop.

Connoisseur's choice: *P. kuntzei.*

Pterocereus, Macdougall & Miranda (1954)

Referred to *Stenocereus.*

Puna Kiesling, *Hickenia* 1(55):289 (1982)

This is a newly proposed generic name for *Opuntia clavarioides* and *Opuntia subterranea.* For the present they are treated herein under *Opuntia.*

Pygmaeocereus Johns. & Backeb., (1957); Buxb., *Kakt.u.a.Sukk.* 20:97 (1969)

Referred to *Arthrocereus.*

Pyrrhocactus (Bgr.) Backeb. & Knuth (1935)

Referred to *Neoporteria.*

Quiabentia B. & R., *The Cact.* 4:252 (1923)

These tree or shrub-like relatives of *Opuntia* are little known or grown in cultivation. They come from Brazil, Bolivia and Argentina. Species named are: *Q. chacoensis* (& var. *jujuyensis*), *Q. pereziensis, Q. pflanzii, Q. verticillata, Q. zehntneri.*

They are not recommended.

Rapicactus Buxb. & Oehme (1942)

Referred to *Neolloydia.*

Rathbunia B. & R. (1909)

Referred to *Stenocereus.*

Rauhocereus Backeb., (1957)

Referred to *Browningia.*

Rebutia Schum., *Monatsschr. Kakteenk.* 5:102 (1895); Donald, *Nat. Cact. Succ. Journ.* 12:3,9 (1957); *Cact. GB* 27:38 (1965)

This is undoubtedly one of the most popular of genera, and is taken these days to embrace former separate genera *Aylostera* and *Mediolobivia*; *Sulcorebutia* is referred hereunder by some authorities, but is regarded separately in this book. The species come from Bolivia and northern Argentina, often in high altitude areas, where they will be subject to temperatures below freezing, and plants in cultivation in England have been overwintered in cold frames successfully for several years. They are undemanding of space, mostly making clumps in time of 6–8 in (15–20 cm) or so, although larger clumps are sometimes seen. They are free in their flower production, with a colour range from white through yellow and various shades of pink to orange and red.

There has been a rash of new species named in the last few years, some of which are doubtfully distinct; they may well be sunk into synonymy when someone takes the genus by the throat and really rationalizes it. Some steps in this direction have been taken, some time ago now, but because of the use of trinomials or even quadrinomials the move has not been taken to heart on the whole by collectors or nurserymen.

220. *Rebutia albiflora*

Species named are: *R. albiareolata, R. albiflora, R. albipilosa, R. albopectinata, R. almeyeri, R. archibuiningiana, R. auranitida* (& fa. *gracilis*), *R. aureiflora* (& subsp. *elegans*, subsp. *elegans* var. *sarathroides*, var. *blossfeldii*, fa. *albiseta*, fa. *boedekeriana*, fa. *duursmaiana*, fa. *kesselringiana*, fa. *rubelliflora*), *R. binnewaldiana, R. buiningiana, R. brunescens, R. brunneoradicata, R. cajasensis, R. camargensis, R. canacruzensis, R. carmeniana, R. christinae, R. cintiensis, R. colorea, R. costata* (& fa. *pilifera*), *R. deminuta* (& fa. *pseudominuscula*), *R. diersiana*, (& var. *atrovirens*, var. *minor*), *R. donaldiana, R. einsteinii* (& var. *columnaris*, var. *columnaris* fa. *conoidea*, var. *gonjianii*, fa. *rubroviridis*, fa. *schmiedcheniana*, fa. *steineckii*), *R. eos, R. euanthema* (& fa. *fricii*, fa. *neopygmaea*, fa. *oculata*), *R. eucaliptana, R. fabrisii* (& var. *aureiflora*, var. *nana*), *R. fiebigiana, R. fiebrigii* (& var. *densiseta*, var. *vulpes*), *R. flavistyla, R. friedrichiana, R. frohlichiana, R. fulviseta, R. fusca, R. gracilispina, R. haagei, R. heliosa* (& var. *cajasensis*, var. *condorensis*), *R. hirsutissima, R. hoffmanii, R. huasiensis, R. iridescens, R. iscayachensis, R. jujuyana, R. kieslingii, R. kupperiana* (& var. *spiniflora*), *R. lanosiflora, R. leucanthema, R. mamillosa* (& var. *australis*, var. *orientalis*), *R. margarethae, R. marsoneri* (& var. *sieperdaiana*, var. *spathulata*, var. *vatteri*), *R. minuscula* (& subsp. *grandiflora*, subsp. *violaciflora*, subsp. *violaciflora* fa. *kariusiana*, subsp. *violaciflora* fa. *knuthiana*), *R. minutissima, R. mixta, R. mixticolor, R. mudanensis, R. muscula* (& var. *luteo-albida*), *R. narvaecensis, R. nazarenoensis, R. nitida, R. nogalesensis, R. orurensis, E. padcayensis, R. pallida, R. patericalyx, R. pauciareolata, R. paucicostata, R. perplexa, R. poecilantha, R. potosina, R. pseudodeminuta* (& fa. *albiseta*, fa. *grandiflora*, fa. *rubrifilamentosa*, fa. *schneideriana*, fa. *schumanniana*), *R. pulchella, R. pulvinosa, R. pygmaea* (& fa. *atrovirens*, fa. *flavovirens*, fa. *fuauxiana*, fa. *haefneriana*, fa. *neosteinmannii*), *R. raulii, R. ritteri* (& var. *nigricans*, fa. *hahniana*, fa. *peterseimii*), *R. robustispina* (& var. *minor*), *R. rosalbiflora* (& var. *amblypetala*), *R. rubiginosa, R. rutiliflora, R. salpingantha, R. sanguinea* (& var. *minor*), *R. schatzliana, R. senilis* (& subsp. *chrysacantha*, subsp. *chrysacantha* fa. *schieleana*, var. *aurescens*, var. *breviseta*, var. *elegans*, var. *iseliniana*, var. *kesselringiana*, var. *lilacino-rosea*, var. *semperflorens*, var. *stuemeri*), *R. simoniana, R. singularis, R. spegazziniana* (& var. *atroviridis*), *R. spinosissima, R. spiralisepala, R. steinmannii* (& var. *cincinnata*), *R. sumayana, R. supthutiana, R. tamboensis, R. tarijensis, R. tarvitaensis, R. torquata, R. tropaeoclinta, R. tropaeolipicta, R. tuberosa, R. vallegrandensis, R. violascens, R. vulpina, R. wahliana, R. wessneriana* (& subsp. *berylloides*, subsp. *berylloides* fa. *calliantha*, var. *gokrausei*, var. *gokrausei* fa. *permutata*, var. *krainziana*), *R. xanthocarpa* (& fa. *citricarpa*, fa. *coerulescens*,

221. *Rebutia aureiflora*

222. *Rebutia donaldiana*

223. *Rebutia einsteinii* var. *gonjianii*

224. *Rebutia fiebrigii* var. *densiseta*

fa. *dasyphrissa*, fa. *graciliflora*, fa. *salmonea*, fa. *violaciflora*),
R. *yuquinensis*, R. *zecheri*.

Rejected names and synonymies:

R. *auranitida* var. *flaviflora* = R. *auranitida* fa. *gracilis*
R. *blossfeldii* = R. *aureiflora* var. *blossfeldii*
R. *brachyantha* = R. *steinmannii*
R. *calliantha* = R. *wessneriana* subsp. *berylloides* fa. *calliantha*
R. *calliantha* var. *berylloides* = R. *wessneriana* subsp. *berylloides*
R. *calliantha* var. *breviseta* = R. *wessneriana* subsp. *berylloides*
R. *carminea* = R. *minuscula* subsp. *violaciflora*
R. *chrysacantha* = R. *senilis* subsp. *chrysacantha*
R. *cincinnata* = R. *steinmannii* var. *cincinnata*
R. *conoidea* = R. *einsteinii* var. *columnaris* fa. *conoidea*
R. *conoidea* var. *columnaris* = R. *einsteinii* var. *columnaris*
R. *corroana* = *Weingartia corroana*
R. *elegans* = R. *aureiflora* subsp. *elegans*
R. *elegans* var. *gracilis* = R. *aureiflora*
R. *'espinosae'* = R. *narvaecensis*
R. *gonjianii* = R. *einsteinii* var. *gonjianii*
R. *graciliflora* = R. *xanthocarpa* fa. *graciliflora*
R. *graciliflora* var. *borealis* n.n. = R. *camargensis* or R. *mamillosa* var. *australis*
R. *graciliflora* var. *orientalis* = R. *mamillosa* var. *orientalis*
R. *grandiflora* = R. *minuscula* subsp. *grandiflora*
R. *haefneriana* = R. *pygmaea* fa. *haefneriana*
R. *hyalacantha* = R. *wessneriana*
R. *ithyacantha* = R. *fiebrigii* var. *vulpes*
R. *kariusiana* = R. *minuscula* subsp. *violaciflora* fa. *kariusiana*
R. *krainziana* = R. *wessneriana* var. *krainziana*
R. *leucanthema* var. *cocciniflora* = R. *tarvitaensis*
R. *neopygmaea* = R. *euanthema* fa. *neopygmaea*
R. *nigricans* = R. *ritteri* var. *nigricans*
R. *oculata* = R. *euanthema* fa. *oculata*
R. *odontopetala* = R. *friedrichiana*
R. *pectinata* = R. *pygmaea*
R. *pectinata* var. *atrovirens* = R. *pygmaea* fa. *atrovirens*
R. *pectinata* var. *digitiformis* = R. *pygmaea*
R. *pectinata* var. *neosteinmannii* = R. *pygmaea* fa. *neosteinmannii*
R. *pectinata* var. *orurensis* = R. *orurensis*
R. *permutata* = R. *wessneriana* var. *gokrausei* fa. *permutata*
R. *pseudominuscula* = R. *deminuta* fa. *pseudominuscula*
R. *rauschii* = R. *steinmannii*
R. *salmonea* = R. *xanthocarpa* fa. *graciliflora*
R. *schmiedcheniana* = R. *einsteinii* fa. *schmiedcheniana*
R. *schmiedcheniana* var. *karreri* = R. *einsteinii* fa. *rubroviridis*
R. *schmiedcheniana* var. *steineckei* = R. *einsteinii* fa. *steineckii*
R. *senilis* var. *sieperdaiana* = R. *marsoneri* var. *sieperdaiana*
R. *violaciflora* = R. *minuscula* subsp. *violaciflora*
R. *violaciflora* var. *knuthiana* = R. *minuscula* subsp. *violaciflora* fa. *knuthiana*

225. *Rebutia haagei*

226. *Rebutia heliosa* var. *condorensis*

227. *Rebutia kupperiana*

228. *Rebutia marsoneri* var. *marsoneri*

R. xanthocarpa var. *elegans* = *R. senilis* var. *elegans*
R. xanthocarpa var. *luteorosea* = *R. xanthocarpa.*
Recommended species: many new names have appeared in the last few years, which are as yet unavailable to collectors, or are only just getting into commercial listings, and their validity as separate species is yet to be tested. The following recommended species are those generally available with a little diligent seeking, which have outstanding characteristics.
R. albiflora, with, as the name indicates, white flowers

freely produced covering the tiny stems. It forms dense moss-saxifrage like clumps, the glassy white spines completely covering the plant bodies.
R. aureiflora has beautifully coloured deep yellow flowers, on globular stems an inch (2·5 cm) or so wide, forming clusters.
R. deminuta is a well-known species, forming clumps of heads about an inch (2·5 cm) or less, with fiery red flowers in abundance.
R. donaldiana is a recent introduction, and like many other

229. *Rebutia minuscula* subsp. *violaciflora* fa. *kariusiana*

230. *Rebutia muscula*

recent finds in this genus has flowers of a distinctly orange colouring. They are on long, slim tubes on a slowly clustering plant making elongated stems.

R. einsteinii in its many forms is a small-growing attractive species; in particular *R. einsteinii* var. *gonjianii* has tiny, tightly growing stems and orange flowers.

R. fiebrigii is wonderfully spined with a mixture of brown and white spines and has orange flowers; the variety *densiseta* is particularly attractive with even denser spines than the type.

R. flavistyla is a standard *Rebutia*, forming a low mound of stems each about 1·5 to 2 in (4 to 5 cm) wide with bright orange flowers.

R. haagei has small fingertip-sized stems forming a dense low clump and with delightfully coloured salmon-pink flowers.

R. heliosa was one of the best finds in the genus only a few years ago, with silvery very short spines completely covering the body in a close fitting armour, the stems each about $\frac{1}{2}$—$\frac{3}{4}$ in (1–2 cm) tall and wide, and forming dense clumps, with long-tubed orange flowers; the varieties *cajasensis* and *condorensis* are somewhat different in appearance, with red flowers, but with very neat spination too.

R. kupperiana is an old favourite, with long, dark red-brown spines and fiery red flowers; it forms clumps of stems each about 1·5–2 in (4–5 cm tall and wide).

R. leucanthema has white flowers contrasting well with the typical *Mediolobivia* dark, shining body colour.

R. marsoneri is one of the first to flower with many bright yellow flowers with a characteristic purple fleck on the outer petals.

R. minuscula, although fairly ordinary in the type, now has had ascribed to it three very attractive forms as far as flower colour is concerned: ssp. *violaciflora* is well known for its pinkish-violet flowers; ssp. *violaciflora* fa. *knuthiana* has similar form and deep carmine flowers; and ssp. violaciflora fa. *kariusiana* has pale pink flowers.

R. muscula is perhaps the neatest spined *Rebutia*, covered with short, even, dense white spines contrasting well with the bright orange flowers.

R. narvaecensis (syn. R. 'espinosae') is neatly white spined with brown tips to the spines, but the outstanding feature is the white, flushed pink or pink-edged flowers.

R. perplexa has short, neat brownish spines on small stems, no more than about $\frac{1}{2}$—$\frac{3}{4}$ in (1–2 cm) tall and wide, with bright pink flowers.

R. ritteri is densely covered with red-brown spines and has bright red flowers.

R. senilis, the type, is worth seeking out for its dense covering of white spines and bright red flowers, as well as the varieties, two of which are outstanding: var. *kesselringiana*, with yellow flowers arising from green buds, and var. *lilacino-rosea* with lovely lilac-pink flowers.

R. wessneriana has a very dark purplish-brown body colour with contrasting long white spines and deep red flowers; the short spined var. *krainziana*, although often misidentified, is an outstanding variety.

Connoisseur's choice: *R. flavistyla, R. haagei, R. heliosa, R. narvaecensis, R. perplexa, R. wessneriana* var. *krainziana*.

Reicheocactus Backeb. (1942)

Referred to *Neoporteria*.

135

231. *Rebutia ritteri*

232. *Rebutia senilis* var. *lilacino-rosea*

Rhipsalidopsis B. & R. (1923)

Referred to *Rhipsalis*.

Rhipsalis Gaertn. *Fruct. Sem.* 1:137 (1788)

The modern application of this old generic name is by way of an overview of the proliferation of generic names for the many forms of what is regarded as a large, epiphytic genus, taking in such commonly used generic names as *Hatiora, Cassytha, Lepismium, Pfeiffera, Acanthorhipsalis* and *Erythrorhipsalis*.

Most are of little, or passing interest to the majority of collectors, except for those who are enthusiastic about epiphytic cacti as a whole; they (the enthusiasts) are few and far between, but are liable to produce such a seashore of seaweed-like plants if asked to talk about them that defies belief in the number there are and their variability. They are the jungle cacti of the rain-forests or damp mountain areas of tropical and sub-tropical America, the West Indies, and, to confound the concept of cacti being confined to the Americas, West Africa, Madagascar, the Mascarene Islands and Sri Lanka. They generally grow in the form of long, narrow stems, often branching, pendant, with little or weak spination. They produce usually small, white, pink or yellow flowers, often followed by mistletoe-like berries. They require different treatment from the more arid area cacti, with a humus-rich compost and preferably daily overhead spraying rather than too much water at the root; and many will tolerate and even prefer less strong sunlight than the desert cacti.

Species named (with former allegiances in brackets, abbreviated) are: *R. aculeata, R. alboareolata, R. angustissima, R. baccifera, R. (Hat)bambusoides, R. boliviana, R. (Aca)brevispina, R. burchellii, R. campos-portoana, R. capilliformis, R. cassutha, R. cassuthopsis, R. cereoides, R. cereuscula* (& var. *rubrodisca*), *R. chloroptera, R. (Lep)chrysanthum, R. clavata, R. clavellina, R. coralloides, R. coriacea, R. (Aca) crenata, R. cribrata, R. crispata, R. crispimarginata, R. (Lep) cruciforme* (& var. *anceps,* var. *cavernosum,* var. *knightii,* var. *myosurus*), *R. cuneata, R. (Hat)cylindrica, R. densiareolata, R. (Lep)dissimile, R. elliptica* (& var. *helicoidea*), *R. (Lep)epiphyllanthoides, R. (Pf)erecta, R. fasciculata, R. (Lep)floccosa* (& var. *gibberula*), *R. flosculosa, R. (Sch) gaertneri, R. goebeliana, R. gonocarpa, R. (Pf)gracilis, R. (Lep)grandiflora, R. hedrosoma, R. heptagona, R. (Hat)herminiae, R. heteroclada, R. hohenauensis, R. horrida, R. houlletiana, R. hylaea, R. (Pf)ianthothele* (& var. *boliviana,* var. *tarijensis*), *R. incachacana, R. (Aca)incahuasina, R. jamaicensis, R. leiophloea, R. leucorhaphis, R. lindbergiana, R. linearis, R. loefgrenii, R. lorentziana, R. lumbricoides, R. madagascarensis, R. (Lep)marnierana, R. (Pf)mataralensis* (& var. *floccosa*), *R. (Lep)megalantha, R. mesembryanthemoides, R. minutiflora, R. (Aca)monacantha* (& var. *samaipatana*), *R. monteazulensis, R. (Pf)multigona, R. (Lep)neves-armondii, R. oblonga, R. (Lep) pacheco-leonii, R. pachyptera, P. (Lep)paradoxa, R. (Aca) paranganiensis, R. penduliflora, R. pentaptera, R. (Ery) pilocarpa, R. pilosa, R. (Lep)pittieri, R. platycarpa, R. prismatica, R. pulchra, R. (Lep)pulvinigera, R. (Lep)puniciodisca* (& var. *chrysocarpa*), *R. purpusii, R. quellebambensis, R. ramulosa, R. rhombea, R. (Lep)rigida, R. robusta, R. (Rhipsalidopsis)rosea, R. roseana, R. russellii, R. (Hat)salicornioides* (& var. *gracilis,* var. *stricta,* var. *villigera*). *R. (Lep)saxatile,*

233. *Rhipsalis cruciforme*

234. *Rhipsalis ianthothele*

R. shaferi, R. simmleri, R. sulcata, R. teres, R. tonduzii, R. triangularis, R. (Lep)trigona, R. (Lep)tucumanensis, R. virgata, R. warmingiana, R. werklei.

Many of these species are not generally available, and, not unrelated to this perhaps, many are similar in appearance, with thin, plain, green stems and very small white flowers. But some are popular for one or another feature, either for attractively coloured stems, or for attractive shapes, or, in a few, for their abundantly produced colourful flowers.

Recommended species: R. (Lepismium) cruciforme. This has narrow, four-angled, purple coloured stems, with wispy, white hair-like spines and bunches of charming small, pink flowers on the areoles for a good length of the stems.

R. (Schlumbergera) gaertneri is the popular so-called 'Easter cactus', with flat, rectangular segments, rounded at the ends, with no teeth on the edges as in *Schlumbergera russelliana*, the Christmas cactus, and tufts of gingerbrown bristles at the segment ends from which the bright, pillar-box red flowers appear in early spring, several to each segment of the new growth. The flowers are regular in shape, not zygomorphic as in *Schlumbergera*, hence the transfer. Hybrids of this species and *Rhipsalis rosea* are sometimes seen, with the tell-tale ginger tufts of bristles, segments more or less intermediate in size between the two species, and with pinkish flowers.

R. houlletiana has flat, leaf-like stems, deeply toothed like a circular-saw blade, bright, light green in colour, with small, white to pale yellow flowers in each indentation.

R. (Pfeiffera) ianthothele is often seen, but more often not grown as well as it might be. If given a spot out of full sun, a rich compost and fairly generous spraying and occasional feeding during the spring and summer months it will make several inches of the quadrangular, wispily spined stems, with white, insignificant flowers followed by the more decorative mistletoe-like berries for which it is well known.

R. (Acanthorhipsalis) monacantha has flat, or three angled, leaf-like stems, similar to the well-known Epiphyllum hybrids, with small, orange flowers along the margins, followed by purple-pink berries.

R. (Erythrorhipsalis) pilocarpa has thin, cylindrical, springy stems, quite densely covered with short, white, hair-like spines lying close to the stem. The small, white flowers are borne in the late autumn or winter months.

R. platycarpa has flat, almost round, disc-like segments to the arching stems, similar to *Schlumbergera* species, and bears many small bunches of flowers, creamy-white, at the margins.

R. (Rhipsalidopsis) rosea is a deservedly popular species with segmented stems in the style of *R. gaertneri*, but half or less the size, with colour from green to purple in strong light. It smothers itself with flowers in the spring, which are a lovely lilac-pink.

R. (Hatiora) salicornioides makes a dense mass of its tiny jointed stems, like tiny bottles, an inch or less (2 cm) long, dark green and growing upright for some time before sprawling under their own weight. It bears masses of small, deep yellow flowers.

Connoisseur's choice: R. houlletiana. R. rosea.

137

Rhodocactus (Bgr.) Backeb. & Knuth (1935)

Referred to *Pereskia*.

Ritterocereus Backeb. (1942)

Referred to *Stenocereus*.

Rodentiophila Ritt. nom. nud.

Referred to *Eriosyce*.

Rooksbya Backeb. (1960)

Referred to *Stenocereus*.

Roseocactus Bgr. (1925)

Referred to *Ariocarpus*.

Roseocereus Backeb. (1938)

Referred to *Echinopsis*.

Samaipaticereus Card. (1952)

Referred to *Corryocactus*.

Schlumbergera Lem., *Rev. Hort.* ser. 4, 7:253 (1858); D. R. Hunt, *Kew Bull.* 23:260(1969); Barthlott & Rauh, *Kakt.u.a.Sukk.* 28:273 (1977)

This is a genus of few species, but much worked on in recent years by the hybridizers to produce a wide variation in the flower colours, from deep purple-pink, through orange-pinks to reds in all shades, to pale pink or almost white, and latest of all, yellow. A good idea of the variation may be gained from the cover of the December issue of the West German society's journal (*Kakteen und andere Sukkulenten*), 1984. These are the popular Christmas cacti, which appear in abundance at Christmas time in florists' shops. Choice of these hybrids is a matter of personal taste, and beyond the scope of this book. The wild species come from Brazil, where they grow either epiphytically or on rocks. As with many epiphytic plants they appreciate frequent spraying rather than overmuch water at the roots, and a change of position should be avoided when they are in bud, as this can lead to loss of the flowers before they open. A lighter, more spongy medium should be used for potting them in, and peat-based composts are preferred, or even bark or sphagnum-moss composts can be used, for anchorage more than as a source of nutrient. For both species and hybrids, 50° F (10° C) is to be preferred from October until flowering time to ensure full bud development. *Epiphyllanthus* and *Zygocactus* are referred hereunder.

Species named are: *S. obtusangula, S. opuntioides, S. orssichiana, S. russelliana, S. truncata*.

Rejected names and synonymies:

S. bridgesii = S. × buckleyi
S. buckleyi = S. × buckleyi (hybrid, *S. truncata* × *S. russelliana*)
S. candida = *S. obtusangula*
S. × exotica = hybrid, *S. truncata* × *S. opuntioides*
S. gaertneri = *Rhipsalis gaertneri*
S. microsphaerica = *S. obtusangula*
(*Epiphyllanthus*) *obovatus* = *S. opuntioides*.

Recommended species: *S. opuntioides* is one of the most intriguing species, quite unlike the others in appearance, and more than anything resembling an *Opuntia* species, with its segments doing as good an imitation of an *Opuntia* pad in miniature as can be seen. But the growth habit is the same as other *Schlumbergera* species, and the flowers are similar to *S. russelliana*, the well known 'Christmas cactus' in a purple-pink, although they are not nearly so readily or regularly produced as in that species and the hybrids. It is also much more difficult to cultivate successfully, being prone to drop its segments if overwatered, or if potted in an unsuitable compost. *S. orssichiana* is an exciting new discovery, which flowers in the autumn, making its use in hybridizing difficult, but not impossible. It is in any case good looking in its own right, with larger flowers than most other species, deep pinkish-purple with white lower parts to the petals. The segments too are half as big again as any others. It is becoming more available now, although it was described only in 1978, and comes from near Parati in the Serra do Mar, Brazil.

S. russelliana, the 'Christmas cactus' has distinct tooth-like edges to the segments; the untoothed 'Christmas cactus' common some ten years or more ago is the hybrid *S. × buckleyi*, a cross between *S. truncata* and *S. russelliana*. As indicated above, this species has now become so worked at by the hybridizers, that the original wild plant is seldom seen with any certainty that it is such. Suffice it to say that it has purple-pink flowers, which many of the hybrids depart little from. The recent colour break *Schlumbergera* 'Gold Charm' with yellow flowers will rapidly become popular.

Connoisseur's choice: *S. opuntioides*.

Sclerocactus B. & R. (1922)

Referred to *Thelocactus*.

Selenicereus (Bgr.) B. & R., *Contrib. U.S. Nat. Herb.* 12:429 (1909)

This is a genus of very long-stemmed, finger-thick, clambering cacti from tropical and subtropical America and the West Indies. They are of little interest to collectors, although the necessary room is often found for one species for the sake of their huge, nocturnal, white flowers. A plant given sufficient room at the root will make yards (metres) of growth each season, and produce the large nocturnal flowers which have given rise to the popular name 'Queen of the Night'. They can be rooted in a large pot or planted direct into the soil, and trained along the ridge-bar, probably a better proposition than trying to contain the growth to a framework above a pot, which can be done if constraints of space dictate, training the young growth into the desired place before it gets too woody and unmanageable. Rowley includes here the little known genera *Cryptocereus, Deamia, Mediocactus* and *Strophocactus*.

Species named (with former allegiances abbreviated in brackets) are: *S.* (*Crypt*)*anthonyanus, S. boeckmannii, S. brevispinus, S.* (*Med*)*coccineus, S. coniflorus, S.* (*Deam*) *diabolicus, S. donkelaari, S. grandiflorus* (& var. *affinis,* var. *barbadensis,* var. *irradians,* var. *ophites,* var. *tellii*), *S.* (*Med*)*hahnianus, S. hallensis, S. hamatus, S.* (*Med*)*hassleri, S. hondurensis, S.* (*Crypt*)*imitans, S. inermis, S. innesii, S. knuthianus, S.* (*Med*)*lindbergianus, S.* (*Med*)*lindmanii, S. macdonaldiae* (& var. *grusonianus*), *S. maxonii, S.* (*Med*) *megalanthus, S. mirandae, S. murrillii, S. nelsonii, S.* (*Med*) *pomifer, S. pringlei, S. pseudospinulosus, S. pteranthus, S. radicans, S.* (*Crypt*)*rosei, S. rothii, S. spinulosus, S.* (*Deam*) *testudo, S. urbanianus, S. vagans, S. vaupelii, S. wercklei, S.* (*Stroph*)*wittii*.

Recommended species: without knowing the wild origins of any plant obtained of this genus it is difficult to determine which species it might be. This is not so terribly important, since most in cultivation have been passed from collector to collector, and most will grow and flower well. No particular species is therefore recommended or offered as a connoisseur's choice.

Seticereus Backeb. (1937)

Referred to *Borzicactus*.

Seticleistocactus Backeb. (1963)

Referred to *Cleistocactus*.

Setiechinopsis (Backeb.) De Haas (1940)

The position of this monotypic genus (*S. mirabilis*) has been the subject of some speculation, but it seems now to have been referred to *Arthrocereus*.

Soehrensia Backeb. (1938)

This is a genus of massive, barrel-size stemmed plants, now referred to the wider concept of *Lobivia*.

Solisia B. & R. (1923)

This monotypic genus (*S. pectinata*) is referred to synonymy with *Mammillaria*. Because of prior use of this name, albeit now discredited, the name *M. pectinifera* is applied to this species.

Stenocactus (Schum.) Backeb. & Knuth, *Kaktus ABC* 353 (1935); D. R. Hunt, *Cact. GB* 42(4):105 (1980); N. P. Taylor, l.c.108 (1980; D. R. Hunt, l.c. 43(1): 12 (1981)

This more popularly used name is preferred to the prior, but unwieldy name *Echinofossulocactus*, which had a brief, grudging revival in the 1970s. Hunt and Taylor combined to resurrect *Stenocactus*, so that Taylor could reduce it to subgeneric rank beneath his wider concept of *Ferocactus*, and so made no move to conserve *Stenocactus* at generic level, since at that stage it was not necessary. Hunt subsequently determined that *Stenocactus* was preferred to *Brittonrosea*, and so the name *Stenocactus* can now be properly used at generic rank again.

The species of this genus all come from Mexico; from the central states of Hidalgo, Zacatecas, to northern Coahuila. They are generally modest-sized plants in cultivation, attaining no more than about 7–8 in (20 cm) in height, and half as wide, often solitary, but a few will form clusters to 10–12 in (to 30 cm) wide. Their main

235. *Stenocactus vaupelianus*

distinguishing characteristic is the fine wavy rib structure, not found in any other genus. Flowers are either yellow, cream or purple, sometimes striped white and purple. They are fairly slow growing, but present no difficulties in cultivation.

Nigel Taylor, at the same time that he reduced the genus to subgeneric rank beneath *Ferocactus*, cast considerable doubt on the good standing of many of the species described. He reduced them to four species, beneath which he listed as synonymous most of the rest, except for a few which he considered inadequately typified, i.e. dubiously identifiable, and which he recommended should be discarded as names. The four maintained are as follows: 1. *S. coptonogonus*, 2. *S. crispatus* (beneath which most species fall into synonymy), 3. *S. phyllacanthus*, 4. *S. vaupelianus*. The full list of species below is numbered for ease of reference to indicate to which of the four species above Taylor ascribed them; the figure 0 indicates those which he considered inadequately described.

Species named are: *S. acroacanthus* (0), *S. albatus* (4), *S. anfractuosus* (0), *S. arrigens* (2), *S. boedekerianus* (2?), *S. bustamantei* (2), *S. caespitosus* (2) (& var. *gracilispinus*), *S. confusus* (2), *S. coptonogonus* (1), *S. crispatus* (2), *S. densispinus* (2?), *S. dichroacanthus* (0), *S. erectocentrus* (2), *S. flexispinus* (0), *S. gladiatus* (0) (& var. *carneus*), *S. grandicornis* (0), *S. guerraianus* (2), *S. hastatus* (2), *S. heteracanthus* (0), *S. kellerianus* (2), *S. lamellosus* (2), *S. lancifer* (2), *S. lexarzai* (2), *S. lloydii* (2), *S. multicostatus* (2), *S. obvallatus* (2), *S. ochoteranaus* (2?), *S. pentacanthus* (0) (& var. *david-bondetianus*), *S. phyllacanthus* (0) (& var. *hookeri*), *S. rosasianus* (2?), *S. sulphureus* (2), *S. tetraxiphus* (2?), (& var. *longiflorus*), *S. tricuspidatus* (2?) (& var. *longispinus*), *S. vaupelianus* (4) (& var. *rectispinus*), *S. violaciflorus* (2), *S. wippermannii* (0), *S. xiphacanthus* (0), *S. zacatecasensis* (2) (& var. *moranensis*).

Recommended species: most 'species' available through commercial sources fall under Taylor's definition of *S. crispatus*, with *S. vaupelianus* (syn. *S. albatus*) running a good second, the latter characterized by dense, fine spination almost completely hiding the plant body, and yellow flowers. Few of the names seen on plants stand up to comparison with their descriptions, and pot luck is often taken with such offerings, seldom carrying habitat information. And Taylor's article is not much help in letting us know what the constituents of each species are, as there are no accompanying descriptions or photographs.

Those illustrated herein follow closely the original description, but in view of the variability of these species should not be taken as typical of Taylor's wider concept. *S. crispatus* (*S. arrigens*) is quite quick growing for this genus, making a club-shaped, solitary stem to about 6 in (15 cm) in six or eight years from seed. It has the charac-

teristic wavy ribs, clusters of spines, with the characteristic wider, more central spines at the top of each cluster, red-brown in colour, compared with, usually, white for the finer radials, and purple flowers.

S. vaupelianus has a dense covering of fine spines in white, yellowish-brown and black, through which the somewhat smaller creamy yellow flowers push with difficulty.

Connoisseur's choice: *S. crispatus*.

Stenocereus (Bgr.) Riccob., *Bol. R. Orto. Bot. Palermo* 8:253 (1909)

This is now the preferred name for a widespread group of columnar cacti from central America, the West Indies, Colombia and Venezuela. It embraces former generic names *Anisocereus*, *Heliabravoa*, *Hertrichocereus*, *Isolatocereus*, *Lemairocereus*, *Machaerocereus*, *Marshallocereus*, *Polaskia*, *Pterocereus*, *Rathbunia*, *Rooksbya* (wrongly referred by some authorities to *Cephalocereus*) and *Ritterocereus*, several of which were erected for one or two species. They are in the main nocturnal flowering, columnar, shrub or tree-like, branching, large growing plants, few of which are seen in cultivation; one, *S.* (*Machaerocereus*) *eruca*, is prostrate.

Species named (with former allegiances in brackets, abbreviated) are: *S.* (*Roth*)*alamosensis* *S.* (*Marsh*)*aragonii*, *S.* (*Hert/Lem*)*beneckei*, *S.* (*Marsh*)*chacalapensis*, *S.* (*Hel*)*chende*, *S.* (*Pol*)*chichipe*, *S. chrysocarpus*, *S.* (*Ritt*)*deficiens*, *S.* (*Isol*)*dumortieri*, *S.* (*Ritt*)*eichlamii*, *S.* (*Mach*)*eruca*, *S.* (*Rook*)*euphorbioides* (& var. *olfersii*), *S.* (*Ritt*)*fimbriatus*, *S.* (*Pter*)*foetidus*, *S. fricii*, *S.* (*Anis*)*gaumeri*, *S.* (*Ritt*)*griseus*, *S.* (*Mach*)*gummosus*, *S.* (*Lem*)*hollianus*, *S.* (*Ritt*)*hystrix*, *S.* (*Rath*)*kerberi*, *S.* (*Ritt*)*laevigatus*, *S.* (*Anis*)*lepidanthus*, *S.* (*Lem*) *longispinus*, *S.* (*Lem*)*martinezii*, *S.* (*Lem*)*montanus*, *S.* (*Ritt*) *pruinosus*, *S.* (*Ritt*)*queretaroensis*, *S.* (*Lem*)*quevedonis*, *S.* (*Lem*) *schumannii*, *S.* (*Rath*)*sonorensis*, *S.* (*Ritt*)*standleyi*, *S. stellatus*, *S.* (*Marsh/Lem*)*thurberi* (& var. *littoralis*), *S. treleasei*.

Recommended species: as indicated above few species are seen in cultivation, but some of the more interesting are offered from time to time.

S. beneckei is often grown as a small seedling, but rarely seen to achieve any real size, since it is prone to rot off if kept at too low a temperature, i.e. 50° F (10° C) minimum is needed for safety. It is covered with white meal, which sets off the red-brown spines in the young growth turning black with age wonderfully. Flowers may be achieved when the arm-thick stem gets to about three feet (1 m) tall, the black buds appearing near the top of the stem, opening to creamy-white flowers flushed with red.

S. eruca is unique in the cactus family for its habit of growing along the ground, rooting as it goes, the hinder part of the growth withering away. In habitat it is an awesome sight with the growing points curving upwards as if checking which way it is heading. It can be grown as an upright plant in cultivation, but tries to make its way to a prostrate habit, and will develop roots on the lower part of the stem in preparation for the start of its creeping habit (hence the popular name 'the creeping devil'). It is best grown as a prostrate plant, but will take up a good deal of room as it develops. It is endemic to Baja California, Mexico.

S. euphorbioides does somewhat resemble a *Euphorbia* species, with its grass-green stem and prominent black, long spines neatly arranged on the straight, vertical ribs. As with others in this genus a little extra warmth is needed to prevent it marking in the winter months. Flowers are unlikely until the stem, which stays solitary for a long time, reaches six feet or so, produced near the top of the stem, but not from a cephalium as would be indicated by its placing in *Cephalocereus*. It comes from the states of Tamaulipas and Jaumave in southern Mexico.

S. griseus soon develops the subtle grey-green colouring for which it is named from a thin bloom on the surface, and which makes it a most welcome addition to a collection of these columnar cacti. The fairly short brown spines become grey as they age. It comes from central and southern Mexico, and in the wild reaches a height of about 20 ft (7 m).

S. thurberi is the well-known 'organ-pipe cactus' of southern Arizona and Mexico. In cultivation it presents some difficulty in attaining any size without either succumbing completely or marking badly from too low temperatures in winter. Keep above 50° F (10° C) for safety. Its attraction lies in the felty brown prominent areoles from which the short dark brown spines emerge. Flowers are unlikely in cultivation at less than about 4–5 ft/(1·5 m) stem height.

Connoisseur's choice: *S. beneckei, S. eruca.*

Stephanocereus Bgr. (1926)

Referred to *Cephalocereus.*

236. *Stenocereus beneckei* (seedling showing commencement of farina development)

237. *Stenocereus euphorbioides*

238. *Stenocereus thurberi*, in habitat, Organ Pipe National Monument, Arizona, USA, with admiring *Cereus* enthusiast Derek Bowdery. Other cacti in the background include a *Ferocactus* and a cholla

239. *Stetsonia coryne*

Stetsonia B. & R., *The Cact.* 2:64, t.9, figs 95, 96 (1920)

This monotypic genus has withstood the onslaughts of the 'lumpers', who have invariably left it to stand. It is a large tree-like cactus from north-west Argentina, where it grows to about 25 feet (8 m) tall, branching from a thick basal trunk. In cultivation it makes quite attractive small plants, with dark green body colouring, prominent white areoles and long black and brown spines, to about 2 in (5 cm) long, penetratingly sharp.

Recommended species (the only one): *S. coryne* (& var. *procera*).

Strombocactus B. & R., *The Cact.* 3:106 (1922); Glass & Foster, *Cact. Amer.* 49:161 (1977); Riha, *Kakt. u.a. Sukk.* 36:178 (1985)

Until fairly recently this genus was regarded as monotypic, with *S. disciformis* as the sole representative. But the pendulum of opinion has swung back and it is now taken to include *Obregonia, Pelecyphora* (the *Normanbokea* species), and *Turbinicarpus*, of which several species were

142

originally described as *Strombocactus*, but hived off to form a somewhat tenuous genus of their own.

All the species now included come from Mexico, and all are regarded as among the most desirable small plants of the cactus family. None get to more than a few inches tall and wide (to 10 cm or so).

Species named (with previous allegiances abbreviated in brackets) are: *S. (Obr)denegrii, S. disciformis, S. (Turb)laui, S. (Turb)lophophoroides, S. (Turb)pseudomacrochele* (& var. *krainzianus), S. (Pel/Norm)pseudopectinatus, S. (Turb)sch-miedickeanus* (& var. *dickisoniae,* var. *flaviflorus,* var. *gracilis,* var. *macrochele,* var. *schwarzii), S. (Pel/Norm)valdezianus.*

Rejected names and synonymies:

S. (Turb)flaviflorus = S. schmiedickeanus var. *flaviflorus*
S. (Turb)gracilis = S. schmiedickeanus var. *gracilis*
S. (Turb)klinkerianus = S. schmiedickeanus var. *klinkerianus*
S. (Turb)krainzianus = S. pseudomacrochele var. *krainzianus*
S. (Turb)macrochele = S. schmiedickeanus var. *macrochele*
S. (Turb)polaskii nom. inval. = S. schmiedickeanus var. *schwarzii*
S. (Turb)roseiflorus nom. inval. = S. laui?
S. (Turb)schwarzii = S. schmiedickeanus var. *schwarzii.*
S. (Pel/Norm)valdezianus var. *albiflorus = S. valdezianus.*

Recommended species (all of them):

S. denegrii is a well known, slow growing species, with flat triangular, overlapping tubercles, giving it the appearance of an opened-out pine cone, with lightly attached wispy spines at the apex of each tubercle, often absent on older growth, having fallen. The cream-coloured flowers are produced from the woolly centre of the solitary, globular stem, which gets to about 4 in (10 cm) in a very long time. It comes from seed readily, and makes a charming little plant which will flower at about an inch (2·5 cm) wide. It comes from north-eastern Mexico.

S. disciformis is the type species of the genus, and was for many years considered the only one. It is often still seen as a rock like, crusty plant which has been imported from the wild, the lower part brown and corky, with a patch of green growth at the top and the readily falling spines present only at the very apex. But with improved seed raising methods, more and more seedling plants of this and other previously 'impossible' cactus species are appearing for sale, and wonderfully clean, attractive additions to the collection they make, helping at the same time to do away with the depredation of former times of these ancients of the deserts. The flowers are cream coloured, the subsequent fruits splitting down the sides to spill the fine seed over the woolly crown. If you want a real challenge, try growing this species from seed; it is possible, but not easy, nor quick. It comes from central Mexico.

S. laui (syn. *Turbinicarpus roseiflorus?*) is a beauty, and somewhat different in body texture, being shining green

240. *Strombocactus laui*

rather than the more usual matt, bluish-grey, and with clearly defined rounded tubercles. The short, dark brown spines recurve. Flowers are white to pink. It comes from gypsum hills near Buenavista, in San Luis Potosi, Mexico.

S. lophophoroides is perhaps the most likely to fail out of all these species, being susceptible to an injudicious watering at any time, but getting by with good drainage and watering confined to warm weather and sunny days, so that it can dry out fairly quickly. It has similar bluish body-colouring to the genus which it is likened to (*Lopho-phora*), and is slow growing, making a stem some 2 in (5 cm) tall and wide in four or five years from seed, with plenty of wool at the apex in the growing area, from which the large, wide opening, pale pink flowers arise in succession over several weeks. It comes readily from seed, but will not be hurried in the first few years. It grows in San Luis Potosi, Mexico.

S. pseudomacrochele is a delight of fine, curling spines around the crown of the globular stem, which gets to about 1 in (2·5 cm) tall and wide, later clustering to form small clumps, covered with the gingery, yellowish-brown spines, curling and interlacing over the plant. Flowers vary from white to pink. It comes from north of Cadereyta in Queretaro, and in Hidalgo, Mexico.

S. pseudomacrochele var. *krainzianus* is noted for the very

241. *Strombocactus pseudomacrochele* var. *krainzianus*

242. *Strombocactus schmiedickeanus* var. *flaviflorus*

different, pectinate spines of the young growth compared with the more standard, grey, fewer, more central spines in maturity. It clusters more readily too, forming flat clusters, little more than an inch or so (2–3 cm) tall or less, each stem about an inch or so (2·5 cm) wide. Flowers are greenish-cream to yellowish. It comes from Queretaro and Hildalgo in Mexico.

S. pseudopectinatus is a very individual species, popular with collectors for its neat spination, white, radiating evenly from the side of each areole, and overlapping to completely obscure the plant body. In England it flowers very early in the year, and will often produce a second flush in the autumn; flowers are variable from white, through peach-pink to reddish-violet on different plants. It takes some years to get to golf ball size, and is seldom

seen larger than this. It comes from Palmillas in Tamaulipas, Mexico.

S. schmiedickeanus has been expanded by Glass and Foster to include several former species at varietal level. The type, which with the erection of these varieties becomes known as *S. schmiedickeanus* var. *schmiedickeanus*, makes probably the largest clumps in this genus, clustering to form mounds of 6 in (15 cm) or more in time, covered with the grey curling, wispy spines, and producing a succession of white to pale pink flowers generally later in the year than most other species.

S. schmiedickeanus var. *dickisoniae* was described in 1982, from a range of mountains only a few miles from where *S. schmiedickeanus* var. *gracilis* was found. It differs from others in the number of persistent radial spines it has, and

144

the copious wool from the crown. Flowers are white. It is from Aramberri, Nuevo Leon, Mexico.

S. schmiedickeanus var. *flaviflorus* has been available only in the last couple of years since its description, having the distinction of greenish yellow flowers. It is a small growing variety apparently, to about 3 cm tall, with incurving brown spines in youth. It is from near Santa Rita, San Luis Potosi, Mexico.

S. schmiedickeanus var. *gracilis*, from Aramberri in Nuevo Leon, Mexico, is noted for its neat, incurving, long central spines, and copious wool produced in the growing area at the top of the smallish stem (to about an inch or so (3 cm) tall. Flowers are white.

S. schmiedickeanus var. *klinkerianus*, from near Huizache junction in San Luis Potosi, Mexico, grows in rock crev-

243. *Strombocactus schmiedickeanus* var. *gracilis*

244. *Strombocactus schmiedickeanus* var. *klinkerianus*

ices in full sun. It is shorter spined than most (less than $\frac{1}{2}$ in/9 mm), with well defined tubercles. Flowers are white to cream.

S. schmiedickeanus var. *macrochele* from near Matehuala in San Luis Potosi, Mexico, presents no problems in growing, although it never gets to any great size, with stems about an inch or so (2 to 3 cm) tall and wide, with white to pink flowers and shortish spination.

S. schmiedickeanus var. *schwarzii* (syn. *Turbinicarpus pola-*

skii?), comes from near Matehuala and from Cerros Blacos in San Luis Potosi, Mexico. It has generally more flattened growth, with less spines than other varieties. Flowers are white to lavender-pink.

S. valdezianus, from near Saltillo in Coahuila and from Nuevo Leon in Mexico, is a very individual, tiny species, making globular stems no more than an inch (2·5 cm) tall and wide or less, staying solitary, and flowering at no more than $\frac{1}{4}$ in (1 cm) tall. It is closely covered with tiny, white, plumose radiating spines, 30 or more to each areole, hiding the plant body. Flowers vary from deep reddish-violet to white ('var. *albiflorus*').

Connoisseur's choice: *S. denegrii, S. disciformis, S. lophophoroides, S. pseudomacrochele, S. pseudopectinatus, S. schmiedickeanus, S. valdezianus.*

Strophocactus B. & R. (1913)

Referred to *Selenicereus.*

Submatucana Backeb. (1959)

Referred to *Borzicactus.*

Subpilocereus Backeb. (1938)

Referred to *Cephalocereus.*

Sulcorebutia Backeb. *Cact. GB* 13:96 (1951)

Brinkmann, *Die Gattung Sulcorebutia* (1976); Pilbeam, *Sulcorebutia & Weingartia – A Collector's Guide* (1985)

This comparatively newly-discovered genus from high altitudes in Bolivia has proved a most popular one with collectors for its ease of cultivation, its attractive spination, modest size, and above all, the extremely free flowering capabilities of most species. New species are still being discovered, and the relationship of those already found need some elucidation, which will no doubt form the subject of some heavy debate over the next few years. Even their generic relationships have been the subject of some speculation: from an early (and still maintained by some authorities) allocation to synonymy with *Rebutia*, opinion has swung round to a closer relationship to *Weingartia*, thence to *Gymnocalycium*. Their separate standing is in jeopardy, but their individuality will ensure they survive in collections, whatever their fate.

Species named are: *S. alba, S. albissima, S. arenacea, S. breviflora, S. candiae, S. canigueralii, S. caracarensis, S. cardenasiana, S. cochabambina, S. crispata, S. cylindrica, S. flavissima, S. frankiana* (& var. *aureispina*), *S. glomeriseta, S. glomerispina, S. hoffmanniana, S. inflexiseta, S. krahnii, S.*

krugeri, S. losenickyana, S. markusii, S. menesesii (& var. *kamiensis*), *S. mentosa, S. mizquensis, S. muschii, S. oenantha, S. pampagrandensis, S. pulchra, S. purpurea, S. rauschii, S. santiaginiensis, S. steinbachii* (& var. *gracilior*, var. *horrida*, var. *polymorpha*), *S. swobodae, S. tarabucoensis, S. taratensis, S. tarijensis, S. tiraquensis* (& var. *electracantha*), *S. torotorensis, S. totorensis* (& var. *lepida*), *S. tunariensis, S. unguispina, S. vasqueziana, S. verticillacantha* (& var. *albispina*, var. *applanata*, var. *aureiflora*, var. *cuprea*, var. *minima* & fa. *brevispina*, *S. vizcarrae* (& var. *laui*), *S. zavaletae.*

Rejected names and synonymies:
S. 'albida' nom. nud. = *S. albissima*
S. bicolor Hort. = *S. steinbachii*
S. clizensis = *S. cochabambina*
S. cupreata Hort. = *S. flavissima*
S. langeri nom. prov. (not yet validated as a good species)
S. lepida = *S. totorensis* var. *lepida*
S. oenantha var. 'Epizana' Hort. = strong spined variant
S. pojoniensis = *S. cochabambina*
S. polymorpha = *S. steinbachii* var. *polymorpha*
S. rauschii var. *frankiana* Hort. = *S. rauschii*
S. steinbachii var. *rosiflora* = *S. steinbachii* (a pink flowered variant)
S. steinbachii var. *violaciflora* = *S. steinbachii* (a violet-pink flowered variant)
S. taratensis var. *minima* = *S. verticillacantha* var. *minima*
S. tiraquensis var. *bicolorispina* nom. prov. (not yet validated as a good variety)
S. tiraquensis var. *horrida* Hort. = strong spined variant
S. vasqueziana var. *albispina* = *S. verticillacantha* var. *albispina*
S. verticillacantha var. *chatajillensis* = *S. alba*
S. verticillacantha var. *ritteri* = *S. verticilloacantha* var. *albispina*
S. verticillacantha var. *verticosior* = *S. verticillacantha.*

Recommended species: *S. arenacea.* Although varying in spine length and colouring, this is a most attractively-spined species. It forms neat rows of the clusters of short white or brown spines, forming a geometric delight in their arrangement on the brownish-green body, which is globular and tends to stay solitary for some years before clustering from around the base. The flowers are a rich, deep yellow, smaller than many other species.

S. candiae has dark purple-brown bodies and golden yellow to brownish-yellow spines in orderly combs. It clusters readily, to form low mounds to 8 in (20 cm) or more wide, and produces its deep yellow flowers freely.

S. canigueralii has purple-brown bodies with short brown spines lying flat against the body, and forms low clusters of its inch wide (2–3 cm) stems. Flowers are bicoloured, red and yellow, the latter colour in the throat of each bloom and varying in its amount from plant to plant.

S. crispata is variable in spine length and colour of spines,

245. *Strombocactus schmiedickeanus* var. *macrochele*

246. *Sulcorebutia candiae*

247. *Sulcorebutia crispata*

248. *Sulcorebutia cylindrica*

from pinkish-brown to white, short in some plants (3–4 mm long) to 2–3 cm in others, the spines usually curling and twisting erratically, and all but obscuring the brownish-green plant body, which clusters readily to form low mounds. Flowers are magenta, sometimes with a whitish throat.

S. flavissima has bright yellow, dense spines and wonderfully contrasting bright magenta-pink flowers. It is slow to form a clustering plant, making quite large stems before doing so, to about 3 in (8 cm) or so.

S. glomeriseta is completely obscured by its fine, bristle-like cream-yellow to brownish-yellow spines, forming lumpy, untidy clusters of stems, each about 2½–3 in (7–8 cm) wide. It has a succession of small deep yellow flowers.

S. langeri, although only a provisional name is likely to be ratified as it is an individual species in the style of *S. arenacea*, but in miniature, with very short spines in neat clusters and yellow flowers freely produced.

S. mentosa has wonderfully dark, mahogany red-brown spines, and generally remains solitary for some years before producing random offsets in cultivation. Flowers are magenta with paler throat.

S. mizquensis is a delightful, small-headed species, densely white spined with lilac flowers, clustering to form small, hand sized clumps.

S. rauschii is very variable, but usually of a very low-growing habit, barely getting above soil level often. It has tiny clusters of spines, usually black, in money-spider like clusters, and deep purple-magenta flowers. The body

147

249. *Sulcorebutia glomeriseta*

250. *Sulcorebutia mentosa*

251. *Sulcorebutia rauschii* form

252. *Sulcorebutia tiraquensis* var. *tiraquensis*

colour varies from dull green to purple.

S. tiraquensis is densely and finely spined, and the best of the varieties, although still only provisionally named, is *S. tiraquensis* var. *bicolorispina*, with silvery-white and deep red-brown spines, and magenta to purple-red flowers. Individual stems are about 2–2½ in (5–8 cm) tall and wide, getting taller in age, and eventually forming quite large clusters.

S. verticillacantha is probably the most variable species, and threatens to engulf a few more of the presently recognized species. Two already named as such stand out: *S. verticillacantha* var. *aureiflora*, with small, acorn-sized stems, densely clustering and smothering itself with flowers varying from plant to plant, from all yellow, through orange to deep red with yellow throat.

S. verticillacantha var. *cuprea* has a copper-brown coloured body and deep fire-red flowers, developing into clusters with heads about 2½–3 in (7 to 8 cm) tall and wide with brown bristly spines.

Connoisseur's choice: *S. arenacea, S. canigueralii, S. flavissima, S. langeri, S. rauschii.*

253. *Sulcorebutia verticillacantha* var. *aureiflora*

254. *Sulcorebutia verticillacantha* var. *cuprea*

Tacinga B. & R. *The Cact.* 1:39 (1919)

A slender-stemmed *Opuntia*-like shrubby genus from Brazil, almost unknown in cultivation, and with nothing to recommend it. It is separated from *Opuntia* because of the odd construction of the flowers.

Species named are *T. atropurpurea* (& var. *zehntnerioides*), *T. funalis*.

They are not recommended.

Tephrocactus Lem (1868)

Referred to *Opuntia*.

Thelocactus (K. Schum,) B. & R., *Bull. Torr. Bot. Club* 49:251 (1922)

Gordon Rowley's view of this genus is preferred herein, although Nigel Taylor, subsequent to Gordon's exposition in his excellent book, *Name that Succulent,* has taken the view that this genus should be incorporated in the broad view of the genus *Ferocactus,* along with *Ancistrocactus, Hamatocactus, Gladulicactus, Stenocactus* and *Sclerocactus,* hiving off *Echinomastus* to *Neolloydia.* Rowley puts together beneath *Thelocactus* these genera, excluding *Stenocactus* (and *Ferocactus,* of course), as well as the two wayward genera, *Echinomastus* and *Coloradoa,* the latter also ascribed by Taylor to *Neolloydia. Hamatocactus hamatacanthus* and *H. sinuatus,* however, have been transferred to *Ferocactus.*

All are popular with collectors for their attractive, sometimes fierce spines and good flowering capabilities. *Thelocactus* in the narrow sense presents few problems in cultivation, making slow but steady growth to form quite large, usually squat plants, and flowering readily, with mostly sumptuous, large flowers. The new boys to the genus are a different kettle of fish, and are generally not easy at all, being subject to attack by fungal disorders at the least excuse, and, in England at least, are probably safer grown as grafted plants, maintaining their solitary state even on the graft for a considerable time if not rushed, and growing good spines and flowering well. They are also prey to sooty moulds, which forms on the sugar solution exuded from the glands common to all species in this genus (see p. 14).

Species named (with more usually seen names in brackets, abbreviated) are: *T. bicolor* (& var. *bolansis,* var. *flavidispinus,* var. *pottsii,* var. *schottii,* var. *schwarzii,* var. *texensis,* var. *tricolor*), *T. bueckii, T. conothelos* (& var. *argenteus,* var. *aurantiacus,* var. *mcdowellii*), *T.(Scl)contortus, T.(Ech)erectocentrus* (& var. *acunensis*), *T.(Scl)glaucus, T. hastifer, T. (Scl)havasupaianus* (& var. *roseus*), *T. heterochromus T. hexaedrophorus* (& var. *decipiens,* var. *droegeanus,* var. *fossulatus*(, *T. (Ech)intertextus, T. (Ech)johnsonii* (& var. *lutescens,* *T. krainzianus, T. (Ech) krausii, T. leucacanthus* (& var. *ehrenbergii,* var. *porrectus,* var. *sanchez-mejoradai,* var. *schmollii*). *T. lloydii, T. lophothele, T. (Ech)mapimiensis, T. (Ech)mariposensis, T. mathssonii, T. matudae, T. (Col)mesaverdae, T. (Scl)parviflorus* (& var. *blessingiae,* var. *intermedius*), *T. (Scl)polyancistrus, T. (Scl)pubispinus, T. rinconensis* (& var. *nidulans,* var. *phymatothele*), *T. saussieri, T. (Anc)scheerii* (& fa. *brevihamatus,* fa. *megarhizus*), *T. (Ham)setispinus* (& fa. *flavibaccatus*), *T. (Scl)spinosior, T. (Scl)terrae-canyonae, T. (Anc)tobuschii, T. tulensis, T.*

(*Anc/Gla*)*uncinatus* (& var. *wrightii*), *T.* (*Ech*)*unguispinus* (& var. *durangensis*, var. *laui*), *T. wagnerianus*, *T.* (*Ech*)*warnockii*, *T.* (*Scl*)*whipplei* (& var. *heilii*, var. *reevesii*, var. *roseus*), *T.* (*Scl*)*wrighti*

Rejected names and synonymies:

T. (*Ech*)*acunensis* = *T. erectocentrus*
T. (*Anc*)*crassihamatus* = *T. mathssonii*
T. (*Ech*)*durangensis* = *T. unguispinus* var. *durangensis*
T. ehrenbergii = *T. leucacanthus* var. *ehrenbergii*
T. flavidispinus = *T. bicolor* var. *flavidispinus*
T. fossulatus = *T. hexaedrophorus* var. *fossulatus*
T. (*Scl*)*intermedius* = *T. parviflorus* var. *intermedius*
T. (*Ech*) *laui* = *T. unguispinus* var. *laui*
T. (& *Ech*)*macdowellii* = *T. conothelos* var. *mcdowellii*
T. (*Anc*)*megarhizus* = *T. scheerii* fa. *megarhizus*
T. nidulans = *T. rinconensis* var. *nidulans*
T. phymatothele = *T. rinconensis* var. *phymatothele*
T. (*Anc*)*scheerii* fa. *crassihamatus* = *T. mathssonii*
T. schwarzii = *T. bicolor* var. *schwarzii*

Recommended species:
T. bicolor has been a deserved favourite for many years because of its strong, two coloured spination and large, silky textured pink flowers flushed with red in the throat. Its varieties are less well known and somewhat neglected, and *T. bicolor* var. *bolansis* in particular is a lovely harmony of yellow dense spines on a more narrowly columnar plant and with lilac flowers with white throat.

T. conothele in its various varieties is worth a place. *T. conothele* var. *aurantiacus* has a good covering of silver and dark brown spines, and yellow flowers, while *T. conothelos* var. *mcdowellii* (still seen erroneously labelled as *Echinomastus macdowellii*) is a delight of dense silvery white spines completely covering the globular plant and with deep purple-pink flowers from the centre.

T. erectocentrus is one of the most attractively spined of the former *Echinomastus* species, with white radial spines lying flat against the stem, and strong, erect, dark brown central spines. Flowers are pale pink with yellow throat.

T. johnsonii is one of the more fiercely spined of the *Echinomastus* species, covered with strong, projecting spines in grey and red. Flowers are pale to purplish pink.

T. leucacanthus is not easy to flower in England, although in a good year it will oblige if it gets sufficient sunshine. Spines are sparsely set and weak, and flowers are deep yellow; *T. leucacanthus* var. *schottii* has deep purple flowers.

T. (*Sclerocactus*) *polyancistrus* is perhaps the doyenne of the former Sclerocactus species, making large, pineapple

255. *Thelocactus bicolor*

256. *Thelocactus conothele* var. *aurantiacus*

257. *Thelocactus leucacanthus*

258. *Thelocactus mapimiensis*

size plants, covered with a glorious, twisting basketwork of spines in red and white, with long, fiercely hooked central spines also curling this way and that, surmounted with large flowers in a delicate shade of reddish-pink. But it is difficult in cultivation in England at least, and needs maximum light and careful watering with a well-drained compost for success; heat is not so important as one might think, since these plants come from areas which regularly get sub-zero temperatures although with our winter humidity accompanying the low temperatures such treatment might not be so desirable.

T. rinconensis in any of its three varieties, the type and var. *nidulans* with long spines, var. *phymatothele* with very short ones, is a worthwhile plant to grow, producing its pale pink flowers in succession throughout the growing season at the centre of the plant, and if kept in full light maintaining its wild heavy spination for the former two, and the beautiful blue body colouring, so prominent a

feature in the last named.

T. saussieri is getting into cultivation now as seed has become available in the last few years, and is an attractive plant to grow, with dense, white spines covering the plant, and strong, contrasting, blackish-brown central spines projecting through them; flowers are

T. scheerii in its various forms has been a challenge to grow for some years, and many have failed to keep it going for any real length of time. But it is worth the effort, which seems to require a careful hand with the watering-can, especially early and late in the season, and a well-drained compost and light position to induce flowering in its intriguing shade of green to yellowish-green, darkly marked on the outer petals.

T. setispinus is a splendidly flowering species, providing that measures against the scourge of sooty mould forming on the exuded nectar from the glands above the areoles, which in this species tends to be profuse, although all

151

259. *Thelocactus mariposensis*

260. *Thelocactus rinconensis* var. *phymatothele*

261. *Thelocactus scheerii*

262. *Thelocactus setispinus*

species in this genus suffer from this disfiguring ailment (see p. 14). They remain solitary for some time, eventually offsetting, making short columnar bodies to about a foot (30 cm) tall and some 4 to 6 in (10 to 15 cm) wide, with thin, flexible, very long spines, the centrals hooked viciously. The readily produced flowers are yellow and become more and more numerous as the plants increase in size, making a wonderful show.

T. uncinatus, known for many years as *Glandulicactus uncinatus* has been a popular plant for many years, and a challenge to grow too, being prone to marking up badly with sooty mould forming on the sugary secretion of the glands so prominent on the plant's tubercles – a problem with many species of this genus – but the long curving and hooked spines and the unusually coloured wine-red or red-brown flowers make it worth the trouble of trying to keep clean by frequent spraying in the growing season, or by regular applications of a fungicide to keep the sooty mould at bay.

T. unguispinus has very thick, recurving spines in dark brown, aging to grey, and with lighter brown radial spines. Flowers are green.

T. unguispinus var. *laui* has become readily available in recent times and grows well either on a graft, or on its

own roots in a well drained compost and with careful watering.

T. (Sclerocactus) whipplei is the most often seen in collections, although it too does present difficulties in cultivation for any length of time, and the most long lived plants in England at least are those which have been grafted. It has two-coloured spines, not so long or as dense as in *T. polyancistrus*, but still clothing the plant thoroughly with a mixture of red-brown and white somewhat straighter spines, and producing fairly readily its dark red flowers at the apex. It grows well as a graft, not offsetting excessively or too early.

Connoisseur's choice: *T. bicolor* var. *bolansis, T. erectocentrus, T. johnsonii, T. mapimiensis, T. mariposensis, T. polyancistrus, T. saussieri, T. scheerii, T. uncinatus, T. unguispinus, T. whipplei.*

Thelocephala Ito (1957)

Referred to *Neoporteria.*

Thrixanthocereus Backeb. (1937)

Referred to *Espostoa.*

Toumeya B. & R. *The Cact.* 3:91 (1922)

Although this monotypic genus (*T. papyracantha*) from New Mexico has been referred by some authorities to *Pediocactus,* the combination has been challenged by others, and the rank and file collectors and nurserymen have closed ranks and still use the name for this very individual plant. It is dealt with separately here while the doubts remain.

Recommended species: *T. papyracantha* is a tiny plant in the wild, barely half a finger length long and usually solitary, with flexible, papery spines curling over the top of the plant and concealing its presence very effectively by mimicking dead grass clumps among which it grows at about 6000 feet altitude, suffering well below zero temperatures at times. In cultivation it is very often grown as a graft, when it forms clusters which after a few years get leggy and need starting again.

Connoisseur's choice: *T. papyracantha.*

263. *Thelocactus uncinatus,* in habitat in limestone, Texas, USA

264. *Thelocactus wagnerianus*

Trichocereus

Trichocereus (Bgr.) Riccobono, *Boll. R. Ort. Bot. Palermo* 8:236 (1909); Fried. & Rowl., *I.O.S. Bull*, 3 (1974)

Referred to *Echinopsis*.

Turbinicarpus Buxb. & Backeb. (1937)

Referred to *Strombocactus*.

Uebelmannia Buining, *Succulenta* 46:159 (1967)

This is the most exciting discovery in recent years in the cactus world. To discover new species is not so surprising in view of the vast areas where these plants grow in the wild, and many more will no doubt be discovered as the intrepid collectors get into the more remote, unexplored parts, but to find a new genus is extraordinary indeed. The first few found were ascribed to Parodia, to which they bore a superficial resemblance, but when some of the more striking species were found it became apparent that a new genus had been discovered and it was so described. The species are still far from common in collections, and many that were imported from their native Brazil have perished, since they do present some difficulty in cultivation. Extra heat seems to be one of the requirements, and a minimum of 55° F (13° C) is recommended for safety. Their attraction lies in the neat, vertical ribs clothed with dark brown to black bristle-like spines and the dark brown to purple body colouring. They are slow but not impossible on their own roots, but grafting is often resorted to with good effect as they tend to stay solitary and not grow uncharacteristically as so many plants do on a graft. The flowers are disappointingly small and yellow, appearing in more thickly woolled areas on the ribs near the apex of the plants, but they are not easily produced in England.

Species named are: *U. buiningii, U. flavispina, U. gummifera, U. meninensis* (& var. *rubra*), *U. pectinifera* (& var. *horrida*, var. *pseudopectinifera*).

Recommended species: *U. buiningii* is the smallest of the species and very slow growing, even on a graft. The body colour is a rich purple, and the few ribs have wayward brown wispy spines.
U. pectinifera is probably the most sought after of all species, with an orderly arrangement of spines down the vertical ribs, dark brown or nearly black, and similar purple body colouring to *U. buiningii*, which seems intensified on strongly growing grafted plants.

Connoisseur's choice: *U. pectinifera*.

Utahia B. & R. (1922)

This monotypic genus (*U. sileri*) is referred to *Pediocactus*.

Vatricania Backeb. (1950)

Referred to *Espostoa*.

Weberauerocereus Backeb. (1942)

Referred to *Haageocereus*.

Weberocereus B. & R., *Contrib. U.S. Nat. Herb.* 12:431 (1909)

This is a small genus of epiphytic cacti from Central America and Ecuador, of little interest other than to epiphyte enthusiasts.

Species named are: *W. biolleyi, W. bradei, W. glaber, W. panamensis, W. tonduzii, W. trichophorus, W. tunilla*.

They are not recommended.

Weingartia Werderm., *Kakteenk.* 1937. 21 (1937); Pilbeam, *Sulcorebutia and Weingartia – A Collector's Guide* (1985)

The separate standing of this genus from Bolivia and northern Argentina has been questioned, and there have been moves towards submerging it beneath *Gymnocalycium*. But while some species do have a strong leaning in that direction the more commonly seen *Weingartia* species tend to discredit the amalgamation, and one or two species indicate a closer link with *Sulcorebutia*. With the odd exception Weingartias are excellent species for flowering, producing many flowers on quite small plants, and they have attractive yellow or brownish-yellow spines on globular stems to about 4–5 in (10–12 cm) or more, later becoming short-columnar and sometimes clustering. A few species produce their flowers from the centre of the growing point and are less free flowering and less spiny. These more southerly species are somewhat different in appearance from those usually seen.

Species named are: *W. buiningiana, W. chuquichuquiensis, W. cintiensis, W. corroana, W. erinacea* (& var. *catarinensis*), *W. fidaiana, W. gracilispina, W. hediniana, W. kargliana, W. knizei, W. lanata, W. lecoriensis, W. longigibba, ·W. mataralensis, W. multispina, W. neocumingii* (& var. *koehresii*), *W. neumanniana, W. pilcomayensis, W. platygona, W. pulquinensis* (& var. *mairanensis*), *W. riograndensis, W. saetosa, W. saipinensis, W. sucrensis, W. trollii, W. vilcayensis, W. westii*.

Rejected names and synonymies (apart from the accepted species of *Sulcorebutia* which have mostly been also allotted to this genus at one time or another):
W. aglaia = *Sulcorebutia tiraquensis* var. *bicolorispina* (nom. prov.)

W. albissima = *Sulcorebutia albissima*
W. backebergiana = *Sulcorebutia steinbachii* var. *horrida*
W. brachygraphisa = *W. neocumingii* form
W. brevispina = *Sulcorebutia verticillacantha* fa. *brevispina*
W. chilensis = *Neowerdermannia chilensis*
W. clavata = *S. steinbachii*
W. croceareolata = *Sulcorebutia* sp. (indeterminate)
W. cumingii = *W. neocumingii*
W. flavida = *Sulcorebutia flavissima*
W. formosa = *Sulcorebutia losenickyana*
W. hajekyana Hort. = *W. pulquinensis* var. *mairanensis*
W. mairanana = *W. pulquinensis* var. *mairanensis*
W. margarethae = *Rebutia margarethae*
W. mocharasensis = *W. kargliana*
W. neglecta = *W. neocumingii*
W. neumanniana var. *aurantia* = *W. neumanniana*
W. nigro-fuscata = *Sulcorebutia tiraquensis* var. *spinosior* (nom. prov.)
W. oligacantha = *Sulcorebutia tarijensis*
W. pasopayana = *Sulcorebutia pulchra*
W. perplexiflora = *Sulcorebutia pulchra*
W. pygmaea = *W. kargliana*
W. ritteri = *Sulcorebutia verticillacantha* var. *albispina*
W. sanguineo-tarijensis = *Sulcorebutia tarijensis*
W. saxatilis = *Sulcorebutia verticillacantha* var. *albispina*
W. torotorensis = *Sulcorebutia torotorensis*
W. totoralensis = *Sulcorebutia* (*hoffmanniana*?)
W. viscarrae = *Sulcorebutia vizcarrae*.

Recommended species: *W. neumanniana* is an individual species from the smaller group of Weingartias coming from farther south in Bolivia than most. It is quite a small plant with a thick tap root, constricted at the junction with the upper part of the plant; the part appearing above ground being a purplish brown colour with strong black spines in sparse clusters, and with orange flowers produced at the apex of the plant.

W. pilcomayensis is a good example of the prominently tufted type of *Weingartia*, where the clusters of spines are surmounted with a thick pad of creamy white wool from which the flowers appear. As with most of this type of *Weingartia* the flowers are abundant, appearing two or three to an areole often, and coloured deep yellow.

W. pulquinensis is one of the multitudinously fine-spined Weingartias, absolutely covered with a porcupine coating of long, needle sharp bristle-like spines in brown or yellowish-brown tipped brown. The flowers are yellow and as abundant as in the previous species.

W. trollii has the distinction of having either yellow or red flowers, and falls between the previous two in its spination, with short, strong spines fairly abundant, but with only a slight tuft above each areole.

Connoisseur's choice: *W. neumanniana.*

265. *Weingartia pilcomayensis*

266. *Weingartia pulquinensis*

Werckleocereus B. & R. (1909)

Referred to *Weberocereus.*

Wigginsia D. M. Porter (1964)

Referred to *Notocactus.*

Wilcoxia

Wilcoxia B. & R. (1909)

Referred to *Echinocereus* in part, and to *Peniocereus* in part.

Wilmattea B. & R. (1920)

Referred to *Hylocereus*.

Winteria Ritt. (1962)

Referred to *Hildewintera,* and thence to *Borzicactus*.

Wittia Schum. (1903)

Referred to *Disocactus*.

Wittiocactus Rauschert (1982)

A recent separation of species from *Wittia*, now referred with that genus to *Disocactus*.

Yungasocereus Ritt., *Kakt. Sudamer.* 2:688 (1980)

This is a monotypic genus set up recently by Friedrich Ritter for the former *Samaipaticereus inquisivensis.* It is here regarded as synonymous with *Haageocereus*.

Zehntnerella B. & R., *The Cact.* 2:176, figs 249, 250 (1920)

Ritter has recently added another species and variety to this formerly monotypic genus from Brazil. They are columnar cacti of little interest except to *Cereus* enthusiasts, or those who want the complete alphabet.

Species named are: *Z. chaetacantha* (& var. *montealtoi*), *Z. squammulosa*

Zygocactus K. Schum. (1890)

It is a pity that this still popularly used name must be referred to synonymy with *Schlumbergera*.

GLOSSARY WITH PARTICULAR REFERENCE TO CACTI

The glossary below is by no means a complete one; for this none can be bettered than that contained in William Stearn's *Botanical Latin* (1966), on which I have leaned heavily. I also gained support from Roger Ivimey-Cook's excellent work for the then National Cactus & Succulent Society, *Succulents – A Glossary of Terms and Descriptions* (1974), sadly now out of print. I have provided below sufficient material to give the reader an insight into cactus names. I have also included some of the more commonly met botanical terms bandied about by the knowledgeable often to the bewilderment of ordinary enthusiasts like myself.

Pronunciation is a pain to beginners and old hands alike, and is not so terribly important, provided that we understand each other. A few ground rules may help. Accent usually falls on the penultimate syllable if it is a 'long' syllable, or if it has only two syllables, e.g. plumōsa, or pīcta. Otherwise it falls on the syllable before the penultimate one, e.g. Mammillāria, Rebūtia. But there are exceptions through common usage. The vowels and consonants most often presenting difficulty are those below, but again there are exceptions:

ae = ee as in 'keep'
au = a as in ball.
c is hard as in 'cap' before a, o or u; and soft as in 'ceiling' before e, i or y
ch is hard as in 'choral' before a, o or u; and soft as in 'chimney' before e, i or y
ei = as in 'height'
g is hard, as in 'game' before a, o or u; and soft as in 'gentle' before e, i or y
oe = ee as in 'keep'
oi is pronounced as two syllables, not as in 'hoist'.

a-, an- without, lacking
acantha spine
-aceae suffix to type genus to indicate family name
-aceus, -a, -um resembling
aciculus, -a, -um; acicularis, -is, -e needle; needle shaped
acro- the top, apex
actino- star-like, radiating
aculeatus, -a, -um spiny
acuminatus, -a, -um tapering gradually, or abruptly from incurving sides to a narrow point
-acus belonging to
acutus, -a, -um acute, narrowed gradually to a point
ad- at, to, near to
adpressed lying flat to, or pressed towards
adscendens ascending
adustus, -a, -um scorched, blackened
adventitious development of part of plant in unusual position, e.g. roots on stem
-ae suffix indicating finder of species is female
aequalis, aequi- equal
aequilateralis with equal sides
aer-, aerial air, of or in the air, e.g. aerial roots
affinis, aff. having affinity to, related, similar to
agavoides like an Agave
agglomeratus, -a, -um heaped closely together
aggregatus, -a, -um clustered together
alatus, -a, -um wing; wing-like
albescens whitish, becoming white
albi- white
albicans tending towards white
albidus, -a, -um whitish, somewhat white
albus, -a, -um white
-alis pertaining to, resembling
-allo- another, different
alpestris nearly alpine
alpinus, -a, -um alpine, growing at alpine heights
alteolatus highly scented
altus, -a, um tall, high

Glossary with particular reference to cacti

amarus, -a, -um   bitter

ambiguus, -a, -um   ambiguous, uncertain

ambly-   blunt, dull

amethystinus, -a, -um   amethyst, violet

ammophilus, -a, um   sand-loving, growing preferentially in sand

amoenus, -a, -um   pleasing, beautiful

amorphus, -a, um   amorphous, without shape

amphi-   double, on both sides, of two kinds

amplexi-   clasping

amplus, -a, um   ample, abundant, large

an-   without, lacking

ancistro-   hooked

andro-, -andrus   male

anemo-   pertaining to the wind

anfractuosus, -a, -um   twisted, tortuous, sinuous

angi-   container

anguinus, -a, -um   lizard-like

angularis   angled

angulus   angle

angusti-   narrowed

aniso-   unequal

annularis   ring-shaped

anomalus, -a, -um   abnormal, different from normal

ante-   before, preceding

anther   part of stamen with the pollen

antho-   of the flower

anti-   against

-anus, -a, -um   belonging to, pertaining to

apertus, -a, -um   open

apex; apici-   apex, top; pertaining to the apex, or top

apo-   from, away from

applanatus, -a, -um   flattened

appressed   lying flat to, or pressed towards

apricus, -a, -um   exposed to the sun

arachn-   spider-like

arachnoideus, -a, -um   cobwebby

arboreus-, -a, -um   tree

arche, archi-   first

arcuatus, -a, -um   bowed, arc-like

arenaceus, -a, -um   sandy

arenicolus, -a, -um   inhabiting sandy places

areole   felty pad from which spines arise

argenteus, -a, -um   silvery-white

aridus, -a, -um   dry

-aris   pertaining to

armatus, -a, -um   armed, spiny

arrigens   erect

arthro-   jointed, articulate

articulatus, -a, -um   jointed, articulate

ascendens   ascending, usually obliquely

-ascens   becoming

asper, -era, -erum   rough

asselliformis   like a woodlouse

astero-, astro-   starry, star-like

ater, atra, atrum   black

atro-   blackish, dark

auctus, -a, -um   enlarged, added to

aurantiacus, -a, -um   orange

aureus, -a, -um   golden yellow

austro-   southern, southerly

australis   south, southern

axil   the junction of different parts of plant, literally armpit, in cacti usually referring to junction of tubercles or ribs

azureus, -a, -um   sky blue

barbatus, -a, -um   bearded, with tufts of bristles or hair

basilaris, -is, -e   basal

bellus, -a, -um   beautiful

bi-   two

bombycinus, -a, -um   silken

bonus, -a, -um   good

borealis   northern

brachy-   short

brevi-   short

brunescens   brownish, becoming brown

brunneus, -a, -um   brown

bumammus, -a, -um   with very large tubercles

caeruleus, -a, -um   pale blue

caesius, -a, -um   lavender blue, grey blue

caespitosus, -a, -um   growing in clumps, tufted

-cal-   beautiful

calcareus, -a, -um   chalky, limey

calcifuge   plant abhorring chalky or limy soil

calli-   beautiful

callus   corky tissue forming over wound

calo-   beautiful

calymm-   sheathed, covered

calyx   protective sepals around flower

campanulate   bell shaped

campestris, -is, -e   growing in plains, or flat areas

campo, campso, campto, campylo-   bent, curved

canaliculatus, -a, -um   with longitudinal grooves or channels

candelaris   candle-like

candicans   becoming pure white

candidus, -a, -um   pure, shining white

canescens   becoming grey

canus, -a, -um   greyish white, usually of hair

capensis, -is, -e   of or from the cape, referring to a cape area

capillus   hair

capitatus, -a, -um   with a blunt head

capricornis, -is, -e   with horns, like a goat

caput   head

cardia-, cardio   of the heart

cardinalis   cardinal red

carinatus, -a, -um   keel or ridge

carmineus, -a, -um   carmine

carneus, -a, um   flesh coloured, pale pink

carnosus, -a, -um   fleshy, succulent

carpus, -a, -um   fruit

caryo-   nut, kernel, nucleus

castaneus, -a, -um   chestnut-coloured

cataphractus, -a, -um   scaly

celsus, -a, -um   high

centralis, -is, -e   central, centrally placed

cephal-   head

cephalium   head differentiated from normal growth, usually applying to woolly or felty growth from which flowers arise

-ceras   horn

cerasinus, -a, -um   cerise, cherry red

cerato-   horned

cereus, -a, -um   waxy, wax candle-like

chaeto-   brittle

chalybeus, -a, -um   steel-grey

chamae-   low-growing, creeping

cheilo-   lip

cheiri-   sleeve

-chilus   lipped

chilensis, -is, -e   from Chile

chion-   snow

chlamys   cloak, covering

chlor-   green, greenish-yellow

chlorophyll   green cells in plant enabling photosynthesis

-chromus, -a, -um   coloured

-chrous   coloured

chrys-, chryso-   golden-yellow

-chylus   sap

ciliatus, -a, -um   fringed, like eye-lashes

cinctus   enclosed

cinereus, -a, -um   ash-grey

cinnabarinus, -a, -um   cinnabar, orange-red

circa, circum   around, near

cirrha   tendril

citri-   lemon, lemon-yellow

clavatus, -a, -um   club-shaped

cleisto-   closed

cline   series of forms of a species

clone   one plant of a species

coccineus, -a, -um   deep red, from scarlet to carmine

coeruleus, -a, -um   pale blue

-cola   inhabitant of, e.g. saxicola, growing in rock

collinus, -a, -um   growing on hill

color   colour

coloratus, -a, -um   coloured, reddish

columnaris, -is, -e   columnar

com-   with

comus, -a, -um; comosus, -a, -um   hair; with long hair

compressus, -a, -um   flattened

con-   with

concinnus, -a, -um   neat, elegant

concolor   of one colour, having the same colour

confinis   adjoining

conglomeratus, -a, -um   clustered

coni, cono-   cone like

conjungens   joining, fusing

connivens   converging

conoideus, -a, -um   almost conical

cordatus, -a, -um   heart, heart-shaped

-cornis   horned

cornutus, -a, -um   horn shaped

coronatus, -a, -um   crown, crown-shaped

coryne   club

costa   rib

crassus, -a, -um   thick

crebri-   closely

crest   cristate growth

cretaceus, -a, -um   chalky-white

crinis   with tufts of hair

crinitus, -a, -um   tufted, with long hairs

crispus, -a, -um; crispatus, -a, -um   curling, wavy, twisted

cristate   with multiple growing point, forming undulating, ribbon like growth

croceus, -a, -um   saffron yellow, orange

cruci-   cross shaped

crypto-   hidden, concealed

cteno-   comb-like

cuneatus, -a, -um   wedge shaped

cupreus, -a, -um   coppery

cuspidatus, -a, -um   sharp pointed

cyaneus, -a, -um   dark blue

cyath-   cup

cylindr-   cylindrical

cymb-   boat, boat shaped

cyto-   cell

dasy-   thickly hairy, shaggy

de-   down, away from

dealbatus, -a, -um   whitened

debilis, -is, -e   weak

deca-   ten

decipiens   deceiving

declinatus   bent or curved downwards or forwards

decumbens   lying prostrate with tip ascending

dejectus, -a, -um   fallen, low

dendr-   tree

dentatus, -a, -um   toothed

denticulatus, -a, -um   small-toothed

denudatus   bare, uncovered (with few spines)

Glossary with particular reference to cacti

depauperatus, -a, -um   dwarfed, starved

dependens   suspended, hanging down

depressus, -a, -um   lying flat, sunken at the centre

dexter, -tra, -trum   to the right, on the right

di-, dis-   two, in different directions

dia-   through, between

dich-   two

dichotomous   branching or dividing in pairs (usually at the apex)

digitatus, -a, -um   with stems radiating from one point; branching, literally with fingers

diminutus, -a, -um   small, diminished

dimorphus, -a, -um   having two forms

dioicus, -a, -um   unisexual, with flowers on one plant either only male or female

diplo-   double

disc-   like a disc, flat and circular in outline

discolor   of different colours

discrete   separate

diurnal   of the day, e.g. day-flowering

divaricatus, -a, -um   widespreading

divergens   diverging, going different ways

diversi-   various, differing

dodeca-   twelve

dolabratus, -a, -um   axe-shaped

dolicho-   long

-doxa   glory, splendour

dubius, -a, -um   doubtful

dumosus, -a, -um   bushy, dwelling in bushes

duo-   two

durus, -a, -um   hard

e-, ex-   out of, from

echinatus, -a, -um   like a hedgehog, armed with spines

echinu-   hedgehog

edulis, -is, -e   edible

egregius, -a, -um   excellent

elatus, -a, -um   tall, lofty

electro-   yellow, amber coloured

elegans   elegant

-ellus, -a, -um   diminutive, used with colours means a pale tint

elongatus, -a, -um   elongated, longer

-enatus   arising from

-end-, endo-   within

endemic   indigenous, native to

-ennea-   nine

-ensis, -ense   belonging to, coming from

epi-   upon, above

epidermis   outer covering, 'skin' of a plant or fruit

epiphyte   plant growing on other plants, but not parasitically

erectus, -a, -um   erect

erem-   desert

erio-   woolly

erubescens   reddening, becoming red or pink

erythro-   red

-escens   becoming, tending towards

esculentus, -a, -um   edible

eu-   thoroughly, truly

eury-   broad

ex-, e-   out of, from

exiguus, -a, -um   weak, feeble

F_1 first generation cross between different taxa

F_2 progeny of F_1 hybrids self fertilized

fallax   false, deceptive

farinosus, -a, -um   with a meal-like coating

-farius, -a, -um   -ranked, e.g. trifarius, three-ranked

fasciatus, -a, -um   fasciated, with multiple growing points, flattened, fanned out

fasciculatus, -a, -um   clustered, in bundles

fastigiatus, -a, -um   with branches clustered, parallel and erect

ferox   fierce

ferrugineus, -a, -um   red-brown, rust coloured

-ferus   bearing

fici-   fig-like

filiformis, -is, -e   thread-like, long and slender

fimbriatus, -a, -um   fringed

fissuratus, -a, -um   split by fissures

flagelliformis, -is, -e   whip-like

flammeus, -a, -um   bright, fiery red, scarlet

flav-   yellow

flexi-   pliable

floccosus, -a, -um   woolly, bearing tufts of hair

flor—   flower

folius, -a, -um   leaf

-form   shape, form

forma   category of taxonomy below rank of *varietas* (variety) referring to wild individual rather than discrete population

formosus, -a, -um   beautiful, finely formed

fossa; fossula   ditch; little furrow

fragilis, -is, -e   fragile, brittle

fragrans   fragrant, sweet smelling

frut-   shrubby

fulgens   brightly coloured

fuliginosus, -a, -um   dirty brown, sooty

fulv-   yellow-brown

funalis   rope-like

funicle   thread of attachment from seed to placenta

furcatus, -a, -um   forked

furfuraceus, -a, -um   scaly, scurfy

fusc-   dark, dark brown

galact- milky

gamo- united

gast- stomach-like, stomach-shaped

gemin- in pairs

gemmatus, -a, -um bearing buds

genus category of taxonomy containing species with some characters in common

geometrizans growing in a geometric or ordered manner

-ger bearing, carrying

gibb- humped, with hump-like swellings

giganteus, -a, -um very large and mighty

glabr- smooth, without hairs

gland secreting organ, as in *Ferocactus*, etc.

glareosus, -a, -um growing in gravelly places

glauc- with waxy bloom

globosus, -a, -um globose, shaped like a globe

glochid hair or bristle which is barbed, as in *Opuntia*

glomeratus, -a, -um clustered, heaped together

gloriosus, -a, -um glorious

gon- angled

gracilis, -is, -e slender

graft one plant united with another; in cacti this is usually done to induce more rapid growth in a slow growing plant, or more ready growth in a difficult one. Nurseries also use it as a means of quickly producing quantities of recently introduced plants, or those difficult on their own roots.

grandis, -is, -e large

granul- with a grain-like appearance, covered with granules

graveolens strong-smelling

gregarius, -a, -um growing in company with others

griseus, -a, -um grey, verging to blue

grossus, -a, -um thick, coarse, larger than usual

gummifera bearing gum, gummy

guttatus, -a, -um spotted, exuding drops

gymno- naked, not hairy or bristly

gyn- female

gyr- ring, circle

habitat place where wild plant grows

haem- blood-red

halo- salt

hamatus, -a, -um hooked at the tip, barbed

hastatus, -a, -um arrowhead-shaped

helio- of the sun

hemi- half

hepta- seven

herbarium place where plant material is stored for reference, usually dried

hetero- different

hexa- six

hilum part of seed where funicle is attached

hirsutus, -a, -um hairy, covered with long hairs

holo- whole, entire

holotype specimen upon which description of species is based

homalo- level, smooth

homo- alike, similar

homonym name which has been used for more than one plant

horizontalis, -is, -e horizontal

horridus, -a, -um very prickly, or bristly, or rough

Hort. of gardens, implying not a wild plant, or a name used commercially but not validly described

humilis, -is, -e low, low-growing

hybo- tuberculate

hybrid progeny of a cross between two different taxa

hydro- water

hygro- wet, damp, moist

hymen- membrane

hyp-, hypo- under, below

hyper- above, over

-ianus, -a, -um suffix indicating belonging to

-ianthinus, -a, -um violet

-ibus suffix meaning usually 'with'

icos- twenty

-icus, a, -um suffix often added to place names, indicating the origin of the plant

igneus, -a, -um bright red, burning

ignotus, -a, -um unknown

im-, in- in, not

incanus, -a, -um grey, hoary

incarnatus, -a, -um flesh-coloured

inconstans changeable

incrassatus, -a, -um thickened

inermis, -is, -e unarmed, spineless

infra- below, underneath

ingens very large, larger than normal

insignis, -is, -e outstanding, notable

insularis, -is, -e insular, isolated, of islands

inter- between, among

intra- within

intro- into

-inus, -a, -um belonging to, pertaining to

ion- violet

iso- like, equal, similar

isotype plant equating to the holotype

-issimus, -a, -um superlative, the most

ithy- straight

jucundus, -a, -um delightful

-jug- joined

junceus, -a, -um rush-like

Glossary with particular reference to cacti

juvenalis, -is, -e juvenile, youthful, sometimes implying perpetual juvenile form

kermesinus, -a, -um crimson
kewensis of or from the Royal Botanic Garden, Kew

labiatus, -a, -um lipped
lachno- woolly
lacteus, -a, -um milky
laete- lightly, brightly
lampro- bright, shining
lanatus, -a, -um woolly
lanceolatus, -a, -um lance shaped: pointed, tapering, narrow
laniferus, -a, -um bearing wool
lanuginosus, -a, -um woolly, downy
lasi- woolly
late-, lati- broadly, widely
lateral side growth
latex sap
latus, -a, -um broad, wide
lavandulus, -a, -um lavender-violet
laxi, laxus, -a, -um loose
lectotype type selected from original collection of taxon, when holotype is not available
lei-, leio- smooth
lentus, -a, -um pliant, flexible, sluggish
lepido- scaly, flaky
leprosus, -a, -um scurfy
lepto- slender, thin
leuc-, leuco- white, pale, whitish-
lineatus, -a, -um lined
litoralis, littoralis, -is, -e pertaining to the seashore
lividus, -a, -um pale bluish-grey, lead coloured
lobatus, -a, -um lobed
loc. cit., l.c. loco citata (at the place cited previously)
longus, -a, -um long
loph-, lopho- crest, crested
loratus, -a, -um strap shaped
lox- slanting, oblique, leaning
lucidus, -a, -um shining, bright, transparent
luridus, -a, -um dirty yellowish brown
luteolus, -a, -um pale yellow
lutescens yellowish, becoming yellow
luteus, -a, -um deep yellow, golden yellow

machaer- dagger
macr-, macro- long, large, great
magni- large
magnificus, -a, -um magnificent
major greater, larger

malaco- soft
-mallus, -a, -um wool
mammilla nipple, nipple-like projection
mammillatus, -a, -um having nipples
mammosus, -a, -um having large breasts or breast-like parts, like a large nipple
marginatus, -a, -um with margins, prominently edged
maritimus, -a, -um growing by the sea
marmoratus, -a, -um marbled
maximus, -a, -um greatest, largest
medi- middle
mega-, megalo- large, great
mei-, meio- less, smaller, fewer
mela-, melano- black, very dark
melo- melon-like
meso- middle
meta- with
micro- little, small
miniatus, -a, -um orange-red, red lead colour
minimus, -a, -um very small, very least
minor smaller
minuscule tiny
minutus, -a, -um very small, minute
mirabilis, -is, -e wonderful
mitis, -is, -e soft, mild, gentle
mitri- mitre
modestus, -a, -um modest, small
mollis, -is, -e soft, soft haired
mon-, mono- single, one
monotypic one type, e.g. genus with only one species
monstrosus, -a, -um monstrose, monstrous, abnormal, with multiple growing points producing a proliferation of offsets or growth
montanus, -a, -um pertaining to or growing on mountains
morph- shape, form
mucro- sharp point
multi- many, much
multiplex of many parts
muricatus, -a, -um rough with many sharp points
musc- moss-like
mutabilis, is-, -e changeable
muticus, -a, -um blunt, without points
myrio- very many, countless
mystax moustache

nanus, -a, -um dwarf
napiformis, -is, -e turnip shaped, usually referring to roots
ne no, not, without
neglectus, -a, -um neglected
neo- new, used usually for new taxon with close connections or similarities to another

nidulans; nidus pertaining to a nest, nest-like

niger, -gra, -grum glossy black, black

niv- pertaining to snow, snow-white

nobilis, -is, -e noble, well-known

noct- night

nom. nud., n.n. nomen nudum: name published without complete or valid description

notabilis, -is, -e noteworthy, remarkable

noto- southern, south

nov. new

nudus, -a, -um naked, bare, without spines etc.

nutans drooping, nodding

nyct- night

ob- inverse, reversed

obtusus, -a, -um obtuse, rounded

obvallatus, -a, -um surrounded with a ridge, or a rampart

occidentalis, -is, -e western

occultus, -a, -um hidden, obscured

oct- eight

ochraceus, -a, -um pale yellowish-brown, yellow ochre

odoratus, -a, -um fragrant, sweet smelling

-oides similar to

-olens sweet smelling

olig- few

olivaceus, -a, -um olive green

-olus, -a, -um diminutive suffix, the least

-opsis like, similar to

orb- ring, circle, globe

oreo- pertaining to mountains

orientalis, -is, -e eastern

ornatus, -a, -um adorned, ornamented

ortho- straight

-osus, -a, -um full of

ovalis, -is, -e oval, elliptical

ovatus, -a, -um egg-shaped, with broadest part downwards

ovi- pertaining to egg

ox-, oxi- acid, sharp

pachy- thick, stout

pacificus, -a, -um pertaining to the Pacific Ocean

papilla; papillosa minute, blunt projection; covered with same

papyr- paper-like

para- beside, near, similar to

paradoxus, -a, -um strange, contradictory, paradoxical

parvus, -a, -um small

pauci- few

pectinatus, -a, -um comb-like

ped- foot, stalk

pend- hanging

penicillatus, -a, -um artist's brush-like, tufted

penni- feather

penta five

per through, entirely

peri- around, surrounding

pes, pedis pertaining to foot or stalk

petr- pertaining to rock or stone

pH symbol for scale of acidity or alkalinity, numbered 0 to 14; pH7 is neutral, lower readings indicate acidity, higher alkalinity

phae- dark, grey-brown

phil- loving, growing in

-phorus, -a, -um bearing, carrying

phyll- leaf

phymato- warty

pictus, picturatus coloured, painted

pili-, pilo- hairy

placent- flat and circular

plan- flat

platensis, -is, -e from the Rio de la Plata, South America

platy- flat, broad

pleio- more than usual

plenus, -a, -um full, double

plumbeus, -a, -um lead-coloured, grey

plumosus, -a, -um feathery

pluri- several, many

politus, -a, -um polished, shiny

poly- many

porphyr- reddish-purple

porrect directed outwards and forwards

prae- early, before

praestans distinguished

primulinus, -a, -um primrose-yellow

primus, -a, -um first

procerus, -a, -um high, very tall

procumbens trailing, lying on the ground

proliferus, -a, -um producing offsets readily

pruinosus, -a, -um pruinose, covered with waxy bloom

pruninus, -a, -um plum-coloured, purple

pseudo- false, i.e. resembling, but not the same

psilo- bald, bare

ptero- pertaining to a wing

pube-, pubi- pubescent, downy, finely hairy

pugioni- dagger-like

pulchellus, -a, -um small and beautiful

pulcher, -chra-, -chrum beautiful

pull- dark brown, blackish

pumilus, -a, -um dwarf, small

pungens pointed, piercing, sharp pointed

purpur- purple

-pus, -pes pertaining to feet or stalks

pusillus, -a, -um very small

pycn- dense, crowded, compact

pygmaeus, -a, -um dwarf, very small

Glossary with particular reference to cacti

pyrrh- fiery red

quadr- four
quin-, quinque- five

radial at the side
recti- straight, upright
recurvatus, -a, -um recurved
repandus, -a, -um with undulating margin
repens, reptans prostrate, creeping
rhodo- rose, rosy-red
rosi- rose coloured, pink
rub-, rubr- red
rufus, -a, -um reddish
rupicolus, -a, -um pertaining to rocks
rubiginosus, -a, -um rusty-brown
rupestris, -is, -e pertaining to rocks
rutilus, -a, -um red and yellow, orange

salmoneus, -a, -um salmon-pink, pink tending towards yellow
sanguini- blood-red
sax- pertaining to rocks
scion top part of graft
sciurus, -a, -um squirrel-like, like a squirrel's tail
sclero- hard
scop- broom-like
scopulinus, -a, -um pertaining to cliffs
seleni- pertaining to moon or moonlight
semi- half
semotus, -a, -um remote, distant
semper always, ever
senilis, -is, -e aged, with white hair or bristles
sept- seven
sericeus, -a, -um silky, with long glossy hairs
serpens creeping, snake-like
seta-, seti- stiff hair or bristle, bristly
sex- six
similis, -is, -e similar, resembling
simplex simple, unbranching
singularis, -is, -e unusual, singular, solitary
sinister left, to the left
sinuatus, -a, -um strongly waved, sinuate
smaragdi- emerald green
solitarius, -a, -um solitary, alone
soma body
sparsi- scattered, sparse
species taxonomic rank below genus, indicating population of interbreeding similar individuals, showing marked discontinuity from other species
speciosus, -a, -um beautiful, showy
spectabilis, -is, -e spectacular

sphacelatus, -a, -um with brown or black speckling
sphaer-, spher- spherical, globular
spini- of spines
spinuli- of small spines
spirali- spiralling, twisted
splendens shining, brilliant
squama- scale
stachy- pertaining to a spike
stamen stalk bearing the anther
stamin- of the stamens
-stele column
stell- star, star-like, radiating from centre
steno- narrow
stepho- crown, wreath
stigma tip of style
stigma lobe lobe at tip of style making up stigma
stock basal part of graft, plant on to which scion is grafted
stolon underground shoot
stolonifer, -a, -um having stolons
stramineus, -a, -um straw-coloured
strepto- twisted
striatus, -a, -um with stripes or lines
strigosus, -a, -um with stiff, straight, close pressed bristles
strobili- with overlapping scales, like a pine-cone
strombo- coiled in spirals
stropho- twisting, turning
style organ supporting stigma through which pollen tube passes to the ovary
sub- nearly, somewhat, almost
sulcatus, -a, -um grooved, with long channels
super- over, above
surculosus, -a, -um having suckers or stolons
sylvestris, -is, -e pertaining to woodland (sylvestrii – named for someone named Sylvester)
sym-, syn- with, together
synonym, syn. a term in taxonomy used for name or names incorrect according to the International Code for Botanical Nomenclature (ICBN)

tabularis, -is, -e plate-like, flattened
taxon, taxa (plural) taxonomic group of any rank
taxonomy study of classification of organisms
tenebrosus, -a, -um of dark places
tenuis, -is, -e slender
tephro- ash-grey
terr- of the earth
tetra- four
thele- nipple
thio- sulphur, or sulphur coloured
thrix- of hair
tinct- of colour

toment- thickly woolly

tort- twisted, tortuous

tot- all, many

trachy- rough

trans- across

tri- three

trich- hairy

tropaeo- nasturtium-red, bright orange-red

tuba- trumpet shaped

tuber swollen underground stem

tubercle small tuber like growth, nipple

tumidus, a-, -um thickened, swollen

tunicatus, -a, -um having tunic or coat of separable material

turbinatus, -a, -um turban-like, shaped like a top

turgidus, -a, -um inflated, swollen

type specimen to which name is attached, that plant originally described

uberi- luxuriant, fruitful

-ulus, -a, -um diminutive ending

umbrinus, -a, -um dark brown

uncinatus, -a, -um hooked

undatus, undulatus, -a, -um with wavy margins, undulating

ungui- claw-like

uni- one, single

vagans wandering

validus, -a, -um strong, well developed

variabilis, -is, -e variable, varying

variegate plant with abnormal colour of pigment in body of plant, usually yellow striped or mottled, sometimes red or reddish

variety, varietas taxonomic rank below species

vascular bundle column of cells transporting sap within a plant; in cacti a clearly differentiated ring revealed on cross sectioning

venustus, -a, -um beautiful, lovely

versi- variously

verticill- whorled

vescus, -a, -um thin, weak

vill- with long, soft hairs or bristles

violaceus, -a, -um violet coloured

viridi- green

vivus, -a, -um living

vulpinus, -a, -um fox-like

xanth- yellow

xero- dry

xiph- sword-like

xyl- woody

zephyr- western

zonatus, -a, -um zoned, with concentric markings

zygo- yoked, joined in pairs

BIBLIOGRAPHY (INCLUDING JOURNALS)

The following list of books includes those used by the author in researching for this book, as well as those recommended for further reading. As well as the books much important information is conveyed by means of the various journals which cater for the hobby. Most of the new descriptions of new species appear in such publications, and battles are fought on rationalization of species within different genera as well as the relationships of genera with each other; the more important of these journals are also listed.

Andersohn, Günter, *Cacti* (1983)
Anderson, Edward F., *Peyote The Divine Cactus* (1980)
Backeberg, Curt, *Die Cactaceae*, vols 1 to 6 (1958–62)
Backeberg, Curt, *Cactus Lexicon* (English edition) (1978)
Barthlott, Wilhelm, *Cacti* (1979)
Benson, Lyman, *The Cacti of the United States & Canada* (1982)
Benson, Lyman, *The Cacti of Arizona*, ed. 3 (1969)
Benson, Lyman, *The Native Cacti of California* (1969)
Bravo-Hollis, Helia, *Las Cactaceas de Mexico*, 2nd ed. vol. 1 (1978)
Britton, N. L. & Rose, J. N., *The Cactaceae* vols. 1 to 4 (1919–23)
Buining, A. F. H., *Discocactus* (1980)
Buxbaum, F. in Krainz, H., *Die Kakteen* (1956 et seq)
Craig, Robert T., *Mammillaria Handbook* (1945)
Cullman, Willy, Gotz, Erich & Groner, Gerhard, *Kakteen;* (*Cacti*, English edition) (1984; 1986)
Glass, Charles & Foster, Robert *Cacti & Succulents for the Amateur* (1977)
Haage, Walther, *Cacti and Succulents* (1963)
Hirao, Hiroshi, *Colour Encyclopaedia of Cacti* (1979)
Hunt, D. R. in Hutchison, J., *Cactaceae* (in *The Genera of Flowering Plants*) (1967)
Ito, Y., *Explanatory Diagram of Austroechinocactinae* (1957)
Ivimey-Cook, R. B., *Succulents – A Glossary of Terms and Descriptions* (1974)

Leighton-Boyce, G. & Iliff, J., *The Subgenus Tephrocactus* (1973)
Mace, Tony, *Notocactus* (1975)
Pilbeam, John, *Mammillaria – A Collector's Guide* (1981)
Pilbeam, John, *Sulcorebutia & Weingartia – A Collector's Guide* (1985)
Rausch, Walter, *Lobivia*, vols 1 to 3 (1975–77)
Ritter, Freidrich, *Kakteen in Sudamerika*, vols 1 to 4 (1979–81)
Rowley, Gordon, *Illustrated Encyclopedia of Succulents* (1978)
Rowley, Gordon, *Name That Succulent* (1980)
Rowley, G., Newton, L. E. & Taylor, N. P., *Repertorium Plantarum Succulentarum* (1960 et seq).
Stearn, William T., *Botanical Latin* (1966)
Taylor, Nigel P., *The Genus Echinocereus* (1985)

Journals

Cactus & Succulent Journal (US)
Journal of the Cactus & Succulent Society of Great Britain (now defunct)
Journal of the National Cactus & Succulent Society (UK) (now defunct)
Journal of the British Cactus & Succulent Society (replacing the former two journals)
Bradleya (yearbook of the British society)
Kakteen und andere Sukkulenten (Journal of Deutsche Kakteen-Gesellschaft, the West German society)
Succulenta (journal of the Netherlands and Belgium society)
Ashingtonia (UK) (now defunct)
The Chileans (UK)
Journal of The Mammillaria Society (UK)
Arbeitskreis für Mammillarienfreunde (West Germany)
Cactaceas y Suculentas Mexicanas (journal of the Mexican society)
Anacampseros (Journal of the Australian society)

INDEX

Since the main part of the book (*Commentary on Genera*) is in alphabetical order, and the species named within each genus likewise, the index below is confined to the other parts of the book.